EDWARD JOHN ROUTH (1831-1907)
From a portrait painted by Herkomer in 1888

STABILITY OF MOTION

STABILITY OF MOTION

by

E. J. ROUTH

Reprinted with additional material
by Routh, Clifford, Sturm and Bôcher

Edited by
A. T. FULLER
Control Engineering Group, University of Cambridge

TAYLOR & FRANCIS LTD
London
1975

First published 1975 by Taylor & Francis Ltd
10–14 Macklin Street London WC2B 5NF

© 1975 Taylor & Francis Ltd

Printed and bound in Great Britain by Taylor & Francis (Printers) Ltd, Rankine Road, Basingstoke, Hampshire.

ISBN 0 85066 091 2

Distributed in the United States of America and its territories by Halsted Press (a division of John Wiley & Sons Inc.), 605 Third Avenue, New York, N.Y. 10016.

Editor's Preface

Routh's celebrated stability criterion is nowadays firmly established as an essential part of the theory of dynamical systems, especially control systems. His method provides the simplest and quickest way of finding whether a system with a given characteristic equation is stable. Routh's work was originally published in 1877 in the form of an essay, which won for its author the Adams Prize of the University of Cambridge. Aside from the well-known stability criterion, this essay contains many other interesting techniques for investigating stability. Routh's book has become rare; it is hoped that the present reprint will help to make his work again easily available.

To fill in the historical and mathematical background, an extensive introduction has been written for the present edition. Two earlier papers of Routh are included, as is a chapter from his book *Dynamics of a system of rigid bodies*. A little-known contribution of Clifford to stability theory is reprinted. A translation of a closely related paper by Sturm is included; and finally a valuable paper by Bôcher on the work of Sturm is also reprinted.

Cambridge
November 1974

Acknowledgements

The original publishers kindly gave permission for material to be reprinted in the present book, as listed below.

Macmillan and Co. (London):

E. J. Routh, *Stability of a given state of motion* (1877).

E. J. Routh, Chapter VI of *The advanced part of a treatise on the dynamics of a system of rigid bodies* (6th ed., 1905).

The London Mathematical Society:

W. K. Clifford, Contribution to stability theory, *Proc. London Math. Soc.*, **2**, (1868), 60–61.

E. J. Routh, Stability of a dynamical system with two independent motions, *Proc. London Math. Soc.*, **5**, (1874), 97–99.

E. J. Routh, On Laplace's three particles, with a supplement on the stability of steady motion, *Proc. London Math. Soc.*, **6**, (1875), 86–97.

The American Mathematical Society:

M. Bôcher, The published and unpublished work of Charles Sturm on algebraic and differential equations, *Bull. Amer. Math. Soc.*, **18**, (1911), 1–18.

Thanks are also due to the Master and Fellows of Peterhouse, Cambridge, for permission to photograph the portrait of Routh which hangs in the dining hall of their college.

Contents

Editor's Introduction

1. *Introduction*

Routh's essay on stability, published nearly a hundred years ago, was one of the foundations of the science of control, feedback and stability. Written in a lively and open style, it still reads freshly today. In these introductory pages we shall explore the historical and mathematical background to Routh's work.

To begin with we shall examine Routh's relations with Airy and Maxwell, two co-founders of control theory in the nineteenth century. Then the closely related work of Cauchy and Sturm on the location of roots will be discussed. To make the present volume self-contained, proofs from first principles will be given of certain of Cauchy's and Sturm's results which Routh took for granted. Finally, we shall look into the historical background to Sturm's work.

2. *Routh*

Edward John Routh (1831–1907) entered Cambridge University as an undergraduate in 1850. After achieving the first place in his final examinations, and thus gaining the coveted title of Senior Wrangler, he became famous as a coach in mathematics at Cambridge. From 1855 to 1888 he was private tutor to more than six hundred pupils, and on twenty-seven occasions it was Routh who prepared the Senior Wrangler—an unequalled feat.

Despite all this pedagogic activity* Routh found the time to write books and original papers. Already, as a young man, he had collaborated with Lord Brougham in publishing (in 1855) a volume entitled *Analytical view of Sir Isaac Newton's Principia*. Forsyth (1907) comments drily ". . . it can hardly be rash to assume that the mathematics belonged to Routh and the opinions to Lord Brougham". Routh's textbook on rigid dynamics, first published in 1860, was gradually expanded into a couple of closely packed volumes and became an encyclopedia of the subject. One chapter treats the stability question and is similar to but not identical with part of Routh's "Essay". For completeness this chapter is reproduced in the present volume.

3. *Airy*

George Biddel Airy (1801-1892) was the Astronomer Royal from 1836 to 1881. Another man of enormous activity, he published over five hundred papers and eleven books. Like Routh, he was the Senior Wrangler in his year (1823). Routh married Airy's eldest daughter in 1864, and on Airy's death in 1892 Routh wrote his obituary. It is clear

---

*See Forsyth (1935) for an account of the system of mathematical teaching then practised at Cambridge.

that Routh was closely acquainted with Airy's work and in particular with his work on control systems.

The control problem treated by Airy was in connection with an astronomical telescope which was turned by clockwork to compensate for the earth's rotation. Accurately uniform speed was required and for this purpose a fly-ball governor was fitted to the clockwork. If the speed became too great, the balls of the governor moved outwards due to centrifugal force and pressed against a surrounding fixed sleeve. The resulting increase of friction tended to slow the clockwork and restore uniform speed. (Similar speed governors are often seen in clockwork toys nowadays.)

This speed control involved a feedback loop, albeit a somewhat disguised one, and it was found to become unstable in some circumstances. Airy studied the phenomenon experimentally (1840, 1850) and used methods of celestial mechanics to treat mathematically this instability. Airy thus became the first person to apply differential equations to control systems, i.e. it was he who initiated the study of the *dynamics* of control.

4. *Maxwell and Clifford*

James Clerk Maxwell (1831–1879) entered Cambridge University as an undergraduate in the same year (1850) as Routh. To begin with he was in the same college, Peterhouse, as Routh.

Maxwell was no ordinary undergraduate, having already published three papers before he arrived at Cambridge. With some justification, then, he could have expected to be Senior Wrangler in his final year, 1854. MacMillan (1956) relates the following anecdote. Apparently Maxwell was so confident of his triumph in the examination that he did not trouble to go to the Senate House to hear the lists of successful candidates read out, but sent his servant instead. On his return Maxwell is said to have inquired of him "Well, tell me who's second", and was somewhat taken aback to receive the reply, "You are, sir", for Routh had gained the first place.

After graduating Maxwell entered an essay for the Adams Prize of 1857; as Routh was to do twenty years later. The subject set by the examiners was the stability of Saturn's Rings and was advertised in the following terms: ". . . different hypotheses may be made concerning the physical constitution of the Rings. It may be supposed (1) that they are rigid; (2) that they are fluid and in part aeriform; (3) that they consist of masses of matter not materially coherent. The question will be considered to be answered by ascertaining on these hypotheses severally whether the conditions of mechanical stability are satisfied by the mutual attractions and motions of the Planet and the Rings . . ."

Maxwell's essay concluded that "the only system of rings which can exist is one composed of an indefinite number of unconnected particles revolving around the planet with different velocities according to their respective distances. These particles may be arranged in a series of narrow rings, or they may move about through each other irregularly. In the first case, the destruction of the system will be very slow, in the second case it will be more rapid, but there may be a tendency towards an arrangement in narrow rings which may retard the process." This essay secured the prize for Maxwell, and was characterized by Airy as one of the most remarkable applications of mathematics to physics that he had ever seen.

Maxwell's technique was to approximate and to linearize the differential equations of the motion, in effect obtaining a characteristic equation which was of only fourth degree and which could be easily factorized.

Thus began Maxwell's interest in stability problems. He used the same techniques in his 1868 paper entitled "On Governors". This paper dealt with control systems* in a more systematic and more direct manner than Airy's. Airy had fitted approximate solutions to the non-linear differential equations involved, whereas Maxwell adopted the simpler procedure of first linearizing the differential equations, then examining the resulting characteristic equation in order to decide whether the system was stable. Maxwell pointed out that for stability all the characteristic roots had to have negative real parts, and posed the problem of interpreting the condition in terms of the coefficients of the characteristic equation. He was not able to solve completely this problem of obtaining stability criteria; but did succeed in treating equations of up to third degree.

In the same year during a discussion at the London Mathematical Society (1868), Maxwell raised the question of finding stability criteria for systems of general order. W. K. Clifford (1848–1879) replied that, by forming an equation whose roots are the sums of the roots of the original equation taken in pairs, and determining the condition for the real roots of this equation to be negative,† we should obtain the condition required. Thus Clifford was the first to solve in principle the problem of finding stability criteria. However, as we shall see, the corresponding purely algebraic problem in terms of roots of equations had already been solved in principle by Cauchy, Sturm and Hermite.

Routh followed up Clifford's idea, in a paper of 1874, and used similar techniques in his 1877 essay. Both the original report of Clifford's contribution and Routh's 1874 paper are included in the present volume.

One of the four examiners who set the subject of stability criteria for the Adams Prize Essay of 1877 was Clerk Maxwell himself.

---

*Maxwell's interest in control arose from the need to govern the speed of a spinning coil used in determining a standard of electrical resistance. See Mayr (1971a, 1971b).

†Conditions for all the real roots of an equation to be negative may be found by means of an algorithm of Sturm, which will be discussed in sections 6 and 9.

For further background material on Airy and Maxwell, see two informative papers by Mayr* (1971a, 1971b). For a brief summary of the history of control, see Fuller (1963).

5. *Cauchy*

Augustin-Louis Cauchy (1789–1857) contributed prolifically to many branches of mathematics. So huge was his output that the publishing resources of the French Academy of Sciences were swamped. The Academy was forced to apply a drastic limit to the length of papers published in Comptes Rendus, a restriction which still holds to the present day.

One of Cauchy's important contributions was the founding of the subject now known as "Functions of a complex variable" together with the associated "Calculus of Residues". In this context he developed methods for finding for a given function the number of zeros inside a given contour drawn in the complex plane. In 1831 he wrote a paper expounding his techniques, but unfortunately this paper was not published.† It was, however, lithographed at Turin.

In particular Cauchy showed in this 1831 paper how to find for a given polynomial the number of zeros with positive real part. As an example Cauchy took the equation

$$z^7 - 2z^5 - 3z^3 + 4z^2 - 5z + 6 = 0 \qquad (5.1)$$

(which had already been studied by Fourier), and showed that it had four roots with positive real part, and three roots with negative real part.

In principle then, Cauchy's work contained a solution of the stability problem. However Cauchy made no such application of his technique to the study of stability, and seemed interested only in the location of roots of equations as an academic question in algebra. Furthermore Cauchy made use of the Sturm division procedure‡ which is a rather tedious algorithm to carry out if the degree of the equation being investigated is high. It is the merit of Routh's contribution to stability theory that this division process is replaced by a much simpler algorithm.

Although Routh made explicit use of one of Cauchy's theorems§, it seems unlikely that he had seen Cauchy's unpublished 1831 paper. It seems probable that Routh obtained the theorem from a subsequent exposition by Sturm (1836); since Routh adopted the same symbols as Sturm.

*Note however that in these papers the criticism of Maxwell's treatment of Thomson's and Foucault's governors seems invalid. Apparently the full significance of equation (5) on Maxwell's page 277 was overlooked.

†It does not as yet appear in Cauchy's *Oeuvres*, though a final volume is projected which it is intended will contain hitherto unpublished papers. A lithograph copy of the original manuscript is in the library of the British Museum.

‡This procedure will be described in detail in section 9.

§This theorem will be described in section 8.

6. Sturm

Charles Sturm (1803–1855) is most well known for his method of finding, for a given polynomial, the number of real zeros between given limits. This method, first published in 1829, requires a certain division process to be carried out on the polynomial and its derivative. When Cauchy's method is used to investigate the number of roots inside a given contour, a similar division process is applied to a pair of polynomials which are more or less arbitrary. Sturm published new proofs of Cauchy's theorem in 1836, and in particular gave this generalization* of the Sturmian division process. Although Cauchy had already used the same generalization in his unpublished 1831 paper, it seems possible (at least to the present writer) that he obtained it from an unpublished 1829 memoir of Sturm's. (Sturm's published 1829 paper was apparently a condensed version of an extensive memoir.)

As already mentioned, Routh was probably acquainted with Sturm's 1836 paper. If so, he could have acknowledged more explicitly his debt to Sturm for the generalized division process. However, it must be remembered that in the nineteenth century it was the usual practice for mathematicians to be cursory in the matter of giving references.

Sturm's paper of 1836, like Cauchy's of 1831, contained in principle a solution of the stability problem, though Sturm made no such application himself. A translation of this paper is included in the present volume.

After describing Cauchy's and Sturm's theorems in detail in sections 7, 8 and 9, we shall discuss the historical background to Sturm's work in section 10.

7. The principle of the angle

As a preliminary step towards proving Cauchy's index theorem (which was used by Routh) let us first prove, for a polynomial, the principle of the angle.† This principle may be stated, in the notation of Routh, as follows:

Let

$$f(z) = p_0 z^n + p_1 z^{n-1} + \ldots + p_n \qquad (p_0 \neq 0) \qquad (7.1)$$

be a polynomial function of the complex variable z which has real and imaginary parts x and y:

$$z = x + yi \qquad (7.2)$$

Let C be a simple closed contour in the (x, y) plane, such that no zero of f(z) lies on contour C. Let the real and imaginary parts of f be P and Q:

$$f = P + Qi \qquad (7.3)$$

---

*Vahlen (1934) erroneously attributes this generalization to Sylvester.

†This is usually called the principle of the argument. Here the term *argument* means the angle associated with a complex number in its Argand diagram representation. Following Osgood (1936) we shall use instead the term *angle* since the term argument has another meaning and in the present context could be confused with z itself.

In the (P, Q) plane the straight line joining the origin to f (in the Argand diagram) will make an angle θ, say, with the positive P-axis, θ being measured in the anti-clockwise direction. We call θ the angle of f, and write

$$\theta = \text{arc } f \qquad (7.4)$$

Let the number of zeros of $f(z)$ inside the contour C be μ. Then when z describes C once in the positive (anti-clockwise) direction, the angle of f increases by μ complete revolutions.

This theorem is usually credited to Cauchy, though apparently Cauchy never stated it exactly in these terms.* The theorem was used by Sturm in his 1836 paper, and the proof that follows is essentially Sturm's.

Polynomial (7.1) can be written in factored form as

$$f(z) = p_0(z - z_1 \ (z - z_2) \ . \ . \ . \ (z - z_n) \qquad (7.5)$$

where $z_1, z_2, \ . \ . \ . \ z_n$ are the zeros. From (7.5)

$$\text{arc } f(z) = \text{arc } p_0 + \text{arc } (z - z_1) + \text{arc } (z - z_2) + \ . \ . \ . + \text{arc } (z - z_n) \qquad (7.6)$$

Suppose z_i is a zero inside contour C. The contribution of z_i to (7.6) is the angle arc $(z - z_i)$, namely the angle ϕ_i between the x-axis and the straight line joining z_i and z, as shown in Fig. 1. This figure shows that

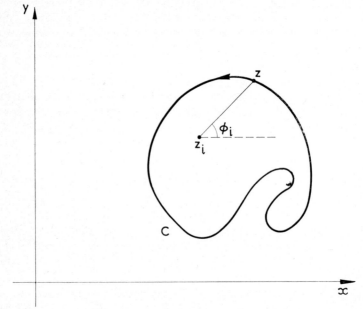

Fig. 1. The angle ϕ_i when z_i is inside contour C.

*He expressed the theorem in terms of the change of log $f(z)$ rather than the change of arc f. See e.g. Cauchy (1855a, 1855b).

when z describes the contour once in the anti-clockwise direction, ϕ_i increases by 2π radians.*

On the other hand, suppose z_j is a zero outside contour C, as in Fig. 2. This figure shows that when z describes the contour once the net change of ϕ_j is zero.

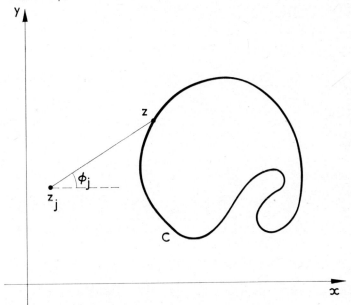

Fig. 2.   The angle ϕ_j when z_j is outside contour C.

Therefore each zero inside C contributes 2π radians to the change of arc $f(z)$, and each zero outside C contributes nothing. Since there are μ zeros inside C, the total change of arc $f(z)$ is $2\mu\pi$. The theorem is thus proved.

8. Cauchy's index theorem

In Routh's 1877 Essay, chapter III starts with a statement of the following theorem.

Let
$$f(z) = p_0 z^n + p_1 z^{n-1} + \ldots + p_n \qquad (p_0 \neq 0) \qquad (8.1)$$
be a polynomial function of the complex variable z. Let z have real and imaginary parts x and y, and let f have real and imaginary parts P and Q:
$$z = x + yi \qquad (8.2)$$
$$f = P + Qi \qquad (8.3)$$
Let C be a simple closed contour in the (x, y) plane, such that no zero of $f(z)$ lies on contour C. Let z describe C once in the anti-clockwise

---

*z is considered as tracing the contour continuously with respect to some appropriate parameter, and ϕ_i is considered as subject to continuous change. (Thus discontinuous jumps of ϕ_i by multiples of 2π are not allowed.)

direction. *Suppose that during the motion of z, the quantity P/Q passes through zero α times from positive to negative, and β times from negative to positive. Then the number of zeros of f(z) inside contour C is* $\frac{1}{2}$ *(α-β).*

This is a special case of Cauchy's index theorem of 1831. The following proof is essentially that given by Sturm (1836).

(8.3) implies that

$$\frac{P}{Q} = \cot \theta \qquad (8.4)$$

where

$$\theta = \text{arc } f(z) \qquad (8.5)$$

Thus P/Q vanishes when $\cot \theta$ vanishes, i.e. when θ is an odd multiple of $\pi/2$:

$$\theta = (2k+1) \frac{\pi}{2} \qquad (k \text{ integer}) \qquad (8.6)$$

Now

$$\frac{d}{d\theta} \cot \theta = -\frac{1}{\sin^2 \theta} \qquad (8.7)$$

From (8.6) and (8.7), when $\cot \theta$ vanishes

$$\frac{d}{d\theta} \cot \theta = -1 \qquad (8.8)$$

(8.8) shows that $\cot \theta$, in vanishing, passes from positive to negative, or from negative to positive, according as θ increases or decreases.

Let the initial value of θ, when z begins to describe C, be σ. Let the number of zeros of $f(z)$ inside C be μ. Then, from the principle of the angle (see section 7), the final value of θ will be

$$\theta = \sigma + 2 \mu\pi \qquad (8.9)$$

The angle θ, changing gradually when z traces C, will become equal (once or several times) to each of the 2μ odd multiples of $\pi/2$ lying between σ and $\sigma + 2\mu\pi$. Consider any one of these multiples, say θ_i. θ must increase through θ_i once more often than it decreases through θ_i; since initially $\theta < \theta_i$ and finally $\theta > \theta_i$. Hence $\cot \theta$, in vanishing at θ_i, passes from + to − once more often than from − to +.

Thus $\cot \theta$, in vanishing at all the 2μ odd multiples of $\pi/2$ between σ and $\sigma + 2\mu\pi$, passes from positive to negative 2μ more times than from negative to positive.

If θ becomes equal to some odd multiple of $\pi/2$ not lying between σ and $\sigma + 2\mu\pi$, say θ_j, then θ must increase through θ_j as often as it decreases through θ_j. Thus $\cot \theta$, in vanishing at θ_j, passes from + to − as often as from − to +.

We conclude that the total number α of decreases through zero of $\cot \theta$ minus the total number β of increases through zero must be

$$\alpha - \beta = 2\mu \tag{8.10}$$

Thus the theorem is proved.

9. Sturm's algorithms

Routh uses an algorithm of Sturm in chapter III of his 1877 Essay, but gives few indications of its origin and proof. We shall fill this gap by stating and proving two algorithms of Sturm. The first is the well-known algorithm for finding the number of real roots of a given real polynomial equation in a given interval.

ALGORITHM 1   (Sturm 1829, 1835)

From the given real polynomial equation

$$f(x) \equiv a_0 x^n + a_1 x^{n-1} + \ldots + a_n = 0 \qquad (a_0 \neq 0) \tag{9.1}$$

form the sequence of functions

$$f_0(x), \, f_1(x), \, \ldots \, f_r(x) \tag{9.2}$$

where

$f_0(x) \equiv f(x)$
$f_1(x) \equiv f'(x)$
$f_2(x) \equiv -$[remainder obtained on dividing $f(x)$ by $f_1(x)$]
$f_3(x) \equiv -$[remainder obtained on dividing $f_1(x)$ by $f_2(x)$]
etc. $\tag{9.3}$

Continue this process until a remainder $(-f_{r+1})$ is obtained which is identically zero. Then the number of real roots of (9.1) between $x = A$ and $x = B$ $(B > A)$ equals the number of variations of sign in the sequence

$$f_0(A), \, f_1(A), \, \ldots \, f_r(A) \tag{9.4}$$

minus the number of variations of sign in the sequence

$$f_0(B), \, f_1(B), \, \ldots \, f_r(B) \tag{9.5}$$

In this rule, a multiple root is only counted once, and any zero terms in (9.4) and (9.5) are omitted from the sequence.*

The proof of algorithm 1 will be deferred until we have proved algorithm 2 below.

Sturm generalized algorithm 1 to deal with the case when $f_1(x)$ is not necessarily the derivative of $f_0(x)$. In this case, when x increases

---

*If *all* the terms of sequence (9.4) are zero, sequence (9.4) is replaced by
$$f_0(A + \epsilon), \, f_1(A + \epsilon), \, \ldots \, f_r(A + \epsilon) \tag{9.6}$$
where ϵ is a small positive quantity. A similar modification is made if all the terms of sequence (9.5) are zero.

through a real root of $f_0(x)=0$, the relative signs of $f_0(x)$ and $f_1(x)$ may change from unlike signs to like signs, or they may change from like to unlike signs. The aim is to count, in a given interval, the number of real roots of $f_0(x)=0$ for which the signs of $f_0(x)$ and $f_1(x)$ change from unlike to like, minus the number of real roots of $f_0(x)=0$ for which the signs of $f_0(x)$ and $f_1(x)$ change from like to unlike. This difference is required in applications of Cauchy's index theorem—see Section 8. The algorithm for this case is as follows (somewhat rephrased as compared with Sturm's version):

ALGORITHM 2   (Sturm 1835, 1836)

From the given two real polynomial equations

$$f_0(x)\equiv a_0x^n+a_1x^{n-1}+ \ldots +a_n=0 \qquad (a_0 \neq 0) \qquad (9.7)$$

$$f_1(x)\equiv b_0x^m+b_1x^{m-1}+ \ldots +b_m=0 \qquad (m \leq n) \qquad (9.8)$$

form the sequence of functions

$$f_0(x), f_1(x), f_2(x), \ldots f_r(x) \qquad (9.9)$$

where

$f_2(x)\equiv-$[remainder obtained on dividing $f_0(x)$ by $f_1(x)$]
$f_3(x)\equiv-$[remainder obtained on dividing $f_1(x)$ by $f_2(x)$]
etc. $\qquad (9.10)$

Continue this process until a remainder $(-f_{r+1})$ is obtained which is identically zero. Then when x increases in the interval $A < x < B$, the number of real roots of $f_0(x)=0$ for which f_0 and f_1 change from unlike to like signs, minus the number of real roots of $f_0(x)=0$ for which f_0 and f_1 change from like to unlike signs, is equal to the number of variations of sign in the sequence

$$f_0(A), f_1(A), \ldots f_r(A) \qquad (9.11)$$

minus the number of variations of sign in the sequence

$$f_0(B), f_1(B), \ldots f_r(B) \qquad (9.12)$$

Here a multiple root is only counted once, and any zero terms are omitted from the sequences (9.11) and 9.12).*

PROOF OF ALGORITHM 2

Relations (9.10) can be written

$$f_{i-1}(x)=q_i(x)f_i(x)-f_{i+1}(x) \qquad (i=1,2, \ldots r) \qquad (9.13)$$

---

*If all the terms of sequence (9.11) are zero, it is replaced by the sequence (9.6). A similar remark applies to sequence (9.12).

with
$$f_{r+1}(x) \equiv 0 \tag{9.14}$$

where $q_i(x)$ is the quotient obtained in dividing $f_{i-1}(x)$ by $f_i(x)$, and $-f_{i+1}(x)$ is the resulting remainder. Thus the degree of the polynomial $f_i(x)$ decreases as i increases from 1 to r. Let us consider first the (usual) case when the last polynomial in sequence (9.9) is simply a (non-zero) constant.

Case (i)
$$f_r(x) = \text{const} \ (\neq 0) \tag{9.15}$$

When x increases, the sequence
$$f_0(x), \ f_1(x), \ \ldots \ f_r(x) \tag{9.16}$$

can change its number of variations of sign only when one or more of the $f_i(x)$ pass through zero. No two neighbouring members $f_i(x)$ and $f_{i+1}(x)$ can become zero simultaneously, because if they could, in view of (9.13) all the $f_i(x)$ ($i=1,2,\ldots r$) would also become simultaneously zero, contradicting (9.15). Thus whenever an intermediate term $f_i(x)$ is zero, its two neighbours $f_{i-1}(x)$ and $f_{i+1}(x)$ are non-zero. Moreover, from (9.13), $f_{i-1}(x)$ and $f_{i+1}(x)$ then have opposite signs.

It follows that the passage of an intermediate term $f_i(x)$ through zero does not change the number of variations of sign in sequence (9.16). Therefore this number can change sign only when the extreme members $f_0(x)$ and $f_r(x)$ change sign. But $f_r(x)$, being constant (see 9.15), does not change sign. Therefore the number of variations of sign can change only when $f_0(x)$ passes through zero.

If, during a passage of $f_0(x)$ through zero, f_0 and f_1 change from like to unlike signs, a variation of sign is gained. If, during a passage of $f_0(x)$ through zero f_0 and f_1 change from unlike to like signs, a variation of sign is lost. These are the only ways in which a variation of sign can be gained or lost.

Therefore the difference between the numbers of sign variations in sequences (9.11) and (9.12) will equal the number of times $f_0(x)$ passes through zero with f_0 and f_1 changing from unlike to like signs, minus the number of times $f_0(x)$ passes through zero with f_0 and f_1 changing from like to unlike signs. This is what we had to prove.

Note that any zero intermediate term can be omitted from sequence (9.11) or (9.12), since its neighbours have opposite signs. Also, if the first term of (9.11) or (9.12) is zero, it can be omitted from the sequence, because x varies in the *open* interval $A < x < B$ rather than the closed interval $A \leqslant x \leqslant B$.

It remains to consider the case when the last polynomial $f_r(x)$ in sequence (9.9) is not simply a constant.

Case (ii)
$$f_r(x) \neq \text{const} \tag{9.17}$$
From (9.13) and (9.14)

11

$$f_{r-1}(x) = q_r(x) f_r(x) \tag{9.18}$$

so that in view of (9.17) $f_{r-1}(x)$ has $f_r(x)$ as a non-trivial factor. Furthermore the recursive relations (9.13) imply that *all* the $f_i(x)$ $(i=0, 1, \ldots r)$ have $f_r(x)$ as a factor. If we divide relations (9.13) by this common factor, writing

$$h_i(x) = \frac{f_i(x)}{f_r(x)} \qquad (i=0, 1, \ldots r) \tag{9.19}$$

we get

$$h_{i-1}(x) = q_i(x) h_i(x) - h_{i+1}(x) \qquad (i=1, 2, \ldots r) \tag{9.20}$$

with

$$h_r(x) = 1 \text{ and } h_{r+1}(x) = 0 \tag{9.21}$$

The sequence of functions

$$h_0(x), h_1(x), \ldots h_r(x) \tag{9.22}$$

thus has the same properties as the sequence (9.16) discussed in case (i). Hence sequence (9.22) loses or gains a variation in sign only when x increases through a zero of $h_0(x)$. Multiplication of the terms of sequence (9.22) by the common factor $f_r(x)$ does not change the variations of sign in the sequence (unless $f_r(x) = 0$, in which case $f_0(x) = 0$ also). Therefore the resulting sequence

$$f_0(x), f_1(x), \ldots f_r(x) \tag{9.23}$$

can lose or gain a variation of sign only when $f_0(x)$ passes through zero. The rest of the proof now follows through as in case (i).

Note that if A is a zero of $f_r(x)$, all the terms in sequence (9.11) are zero. One then replaces sequence (9.11) by (9.6). A similar remark applies if B is a zero of $f_r(x)$.

The proof of algorithm 2 is thus complete.

PROOF OF ALGORITHM 1

The proof of algorithm 1 now follows readily. Visualization of the graph of $f_0(x)$ confirms that when $f_0(x)$ increases through zero, $f_0(x)$ and $f_0'(x)$ change from unlike to like signs; and the same is true when $f_0(x)$ decreases through zero or passes through zero without changing sign. Therefore for the case when $f_1(x)$ is the derivative $f_0'(x)$ there are no changes of f_0 and f_1 from like to unlike signs, when x increases through a zero of $f_0(x)$. This special case of algorithm 2 thus yields algorithm 1.

10. *The historical background to Sturm's algorithms*

At first sight Sturm's algorithms seem to constitute a surprising mathematical discovery. Sturm himself gave little indication of how he was led to his techniques. However, as we shall see, these techniques seem an understandable development when viewed against the historical background. (Of course it needed a mathematician of Sturm's calibre to recognize the possibilities for the first time.)

Sturm acknowledged that he had access to unpublished manuscripts of Fourier on the theory of equations. Now Fourier's main interests were (i) the theory of heat and (ii) the theory of equations (see Grattan-Guinness 1972). Bôcher (1911) has suggested that Sturm could have been led to his technique by consideration of problems in heat flow.* We shall argue that, equally, Sturm could have been motivated by Fourier's work in the theory of equations. Either way, the discoveries of Sturm seem a fairly natural consequence.

Descartes (1637), in his well-known rule of signs, asserted, without proof, that the numbers of positive and negative real roots of an algebraic equation depend on the numbers of sign variations and sign permanences in the sequence of the coefficients.† De Gua (1741), in proving Descartes' rule, also gave in effect the following result.‡ If all the roots of the real equation

$$f(x) \equiv a_0 x^n + a_1 x^{n-1} + \ldots + a_n = 0 \qquad (a_0 \neq 0) \qquad (10.1)$$

are real and if any intermediate coefficient a_i is zero, then its two neighbours a_{i-1} and a_{i+1} must have opposite signs (except for a trivial case§).

Fourier generalized the work of Descartes and De Gua by treating the number of real roots in a given interval.‖ One of Fourier's results was that, for the roots of (10.1) to be all real and distinct, it is necessary and sufficient that in the sequence of $f(x)$ and its derivatives

$$f(x), \ f'(x), \ f''(x), \ \ldots f^{(n)}(x) \qquad (10.2)$$

any value of x which makes an intermediate member $f^{(i)}(x)$ vanish should give its neighbours $f^{(i-1)}(x)$ and $f^{(i+1)}(x)$ opposite signs.¶

*Bôcher's paper is reprinted in the present volume. Gantmacher and Krein (1950) state categorically that Sturm was led to his algorithms by a study of physical problems—but their assertion may be based on a misreading of Bôcher's paper.

†Descartes' treatment was a little ambiguous, and consequently there was some controversy as to whether he had been anticipated by Harriot. See De Gua (1741) and Young (1843) for references.

‡Newton (1707) had already given, without proof, a rule which embraces De Gua's result. Sylvester (1865) proved Newton's rule.

§The exceptional case occurs when the last few coefficients a_r, a_{r+1}, . . . a_n are all zero and a_i is one of these zero coefficients. Then one or both of a_{i-1} and a_{i+1} are zero, so that strictly speaking they do not have opposite signs.

‖Fourier published his results (1820) long after he lectured on them. Meanwhile Budan (1807) published related results, giving rise to another controversy on priority (see Grattan-Guinness 1972).

¶Lagrange (1808) stated the necessity of the above condition. Fourier indicated the sufficiency in 1822, and gave a fuller account of the theory in work published posthumously (1831a, b). Note that Fourier's version of the result differed slightly from that given above, i.e. he did not require the roots to be distinct.

A consequence of this property is that, when x increases from A to B, the number of sign variations in sequence (10.2) changes only when the first member $f(x)$ passes through zero. Thus it can be shown that the number of roots of $f(x)=0$ in the interval $A<x<B$ equals the number $V(A)$ of variations of sign in the sequence

$$f(A), f'(A), f''(A), \ldots f^{(n)}(A) \qquad (10.3)$$

minus the number $V(B)$ of variations of sign in the sequence

$$f(B), f'(B), f''(B), \ldots f^{(n)}(B) \qquad (10.4)$$

(Any zero terms are omitted when sign variations are counted.)

This result is Fourier's rule, adapted to the special case when all the roots are known to be real and distinct.* Sturm's problem was to generalize Fourier's rule so as to determine the number of real roots in the interval $A<x<B$, whether or not (10.1) possessed complex roots. He probably saw that he had to set up a sequence of polynomials

$$f_0(x), f_1(x), \ldots f_r(x) \qquad (10.5)$$

with the same properties as Fourier's sequence (10.2) has when all the roots are real and distinct.
Namely:

    (i) when x increases through a zero of $f(x)$ sequence (10.5) must lose a sign variation;

    (ii) when any intermediate member $f_i(x)$ vanishes, its two neighbours $f_{i-1}(x)$ and $f_{i+1}(x)$ must have opposite signs;

    (iii) the last member $f_r(x)$ must be a constant.

Property (i) can be achieved (see proof of algorithm 1) by making the first two members of sequence (10.5) the same as the first two members of Fourier's sequence (10.2), i.e.

$$f_0(x)=f(x), \qquad f_1(x)=f'(x) \qquad (10.6)$$

The easiest way to obtain property (ii) is to define f_{i+1} in terms of f_i and f_{i-1} by means of a linear equation of the form

$$f_{i+1}(x)=q_i(x)\, f_i(x)-f_{i-1}(x) \qquad (10.7)$$

Finally, to achieve property (iii), $q_i(x)$ in (10.7) should be a polynomial so chosen that $f_{i+1}(x)$ is of degree less than the degree of $f_i(x)$.

With these choices, the $f_i(x)$ are as defined in Sturm's first algorithm. We conclude that Sturm's discoveries were fairly natural in view of the state of development of the theory of equations at the time, and in view of his close acquaintance with Fourier's investigations.

---

*In the general case when the roots are not necessarily all real and distinct, the rule states, that the number of real roots in the interval $A<x<B$ is *not greater than* $V(A)-V(B)$.

11. Conclusions

We have seen that Routh's work on stability criteria had deep roots, going back via the control problems of Maxwell and Airy to the work of Sturm and Cauchy on the location of zeros of polynomials, and even further back to the investigations of Fourier, De Gua and Descartes in the theory of equations.

It should be mentioned that another line of development of stability theory was begun with the work of Hermite (1854). He obtained conditions for roots to have imaginary parts all of the same sign; and apparently did not have applications to stability in mind. His techniques required manipulations with quadratic forms, and originated somewhat obscurely from work Hermite had done earlier in the theory of numbers.

Hurwitz had been asked by the engineer Stodola to solve the problem of stability criteria, which had arisen in the context of the control of hydro-electric turbines. Adapting and modifying Hermite's quadratic form methods, Hurwitz (1895) obtained stability criteria in the shape of determinantal inequalities. These criteria are alternative and equivalent to those of Routh. When the coefficients of the characteristic equation arc given in numerical form, it is usually advantageous to use Routh's algorithm. For an account of the Hermite-Hurwitz approach, see Gantmacher (1954).

12. References

1637 DESCARTES, R. *La Géométrie* (Leyden: Maire), p. 373. Translation: *The geometry of René Descartes* (La Salle: Open Court, 1925), p. 160.
1707 NEWTON, I. *Arithmetica Universalis* (Cambridge), Chapt. II. Translation: *Universal Arithmetic*, 2nd Ed. (London: Senex, 1728). Reprinted in *The mathematical works of Isaac Newton* (New York: Johnson, 1967).
1741 DE GUA, J. P. Demonstration de la règle de Descartes. *Histoire de l'Académie Royale des Sciences* (Paris), *Mémoires*, pp. 72–96.
1807 BUDAN, D. *Nouvelle méthode pour la résolution des équations de degré quelconque* (Paris).
1808 LAGRANGE, J. L. *Traité de la résolution des équations numériques de tous les degrés.* (Paris: Courcier.)
1820 FOURIER, J. B. J. Sur l'usage du théorème de Descartes dans la recherche des limites des racines. *Bulletin des Sciences par la Société Philomathique de Paris*, pp. 156–165, 181–187.
1822 FOURIER, J. B. J. *Théorie analytique de la chaleur* (Paris, Didot). Translation: *The analytical theory of heat* (Cambridge: 1878), p. 294.
1829 STURM, C. Analyse d'un mémoire sur la résolution des équations numériques. *Bulletin des Sciences Mathématiques (de Ferussac)*, **11**, 419–422.
1831 CAUCHY, A. L. Mémoire sur les rapporte qui existent entre le calcul de résidus et le calcul de limites et sur les avantages qu'offrent ces deux nouveaux calculs dans la résolution des équations algébriques ou transcendentes. (27th Nov. 1831, lithographed at Turin.)
1831a FOURIER, J. B. J. *Analyse des équations determinées.* (Paris: Didot.)
1831b FOURIER, J. B. J. Remarques générales sur l'application des principes de l'analyse algébrique aux équations transcendentes. *Mémoires de l'Academie royale des Sciences de l'Institut de France*, **10**, 119–146.
1835 STURM, C. Mémoire sur la résolution des équations numériques. *Mémoires des Savantes Étrangers (l'Académie royale des Sciences de l'Institut de France)*, **6**, 273–318.

1836 STURM, C. Autres démontrations de même théorème. *Journal de mathématiques pures et appliquées*, **1**, 290–308.

1837 CAUCHY, A. L. Calcul des indices des fonctions. *Journal de l'École Polytechnique*, **15**, 176–230.

1840 AIRY, G. B. On the regulator of the clock-work for effecting uniform movement of equatoreals. *Memoirs of the Royal Astronomical Society*, **11**, 249–267.

1843 YOUNG, J. R. *Theory and solution of algebraical equations of the higher orders.* (London: Souter and Law.)

1851a AIRY, G. B. On a method of regulating the clock-work for equatoreals. *Monthly notices of the Royal Astronomical Society*, **11**, 17–18.

1851b AIRY, G. B. Supplement to a paper "On the regulation of the clock-work for effecting uniform movement of equatoreals." *Memoirs of the Royal Astronomical Society*, **20**, 115–119.

1851c AIRY, G. B. On the vibration of a free pendulum in an oval differing little from a straight line. *Memoirs of the Royal Astronomical Society*, **20**, 121–130.

1855 BROUGHAM, H., and ROUTH, E. J. *Analytical view of Sir Isaac Newton's Principia.* (London: Longman.)

1855a CAUCHY, A. L. Mémoire sur les variations intégrales des fonctions. *Comptes Rendus Acad. Sci.*, **40**, 651–658.

1855b CAUCHY, A. L. Sur les compteurs logarithmiques. *Comptes Rendus Acad. Sci.*, **40**, 1009–1016.

1856 HERMITE, C. Extrait d'une lettre sur le nombre des racines d'une équation algébrique compris des limites données. *J. reine angew. Math.*, **52**, 39–51.

1857 MAXWELL, J. C. *On the stability of the motion of Saturn's rings.* (Adams Prize Essay, University of Cambridge.) *Scientific papers of J. C. Maxwell*, **1**, 288–376.

1860 ROUTH, E. J. *Dynamics of a system of rigid bodies.* (London and Cambridge: Macmillan.)

1865 SYLVESTER, J. J. Elementary proof and generalization of Sir Isaac Newton's hitherto undemonstrated rule for the discovery of imaginary roots. *Proc. London Math. Soc.*, **1**, 2nd paper (16 pp.).

1868 CLIFFORD, W. K. (Contribution to a discussion.) *Proc. London Math. Soc.*, **2**, 60–61.

1868 MAXWELL, J. C. On governors. *Proc. Royal Society of London*, **16**, 270–283. Also printed in *Philosophical Magazine, 35* (1868), 385–398.

1874 ROUTH, E. J. Stability of a dynamical system with two independent motions. *Proc. London Math. Soc.*, **5**, 97–99.

1875 ELLERY, R. L. J. The results of some experiments with Huygen's parabolic pendulum for obtaining uniform rotation. *Monthly Notices of the Royal Astronomical Society*, **36**, 72–76.

1875 ROUTH, E. J. On Laplace's three particles, with a supplement on the stability of steady motion. *Proc. London Math. Soc.*, **6**, 86–97.

1877 ROUTH, E. J. *A treatise on the stability of a given state of motion.* (London: Macmillan.)

1892 ROUTH, E. J. Obituary notice of Sir George Airy. *Proc. Royal Society of London*, **51**, i–xxi.

1895 HURWITZ, A. Ueber die Bedingungen unter welchen eine Gleichung nur Wurzeln mit negativen reellen Theilen besitzt. *Mathematische Annalen*, **46**, 273–284.

1896 AIRY, G. B. *Autobiography of Sir George Airy.* (Cambridge: University Press.)

1907 FORSYTH, A. R. Obituary notice of Edward John Routh. *Proc. London Math. Soc.*, **5**, xiv–xx.

1911 BÔCHER, M. The published and unpublished work of Charles Sturm on algebraic and differential equations. *Bulletin American Math. Soc.*, **18**, 1–18.

1911 LARMOR, J. Obituary notice of Edward John Routh. *Proc. Royal Society of London*, **84**, xii–xvi. (Reprinted from *Nature*, June 27, 1907.)

1934 VAHLEN, K. T. Wurzelabzählung bei Stabilitätsfragen. *Zeit. f. angew. Math. u. Mech.*, **14**, 65–70.

1935 FORSYTH, A. R. Old tripos days at Cambridge. *Mathematical Gazette*, **19,** 162–179.
1936 OSGOOD, W. F. *Functions of a complex variable.* (Peking: University Press.) Reprint: New York, Chelsea.
1949 ANDRONOV, A. A., and VOSNESENSKI, I. N. The work of J. C. Maxwell, I. A. Vyshnegradski and A. Stodola in the theory of machine control. In *J. C. Maxwell, I. A. Vyshnegradski, A. Stodola. Theory of Automatic Control.* (Classics of Science.) In Russian. (Acad. Sci. USSR.) Reprinted in Andronov's *Collected Works.*
1950 GANTMACHER, F. R., and KREIN, M. G. *Oscillation matrices and kernels and small vibrations of mechanical systems* (in Russian). Translation: U.S. Atomic Energy Commission, AEC-tr-4481.
1954 GANTMACHER, F. R. *Theory of matrices* (in Russian). Translation: New York, Chelsea, 1959. Chapt. XV.
1956 MACMILLAN, R. H. *Automation: friend or foe?* (Cambridge: University Press), p. 41.
1963 FULLER, A. T. Directions of research in control. *Automatica, **1,** 289–296.
1971a MAYR, O. Maxwell and the origins of cybernetics. *Isis, **62,** 425–444.
1971b MAYR, O. Victorian physicists and speed regulation: an encounter between science and technology. *Notes and Records of the Royal Society of London, **26,** 205–228.
1972 GRATTAN–GUINNESS, I. *Joseph Fourier* 1768–1830. (Cambridge, Massachusetts: M.I.T. Press).

Glossary and Symbols

Routh's term	*Modern equivalent*
force function	potential energy
greatest common measure	greatest common divisor
semi vis viva	kinetic energy
vis viva	mass x (velocity)^2
$\lfloor n$	$n!$

ERRATA

The page numbers in these errata are those at the bottom of the page.

p.34 In the first two equations for x: for m read m_1.

p.34 In the first equation for y: for db_2/dm read db_1/dm_1.

pp.34, 35. For $\overline{\dfrac{n}{em}}\Big|^n$ read $\left[\dfrac{-n}{em}\right]^n$

p.62. For f_6x read $f_6(x)$.

p.83. For $\frac{1}{2}B_1\theta'^2 + \beta_{12}\theta'\phi'$ read $\frac{1}{2}B_{11}\theta'^2 + B_{12}\theta'\phi' + \ldots$

p.83. For

$$\begin{vmatrix} B_{11}-\lambda D_{11}, & D_{12}-\lambda D_{12} & \ldots \\ \\ B_{12}-\lambda D_{12}, & D_{22}-\lambda D_{22} & \ldots \\ \\ & \ldots & \ldots \end{vmatrix} = 0$$

read

$$\begin{vmatrix} B_{11}-\lambda D_{11}, & B_{12}-\lambda D_{12} & \ldots \\ \\ B_{12}-\lambda D_{12}, & B_{22}-\lambda D_{22} & \ldots \\ \\ & \ldots & \ldots \end{vmatrix} = 0$$

p.102. For $\dfrac{k^2}{z}$ read $\dfrac{k^2}{2}$

Reprinted from the first edition published in 1877 by Macmillan and Co.
(London)

E. J. ROUTH

Stability of a given state of motion

A TREATISE

ON THE

STABILITY OF A GIVEN STATE OF MOTION,

PARTICULARLY STEADY MOTION.

BEING THE ESSAY TO WHICH THE ADAMS PRIZE WAS ADJUDGED
IN 1877, IN THE UNIVERSITY OF CAMBRIDGE.

BY

E. J. ROUTH, M.A., F.R.S., &c.

LATE FELLOW OF ST PETER'S COLLEGE, CAMBRIDGE,
AND LATE EXAMINER IN THE UNIVERSITY OF LONDON.

London:

MACMILLAN AND CO.

1877

PREFACE.

In March, 1875, the usual biennial notice was issued, giving the subjects for the Adams Prize to be adjudged in 1877. The following is the chief portion of the notice :

The University having accepted a Fund raised by several members of St John's College for the purpose of founding a Prize to be called the *Adams Prize*, for the best essay on some subject of Pure Mathematics, Astronomy or other branch of Natural Philosophy, the Prize to be given once in two years, and to be open to the competition of all persons who have at any time been admitted to a degree in this University—

The Examiners give notice that the following is the subject of the Prize to be adjudged in 1877 : *The Criterion of Dynamical Stability.*

To illustrate the meaning of the question imagine a particle to slide down inside a smooth inclined cylinder along the lowest generating line, or to slide down outside along the highest generating line. In the former case a slight derangement of the motion would merely cause the particle to oscillate about the generating line, while in the latter case the particle would depart from the generating line altogether. The motion in the former case would be, in the sense of the question, stable, in the latter unstable.

The criterion of the stability of the equilibrium of a system is, that its potential energy should be a minimum; what is desired is, a corresponding condition enabling us to decide when a dynamically possible motion of a system is such, that if slightly deranged the motion shall continue to be only slightly departed from.

The essays must be sent in to the Vice-Chancellor on or before the 16th December 1876, &c., &c.

S. G. PHEAR, *Vice-Chancellor*.

J. CHALLIS.

G. G. STOKES.

J. CLERK MAXWELL.

The pressure of other engagements for some time prevented me from giving my attention to the subject. This essay was therefore almost entirely composed during the year 1876. It is now printed as it was sent in to the Examiners, the changes being merely verbal. Some few additions have been made where explanation appeared to be necessary, but all these have been marked by square brackets, so that they can be at once distinguished from the original parts of the essay.

In order to shorten the essay as much as possible many *merely algebraic* processes have been omitted and the results only are stated. It is hoped that this will add clearness as well as brevity to the reasoning, as the attention of the reader will not be called from the argument to follow a manipulation of symbols which may not present any novelty.

The line of argument taken may be indicated in a general way as follows. Chapter I. begins with some definitions of the terms *stable* and *steady* motions. It is then pointed out that whether the forces which act on the system admit of a force-function or not, the stability of the motion, if steady, is indicated by the nature of the roots of a certain determinantal equation. The boundary between stability and instability being generally indicated by the presence of equal roots, a criterion is investigated to determine beforehand whether equal roots do or do not imply instability. This case being disposed of, the consideration of the determinantal equation is resumed. Two general methods are given by which, without solving the equation, it may be ascertained whether the character of the roots imply stability or instability. These occupy Chapters II. and III. In the first method a derived equation is made use of, and it is shewn that a simple inspection of the signs of the coefficients of the several powers in these two equations will decide the question of stability. In the second method a certain easy process is found which if performed on the determinantal equation will lead to the criteria of stability. At the end of the third Chapter a geometrical interpretation is given to the argument.

In the fourth Chapter the forces which act on the system are supposed to have a force-function. The determinantal equation is then much simplified. Several points are considered in this Chapter which are necessary to the argument, such as the proper method of choosing the steady co-ordinates (if there be any), the distinction between harmonic oscillation about steady motion and that about equilibrium, and the changes which must be made in the determinantal equation when the equations of Lagrange become inapplicable. A method of modifying the Lagrangian function is also given by which, in certain cases, the fundamental determinant may be reduced to one of fewer rows and columns.

In the fifth Chapter a series of subsidiary determinants is formed, and it is shown that at least as many of the conditions of stability are satisfied as there are variations of signs lost in the series in passing from one given state to another. It is also shown that this is equivalent to a maximum condition of the Lagrangian function.

In the sixth Chapter the energy test of stability is considered. It is also shown that, when the motion is steady, this reduces to the same criterion as that indicated in Chap. V.

In the seventh Chapter the question considered is whether the stability of a state of motion can really be determined by an examination of the terms of the first order only. In some cases these are certainly sufficient, and an attempt is made to discriminate between these cases and those in which the terms of the higher order ultimately alter the character of the motion.

If the Hamiltonian characteristic and principal functions be given, the conditions of stability as regards space only, or both space and time may be deduced. But if these be not known as expressed in the Hamiltonian form, we may yet sometimes distinguish between stability and instability if we can determine whether a certain integral ceases to be a minimum at some instant of the motion. This is the subject of the eighth chapter.

As part of the third edition of my treatise on the Dynamics of Rigid Bodies was written at the same time as this essay, there are necessarily points of contact between the two works. Thus the subjects of the first part of the seventh chapter and of a portion of the sixth will be found discussed in the treatise on Dynamics. But as the objects of the two books are not the same, it will be found that in all these cases there are considerable differences in the modes of demonstration.

EDWARD J. ROUTH.

Peterhouse,
    August 14, 1877.

CONTENTS.

CHAPTER I.

CHAPTER II.

CHAPTER III.

CHAPTER IV.

CHAPTER V.

CHAPTER VI.

CHAPTER VII.

29

CONTENTS.

CHAPTER VIII.

CHAPTER I.

Definitions of the terms small quantity, stable motion, steady motion. *Arts.* 1, 2.

A system of bodies in steady motion is stable if the roots of a certain determinantal equation are such that their real parts are all negative. Art. 3.

Effect of equal roots, and a test to determine whether equal roots do or do not introduce terms which contain the time as a factor. Arts. 4—7.

Object of Chapters II. and III. Art. 8.

1. Let us suppose a dynamical system to be set in motion under any forces and to move in some known manner. If any small disturbance be given to the system, it may deviate only slightly from its known motion, or it may diverge further and further from it. Let θ, ϕ, &c. be the independent variables or co-ordinates which determine the position of the system, and let the known motion be given by $\theta = \theta_0$, $\phi = \phi_0$, &c. where θ_0, ϕ_0, &c. are known functions of the time t. To discover the disturbance of the system we put $\theta = \theta_0 + x$, $\phi = \phi_0 + y$, &c. These quantities x, y, &c. are in the first instance very small because the disturbance is small. The quantities x, y, z, &c. are said to be *small* when it is possible to choose some quantity numerically greater than all of them, which is such that, its square can be neglected. This quantity may be called the standard of reference for small quantities.

If, after the disturbance, the co-ordinates x, y, z, &c. remain always small, the undisturbed motion is said to be *stable;* if, on the other hand, any one of the co-ordinates become large, the motion is called *unstable.*

It is clear that the same motion may be stable for one kind of disturbance and unstable for another. But it is usual to suppose the disturbance *general,* so that if the motion can be made unstable by any kind of disturbance (provided it be small) it is said to be unstable. On the other hand, it will be called stable only when it is stable for *all* kinds of small disturbances.

2. To determine whether x, y, z, &c. remain small, we must substitute for θ, ϕ, &c. in the equations of motion their values $\theta_0 + x$, $\phi_0 + y$, &c. Assuming that x, y, &c. remain small, we may neglect their squares, and thus the resulting equations will be linear in x, y, z, &c. The coefficients of x, $\dfrac{dx}{dt}$, $\dfrac{d^2x}{dt^2}$, y, $\dfrac{dy}{dt}$, $\dfrac{d^2y}{dt^2}$, &c. in these equations may be either constants or functions of the time. In the former case the undisturbed motion is said to be *steady* for these co-ordinates, in the latter *unsteady*. In the case of a steady motion x, y, z, &c. are all functions of the time which has elapsed since the disturbance and of certain constants of integration which are determined by the initial values of x, $\dfrac{dx}{dt}$, y, $\dfrac{dy}{dt}$, &c. We may therefore define a steady motion to be such that the same change of motion follows from the same initial disturbance at whatever instant the disturbance is communicated to the system.

If all the coefficients in the equations to find x, y, z are constant, they may be made to contain t by a change of co-ordinates. Thus we may write for x, y, z, &c.

$$x = \alpha\xi + \beta\eta + \dots$$
$$y = \alpha'\xi + \beta'\eta + \dots$$
$$z = \&c.$$

where α, β, &c. are any functions of t we please. Conversely, when the coefficients are functions of t, we may sometimes make the coefficients constant by a proper change of co-ordinates. But this cannot always be done. If there are n co-ordinates, we have n^2 arbitrary functions α, β, &c. at our disposal. In each of the n linear equations of motion we may have three terms for each co-ordinate, and thus we have $(3n-1)n$ coefficients to make constants. We have therefore in general too many equations to satisfy. The proper method of choosing the co-ordinates of reference will be considered in a future chapter.

3. Let us suppose a dynamical system to be making small oscillations under the action of any forces which may, or may not, possess a force function and to be subject to any resistances which vary as the velocities of the parts resisted. The general equations of motion will then be of the form

$$\left.\begin{array}{r}\left(A_2\dfrac{d^2}{dt^2} + A_1\dfrac{d}{dt} + A_0\right)x + \left(B_2\dfrac{d^2}{dt^2} + B_1\dfrac{d}{dt} + B_0\right)y + \&c. = 0 \\[2mm] \left(A_2'\dfrac{d^2}{dt^2} + A_1'\dfrac{d}{dt} + A_0'\right)x + \left(B_2'\dfrac{d^2}{dt^2} + B_1'\dfrac{d}{dt} + B_0'\right)y + \&c. = 0 \\[2mm] \&c. = 0\end{array}\right\}.$$

To solve these equations we write

$$x = Me^{mt}, \quad y = M'e^{mt}, \quad \&c.$$

Substituting we obtain a determinantal equation to find m. If we put

$$A = A_2 m^2 + A_1 m + A_0, \qquad B = B_2 m^2 + B_1 m + B_0,$$
$$A' = A_2' m^2 + A_1' m + A_0', \qquad \&c.$$

this equation may be written in the simple form

$$\begin{vmatrix} A, & B, & C \ldots\ldots \\ A', & B', & C' \ldots\ldots \\ \ldots\ldots\ldots\ldots\ldots \end{vmatrix} = 0.$$

We may also write the equation in the form $f(m) = 0$.

The coefficients M, M', &c. are not independent, but if we represent the minors of A, B, C, &c. by a, b, c, &c. we may easily show that

$$\frac{M}{a} = \frac{M'}{b} = \frac{M''}{c} = \&c.$$

We also have

$$\frac{M}{a'} = \frac{M'}{b'} = \frac{M''}{c'} = \&c.$$

It may be shown by properties of determinants that these equations all give the same ratios. If Δ_2 be the second minor obtained from the determinant $f(m)$ by omitting the first and second rows and columns, we know that

$$\Delta_2 f(m) = ab' - a'b.$$

Hence if $f(m) = 0$ we have $\dfrac{a}{a'} = \dfrac{b}{b'}$.

In the same way we may show that $\dfrac{a}{a'} = \dfrac{c}{c'}$, and so on. This property of Determinants is given in Dr Salmon's *Higher Algebra*, Lesson IV. Ex. 1.

The general solution of the equation may therefore be written in the form

$$\left. \begin{array}{l} x = L_1 a_1 e^{m_1 t} + L_2 a_2 e^{m_2 t} + \ldots \\ y = L_1 b_1 e^{m_1 t} + L_2 b_2 e^{m_2 t} + \ldots \\ z = \&c. \end{array} \right\},$$

where L_1, $L_2 \ldots$ are arbitrary constants, a_1, a_2, &c. the values of the minor a when m_1, $m_2 \ldots$ are substituted for m; b_1, $b_2 \ldots$ the values of the minor b when similar substitutions are made, and so on.

4.   We see that the whole character of the motion will depend on the signs of the quantities $m_1, m_2...$ If any one be real and positive, x, y, &c. or some of them will ultimately become large, and the steady motion about which the system is oscillating will be unstable.   If all the roots are real, negative or zero and unequal, the motion will be stable.

If two of the roots be imaginary we have a pair of imaginary exponentials.   If these imaginary roots be $\alpha \pm \beta \sqrt{-1}$, the terms can be rationalized into

$$e^{\alpha t}(N_1 \cos \beta t + N_2 \sin \beta t).$$

The motion will be stable if α be negative or zero, and unstable if α be positive.

If two roots be equal, the form of the solution is changed.   Let $m_2 = m_1 + h$ where h will be ultimately zero, we then have

$$x = L_1 a_1 e^{m_1 t} + L_2 \left(a_1 e^{m_1 t} + \frac{da_1}{dm} h e^{m_1 t} + a_1 h t e^{m_1 t} \right).$$

If we now make L_1 and L_2 infinite in the usual manner, we find

$$x = \left\{ M_2 a_1 t + M_2 \frac{da_1}{dm} + M_1 a_1 \right\} e^{m_1 t},$$

$$y = \left\{ M_2 b_1 t + M_2 \frac{db_1}{dm} + M_1 b_1 \right\} e^{m_1 t},$$

$$\&\text{c.} = \&\text{c.},$$

where M_1, M_2 are two arbitrary constants which replace L_1, L_2.

In the same way if three roots are equal we have

$$x = \left[M_3 \left(a_1 \frac{t^2}{2} + \frac{da_1}{dm_1} t + \tfrac{1}{2} \frac{d^2 a_1}{dm_1^2} \right) + M_2 \left(a_1 t + \frac{da_1}{dm_1} \right) + M_1 a_1 \right] e^{m_1 t},$$

$$y = \left[M_3 \left(b_1 \frac{t^2}{2} + \frac{db_1}{dm_1} t + \tfrac{1}{2} \frac{d^2 b_1}{dm_1^2} \right) + M_2 \left(b_1 t + \frac{db_1}{dm_1} \right) + M_1 b_1 \right] e^{m_1 t}.$$

This rule will be found convenient in practice to supply the defect in the number of arbitrary constants produced by equal roots.   At present we are only concerned with their effect on the stability of the system.   The terms which contain t as a factor will at first increase with t, but if m be negative, the term $t^n e^{mt}$ can never be numerically greater than $\overline{\dfrac{n}{em}}\Big|^n$.   If m be very small the initial increase of the terms may make the values of x and y become large, and the motion cannot be regarded as a small oscillation. But if the system be not so much disturbed that $M \cdot \overline{\dfrac{n}{em}}\Big|^{n}$ is large, the terms will ultimately disappear and the motion may be regarded as stable. If, however, the real parts of the equal roots are positive or zero, the terms will become large and the motion will be unstable.

5. In some cases, however, the relations which exist between the coefficients are such that the terms which contain t as a factor are all zero. It is of some importance to discriminate these cases, for the stability of the system is then unaffected by the presence of equal roots.

Let us suppose first that the determinantal equation has two roots only equal to m_1, and let the terms depending on these be

$$x = (N_1 + N_2 t)\, e^{m_1 t},$$

$$y = (N_1' + N_2' t)\, e^{m_1 t},$$

$$\&c. = \&c.$$

Substituting in the equations of Art. (3) we have, following the same notation as before,

$$\left.\begin{aligned} A N_2 + B N_2' + C N_2'' + \ldots = 0 \\ A' N_2 + B' N_2' + C' N_2'' + \ldots = 0 \\ \&c. = 0 \end{aligned}\right\} \quad \ldots\ldots\ldots\ldots\text{I.}$$

$$\left.\begin{aligned} A N_1 + B N_1' + \ldots = -\frac{dA}{dm}N_2 - \frac{dB}{dm}N_2' - \ldots \\ A' N_1 + B' N_1' + \ldots = -\frac{dA'}{dm}N_2 - \frac{dB'}{dm}N_2' - \ldots \end{aligned}\right\} \quad \ldots\ldots\text{II.}$$

$$\&c. = \&c.$$

To avoid entering more minutely than is necessary into the properties of linear equations, we shall assume that these equations for the given value of m lead to but one solution with two of the N's arbitrary, unless the determinantal equation has more than two roots equal to m_1. If in this unique solution the N_2's are all zero we must have

$$\left.\begin{aligned} A N_1 + B N_1' + \ldots = 0 \\ A' N_1 + B' N_1' + \ldots = 0 \\ \&c. = 0 \end{aligned}\right\} \quad \ldots\ldots\ldots\ldots\text{III.}$$

Since two of the constants N_1, N_1', &c. are to be arbitrary, let them be N_1, N_1', then since $\dfrac{N_1}{a} = \dfrac{N_1'}{b}$ we must have the minors a and b each equal to zero. Also since $\dfrac{N_1}{a} = \dfrac{N_1''}{c}$, we shall have N_1'' infinite unless $c = 0$. In the same way we may prove that all the other first minors are zero.

And if the first minors are zero, we may show that two of the equations may be deduced from the others. Let the symbol $\begin{bmatrix} A\,B \\ A'B' \end{bmatrix}$ represent the second minor, with the usual sign, formed by omitting the rows and columns in which $AB\,A'B'$ occur.

Then since the minors a, b, c, &c. are zero, we have

$$\left.\begin{aligned} A'\begin{bmatrix} AB \\ A'B' \end{bmatrix} + A''\begin{bmatrix} AB \\ A''B'' \end{bmatrix} + \ldots = 0 \\ B'\begin{bmatrix} AB \\ A'B' \end{bmatrix} + B''\begin{bmatrix} AB \\ A''B'' \end{bmatrix} + \ldots = 0 \\ \text{&c.} = 0 \end{aligned}\right\} \ldots\ldots\ldots\text{IV.}$$

Omitting the first line of III. let us multiply the others by $\begin{bmatrix} AB \\ A'B' \end{bmatrix}\begin{bmatrix} AB \\ A''B'' \end{bmatrix}$ &c., respectively. Adding the results, we have an identity. Hence the second equation may be deduced from the others which follow it. In the same way, the first equation may be deduced from the others.

Rejecting the first two equations, let us transpose the arbitrary constants N_1 and N_1' to the right-hand sides of the remaining equations. If there are to be only two arbitrary constants, these remaining equations must be independent; solving, we have

$$\begin{bmatrix} AB \\ A'B' \end{bmatrix} N_1'' = -N_1 \begin{bmatrix} BC \\ B'C' \end{bmatrix} + N_1' \begin{bmatrix} AC \\ A'C' \end{bmatrix},$$

with similar equations for the others. Hence the constants N_1, N_1', &c., are connected by equations of the form

$$N_1 \begin{bmatrix} BC \\ B'C' \end{bmatrix} - N_1' \begin{bmatrix} AC \\ A'C' \end{bmatrix} + N_1'' \begin{bmatrix} AB \\ A'B' \end{bmatrix} = 0,$$

so that when any two are chosen as the arbitrary ones, the others may be deduced from them.

If the determinantal equation has three roots equal to m_1, and if the terms which contain t as a factor are all zero, the equations III. must admit of a solution with three of the constants

N_1, N_1', &c. arbitrary. If these be N_1, N_1', N_1'', we see that the second minors $\begin{bmatrix} B\,C \\ B'\,C' \end{bmatrix} \begin{bmatrix} A\,C \\ A'\,C' \end{bmatrix} \begin{bmatrix} A\,B \\ A'\,B' \end{bmatrix}$ must be zero.

Next since

$$N_1 \begin{bmatrix} B\,D \\ B'\,D' \end{bmatrix} - N_1' \begin{bmatrix} A\,D \\ A'\,D' \end{bmatrix} + N_1''' \begin{bmatrix} A\,B \\ A'\,B' \end{bmatrix} = 0,$$

we must have $\begin{bmatrix} B\,D \\ B'\,D' \end{bmatrix}$ and $\begin{bmatrix} A\,D \\ A'\,D' \end{bmatrix}$ both zero or N_1''' infinite.

Hence all the second minors are zero. And if the second minors are all zero, we have

$$A'' \begin{bmatrix} A\,B\,C \\ A'\,B'\,C' \\ A''\,B''\,C'' \end{bmatrix} + A''' \begin{bmatrix} A\,B\,C \\ A'\,B'\,C' \\ A'''\,B'''\,C''' \end{bmatrix} + \ldots = 0,$$

and by similar reasoning three equations may be deduced from the remaining ones. We have then

$$N_1 \begin{bmatrix} B\,C\,D \\ B'\,C'\,D' \\ B''\,C''\,D'' \end{bmatrix} - N_1' \begin{bmatrix} A\,C\,D \\ A'\,C'\,D' \\ A''\,C''\,D'' \end{bmatrix} + N_1'' \begin{bmatrix} A\,B\,D \\ A'\,B'\,D' \\ A''\,B''\,D'' \end{bmatrix} - N_1''' \begin{bmatrix} A\,B\,C \\ A'\,B'\,C' \\ A''\,B''\,C'' \end{bmatrix} = 0,$$

with similar equations.

Since $f(m)$ is the determinant formed by eliminating N_1, N_1', &c. from III. we have

$$\frac{df(m)}{dm} = \frac{df(m)}{dA}\frac{dA}{dm} + \frac{df(m)}{dB}\frac{dB}{dm} + \&c. + \frac{df(m)}{dA'}\frac{dA'}{dm} + \&c.$$

$$= a\frac{dA}{dm} + b\frac{dB}{dm} + \&c. + a'\frac{dA'}{dm} + \&c.$$

This vanishes when a, b, &c., a', &c. are all zero. If therefore the first minors of $f(m)$ all vanish when $m = m_1$, the equation $f(m) = 0$ has two roots equal to m_1. In the same way $\dfrac{da}{dm}$ vanishes if all its first minors are zero. But

$$\frac{d^2 f(m)}{dm^2} = a\frac{d^2 A}{dm^2} + \frac{da}{dm}\frac{dA}{dm} + \&c.$$

vanishes if a, $\dfrac{da}{dm}$, &c. are all zero. If therefore the first and second minors of $f(m)$ all vanish when $m = m_1$, the equation

$f(m) = 0$ has three roots equal to m_1. It is evident the proposition may be extended to any number of roots.

The test that, when equal roots occur in the determinantal equation, the terms in the values of x, y, *&c. which contain* t *as a factor should be absent may be stated thus. If there are two equal roots all the first minors must vanish. If three equal roots, all the first and second minors must vanish, and so on. In these cases the equal roots introduce merely a corresponding indeterminateness into the coefficients.*

When there are more equal roots than there are rows in the determinantal equation, it is easy to see that there must be some terms in the integrals which contain t as a factor.

[The following simple example will illustrate the application of this test.

A particle is in equilibrium at the origin of co-ordinates under the action of forces whose force function U is given by

$$U = \tfrac{1}{2} A x^2 + \tfrac{1}{2} B y^2 + \tfrac{1}{2} C z^2 + D y z + E z x + F x y.$$

If the level surfaces are ellipsoids and the force acts inwards, it is clear that the equilibrium of the particle must always be stable. If then any equal roots occur in the determinantal equation, the test should show that the terms which contain t as a factor are absent.

If T be the semi vis viva of the particle and if its mass be taken as unity, we have

$$T = \tfrac{1}{2} x'^2 + \tfrac{1}{2} y'^2 + \tfrac{1}{2} z'^2.$$

Omitting accents and forming the discriminant of $- m^2 T + U$ we have the following determinantal equation :

$$\begin{vmatrix} A - m^2 & F & E \\ F & B - m^2 & D \\ E & D & C - m^2 \end{vmatrix} = 0.$$

This is the "discriminating cubic" which determines the axes of the quadric $U = c$, where c is a constant. The conditions that two of its roots should be equal, i.e. that the quadric should be a spheroid, are well known to be

$$A - \frac{EF}{D} = B - \frac{FD}{E} = C - \frac{DE}{F} = m_1^2,$$

where m_1^2 is equal to either root. These are just the conditions obtained by equating any first minor of the determinant to zero.

The conditions that three of the roots of the cubic should be equal, i.e. that the quadric should be a sphere, are

$$A = B = C, \quad D = 0, \quad E = 0, \quad F = 0.$$

These are the conditions that every second minor should vanish.

In this example we have taken the case of a single particle. Similar remarks however apply when any system of bodies is disturbed from a state of stable equilibrium. The oscillations may be found by the method of Lagrange. The final determinantal equation may be conveniently formed by equating to zero the discriminant of $-m^2 T + U$, where T is the semi vis viva with the accents denoting differentiations with regard to the time omitted, and U is the force function. It is a known theorem that the existence of finite equal roots does not affect the stability of the equilibrium. Hence the conditions for equal roots must be such as to make all the minors equal to zero. Conversely, this theorem will often conveniently give the conditions that Lagrange's determinant has equal roots.]

6. That there should be a difference in the modes in which equal roots affect the motion is no more than we should expect *a priori*. Suppose the coefficients of the equation $f(m) = 0$ to be functions of some quantity n, and that as n passes through the value n_0, two roots become equal to each other. Let the quadratic factor containing these roots be $m^2 + 2\alpha m + \beta$, and let us consider only the case in which α and β are real. We have $\alpha^2 - \beta = 0$ when $n = n_0$. If $\alpha^2 - \beta$ change sign as n passes through the value n_0, the roots will change from a trigonometrical to a purely exponential form, which would indicate a change from oscillatory to non-oscillatory motion. The passage from one kind of motion to the other may be effected through a motion represented by expressions having the time as a factor. But if $\alpha^2 - \beta$ does not change sign, for example, if it be a perfect square for all values of n, there will be no change from one kind of motion to the other, and in this case we should expect that the motion when the roots are equal will be represented by terms of the same character as before. Briefly, we may expect equal roots to introduce terms with t as a factor at the boundary between stability and instability; and to introduce merely an indeterminateness into the coefficients when the motion is stable on both sides.

It is easy to show that in the first of these two cases the minors could not contain either of the factors of $m^2 + 2\alpha m + \beta$. For since $\alpha^2 - \beta$ changes sign, these factors are in one case imaginary; and therefore if one factor occur in any minor the other must also be present. The minors would not only vanish, but must have equal roots also. But as in Art. (3), $\Delta_2 f(m) = ab' - a'b$.

Hence if all the first minors have equal roots it is clear that either $f(m)$ has more than two equal roots, or all the second minors must vanish. The latter is impossible unless $f(m)$ has more than two equal roots.

These general considerations are not meant to replace the proofs given in the last article, but merely to explain how a difference in the effects of the equal roots might arise.

7. Summing up what precedes, we see that if a dynamical system have n co-ordinates its stability depends on the nature of the roots of a certain equation of the $2n$th degree.

If the roots of this equation are all unequal, the motion will be stable if the real roots and the real parts of the imaginary roots are all negative or zero, and unstable if any one is positive. If several roots are equal the motion will be stable if the real parts of those roots are negative and not very small, and unstable if they are negative and small, zero, or any positive quantity. But if, as often happens in dynamical problems, the terms which contain t as a factor are absent from the solution, the condition of stability is that the real roots and the real parts of the imaginary roots of the subsidiary equation should be negative or zero.

8. When the equation $f(D) = 0$ is of low dimensions we may solve it or otherwise determine the nature of its roots; the stability or instability of the system will then become known. But if the degree of the equation be considerable this is not a very easy problem. We shall devote the two next Chapters to the consideration of two methods by either of which, without solving the equation, we can determine the conditions that the real roots and the real parts of the imaginary roots should be all negative. The determination of these conditions has, it appears, never before been accomplished.* The consideration of the equations of motion will then be resumed, and the form of the determinantal equation $f(D) = 0$ when the forces admit of a force function will be more particularly investigated.

---

* [These conditions for the cases of a biquadratic and a quintic had been found by the Author in 1873, and read before the London Mathematical Society in June, 1874. See also the third edition of the Author's *Rigid Dynamics*, Art. 436.]

CHAPTER II.

1. The object of this Chapter has been explained at the end of Chapter I. Briefly, the criterion that the motion of a system of bodies should be stable is that the roots of a certain equation should have all their real parts negative. We propose to investigate these conditions.

Let the equation to be considered be

$$f(x) = p_0 x^n + p_1 x^{n-1} + \ldots + p_{n-1} x + p_n = 0.$$

Let the real roots be a_1, $a_2 \ldots$ and the imaginary roots be

$$\alpha_1 \pm \beta_1 \sqrt{-1}, \quad \alpha_2 \pm \beta_2 \sqrt{-1}, \text{ \&c.}$$

Then

$$f(x) = p_0 (x - a_1)(x - a_2) \ldots (x^2 - 2\alpha_1 x + \alpha_1^2 + \beta_1^2), \text{ \&c.}$$

If then a_1, a_2, \&c. α_1, α_2, \&c. are all negative, every term in each factor, and therefore in the product, must be positive.

It is therefore necessary that every term in the equation $f(x) = 0$ should have the same sign. It will be convenient to suppose this sign to be positive.

It is also clear on the same suppositions that none of the coefficients $p_0, p_1, \ldots p_n$ can be zero, except when the roots of the equation are all of the form $\pm \beta \sqrt{-1}$, or when some of the roots are zero.

2.   Let us now form the equation whose roots are the sums of the roots of $f(x)$ taken two and two.   Let this be

$$F(x) = P_0 x^m + P_1 x^{m-1} + \ldots + P_{m-1} x + P_m = 0,$$

where $m = n \dfrac{n-1}{2}$.   The real roots of this equation will be $a_1 + a_2$, $a_1 + a_3$, &c. $2\alpha_1$, $2\alpha_2$, &c. and the imaginary roots will be $a_1 + \alpha_1 \pm \beta_1 \sqrt{-1}$, &c.   It is clear from the same reasoning as before that if a_1, a_2, &c. α_1, α_2, &c. are all negative, the coefficients P_0, P_1, &c. must all have the same sign.

Conversely, if $p_0, p_1 \ldots$ have all the same sign, the equation $f(x)$ can have no real positive root, and if $P_0, P_1 \ldots P_m$ have all the same sign the equation $F(x)$ can have no positive root, and therefore $f(x)$ can have no imaginary root with its real part positive.

3.   *Our first test of the stability of a dynamical system is that all the coefficients of the dynamical equation* f (D) = 0 *and all the coefficients of its derived equation* F (D) = 0 *should have the same sign.*

It should be noticed that though these conditions are all necessary and sufficient, they are not all independent.   We obtain too many conditions.   In many cases, however, we can at once reduce them to the proper number of independent conditions, and when this is difficult we can have recourse to the second method, to be given in the next Chapter, which is free from this objection.

In order to apply this method with success, it is necessary to have some convenient methods of calculating the coefficients $P_0, P_1 \ldots P_m$.

4.   The first method which suggests itself is one similar to that usually given to determine the coefficients of the equation whose roots are the squares of the differences of the roots of any given equation.

If $S_1, S_2 \ldots$ be the sums of the first, second powers, &c. of the roots of the equation $f(x) = 0$, we have by Newton's theorem

$$S_n + p_1 S_{n-1} + p_2 S_{n-2} + \ldots = 0,$$

where p_0 has been put equal to unity.   If $\Sigma_1, \Sigma_2 \ldots$ be the sums of the powers of the equation $F(x) = 0$, we have in the same way

$$\Sigma_n + P_1 \Sigma_{n-1} + P_2 \Sigma_{n-2} + \ldots = 0 \, ;$$

we may also prove

$$\Sigma_1 = (n-1) S_1,$$
$$\Sigma_2 = (n-2) S_2 + S_1^2,$$
$$\Sigma_3 = (n-4) S_3 + 3 S_1 S_2,$$
$$\Sigma_4 = (n-8) S_4 + 4 S_1 S_3 + 3 S_2^2,$$
$$\Sigma_5 = (n-16) S_5 + 5 S_1 S_4 + 10 S_2 S_3;$$

and the general relation can be found without difficulty.

In this way we find

$$P_1 = (n-1) p_1,$$

$$P_2 = \frac{(n-1)(n-2)}{1.2} p_1^2 + (n-2) p_2,$$

$$P_3 = \frac{(n-1)(n-2)(n-3)}{1.2.3} p_1^3 + (n-2)^2 p_1 p_2 + (n-4) p_3,$$

$$P_4 = \frac{(n-1)(n-2)(n-3)(n-4)}{1.2.3.4} p_1^4 + \frac{(n-2)^2(n-3)}{1.2} p_1^2 p_2$$

$$+ (n-3)^2 p_1 p_3 + \frac{(n-2)(n-3)}{1.2} p_2^2 + (n-8) p_4.$$

But the process becomes longer and longer at every stage. We shall therefore proceed to point out some other methods of obtaining the coefficients.

This method of proceeding has indeed been stated only because it proves in a convenient way that when $p_0 = 1$, all the coefficients $P_1, P_2, P_3 \ldots$ of the derived equation are integral rational functions of the coefficients $p_0, p_1 \ldots p_n$.

5. *The equation* $f(x) = 0$ *being given, to calculate the coefficients of* $F(x) = 0$.

Put $x = y \pm z$ and equate separately to zero the sums of the even and odd powers of z, we have

$$\left. \begin{array}{l} f(y) + f''(y) \dfrac{z^2}{\underline{2}} + f^{iv}(y) \dfrac{z^4}{\underline{4}} + \ldots = 0 \\[2mm] f'(y) z + f'''(y) \dfrac{z^3}{\underline{3}} + \ldots \qquad = 0 \end{array} \right\}.$$

Rejecting the root $z = 0$, let us eliminate z. Then the roots of the resulting equation in y are the arithmetic means of the roots of $f(x) = 0$.

If, on the other hand, we eliminate y we have an equation of an even degree to find z. This, putting $4z^2 = \zeta$, is the equation whose roots are the squares of the differences of the roots of the given equation.

It may be thought that this elimination may prove tedious, but it will be presently shown that only the first and last terms of the result are really wanted. All the others may be omitted in the process of elimination, and thus the labour will be greatly lessened. The method is however most useful when the given equation has several of its terms absent.

6. *Example.* *To determine the condition that the roots of the biquadratic*

$$x^4 + px^3 + qx^2 + rx + s = 0$$

should indicate a stable motion.

Applying the rule we have

$$F(x) = x^6 + 3px^5 + (3p^2 + 2q)\,x^4 + (4pq + p^3)\,x^3$$
$$+ (2p^2q + pr + q^2 - 4s)\,x^2 + (pq^2 + p^2r - 4ps)\,x + pqr - r^2 - p^2s.$$

The first four coefficients contain only positive terms, and need not be considered. If the last three coefficients be called P_4, P_5, P_6, we have

$$p^2 P_4 - 4P_6 = (pq - 2r)^2 + 2p^4q + p^3r,$$
$$pP_5 - 4P_6 = (pq - 2r)^2 + p^3r.$$

If then P_6 is positive, all the other coefficients are positive.

The necessary and sufficient conditions of stability are therefore that p, q, r, s should be finite and positive, and

$$P_6 = pqr - r^2 - p^2s$$

positive or zero.

7. In forming the derived equation $F(x)$ the only difficulty is to form the last term P_m. For when this is known the other terms can be at once derived from it by an easy process.

Let $a, b, c...$ be the roots of $f(x) = 0$ with their signs changed, and let

$$f(x) = p_0x^n + p_1x^{n-1} + ... + p_n.$$

Let Δ stand for the operation

$$\Delta = \frac{d}{da} + \frac{d}{db} + \frac{d}{dc} + ...$$

Then since $\dfrac{p_n}{p_0} = abc \dots$ we have obviously

$$\Delta \frac{p_n}{p_0} = \frac{p_{n-1}}{p_0} .$$

In the same way we have

$$\Delta \frac{p_{n-1}}{p_0} = 2 \frac{p_{n-2}}{p_0} .$$

And generally

$$\Delta \frac{p_{n-\kappa+1}}{p_0} = \kappa \frac{p_{n-\kappa}}{p_0} ,$$

and so on up to

$$\Delta \frac{p_1}{p_0} = n.$$

Let us now operate with Δ on any expression

$$\phi \left(p_0, p_1 \dots p_n \right),$$

which has the same number of factors in every term. Let r be the number of factors, then ϕ may be written

$$\phi = p_0{}^r \dot{\phi}_1 \left(\frac{p_1}{p_0}, \dots \frac{p_n}{p_0} \right),$$

$$\therefore \Delta\phi = p_0{}^{r-1} \left\{ np_0 \frac{d}{dp_1} + (n-1)p_1 \frac{d}{dp_2} + \dots \right\} \phi_1$$

$$= \left\{ np_0 \frac{d}{dp_1} + (n-1)p_1 \frac{d}{dp_2} + \dots + p_{n-1} \frac{d}{dp_n} \right\} \phi. ,$$

Let $P_0, P_1 \dots P_m$ be the coefficients of the derived equation $F(x)$, and let $P_0 = 1$. Then since the roots of $F(x)$ are the sums of the roots of $f(x)$ taken two and two, it is easy to see that

$$P_{m-1} = \tfrac{1}{2}\Delta P_m,$$
$$2P_{m-2} = \tfrac{1}{2}\Delta P_{m-1},$$
$$3P_{m-3} = \tfrac{1}{2}\Delta P_{m-2},$$
$$\&c. = \&c.$$

Thus when P_m is known, the other terms may be calculated without difficulty. The term P_m will be called the *fundamental term* of the equation.

Example. Given in the case of a biquadratic

$$P_6 = p_1 p_2 p_3 - p_0 p_3{}^2 - p_1{}^2 p_4,$$

to calculate P_5.

Performing the operation

$$p_3 \frac{d}{dp_4} + 2p_2 \frac{d}{dp_3} + 3p_1 \frac{d}{dp_2} + 4p_0 \frac{d}{dp_1},$$

on P_5 we find after division by 2,

$$P_5 = p_1 p_2^2 + p_1^2 p_3 - 4p_0 p_1 p_4,$$

which is the result already given.

8.   It should be noticed that in the equation

$$f(x) = p_0 x^n + p_1 x^{n-1} + \ldots + p_n = 0,$$

if we regard x as a number, $p_0 p_1 \ldots p_n$ are all of equal dimensions. It follows from the theory of dimensions, that if any subject of operation be the sum of a number of terms of the form

$$p_0^\alpha p_1^\beta p_2^\gamma, \ldots$$

there must be the same number of factors in every term.   For example, in every term of the expression for P_m we have $\alpha + \beta + \gamma$ &c. the same.

On the other hand, we may regard x as a quantity of one dimension, and in this case $p_0, p_1 \ldots p_n$ have their dimensions indicated by their suffixes.   We must therefore have $\beta + 2\gamma + 3\delta + \ldots$ as well as $\alpha + \beta + \gamma + \ldots$ the same in every term.

These two tests of the correctness of our processes will be found convenient.

9.   *The whole derived equation being known when the fundamental term is known, it is required to find the fundamental term.*

[First Method.]

If we write $-x$ for x in any equation, we have a second equation whose roots are equal and opposite to those of the first equation. If we eliminate x between these two, we shall get a result which must be zero when the two equations have a common root.   The eliminant must therefore contain as a factor the product of the sums of the roots of the given equation taken two and two.

It will afterwards be shown that the last term P_m of the derived equation (when p_0 is put equal to unity) always contains the term

$$p_1 / p_2 / p_3 \ldots$$

with a coefficient which is positive and equal to unity.

Hence we have this rule, to find P_m, eliminate x between

$$\left. \begin{array}{l} x^n + p_2 x^{n-2} + p_4 x^{n-4} + \ldots = 0 \\ p_1 x^{n-1} + p_3 x^{n-3} + \ldots \quad\quad = 0 \end{array} \right\},$$

and divide the result by the coefficient of $p_1 p_2 p_3 \ldots p_{n-1}$.

It is obvious that the result may be written down as a determinant. On trial, however, it will be found more convenient to make the elimination by the method of eliminating the highest and lowest terms than to expand the determinant.

10. *Given the fundamental term of the equation derived from*

$$f(x) = p_0 x^{n-1} + p_1 x^{n-2} + \ldots + p_{n-1} = 0 \ldots\ldots\ldots\ldots(1),$$

to find the fundamental term of the equation derived from

$$p_0 x^n + p_1 x^{n-1} + \ldots + p_{n-1} x + p_n = 0 \ \ldots\ldots\ldots\ldots(2).$$

[Second Method.]

Let Q_n be the product of the sums, two and two, of the roots of the equation (2) taken *with their signs changed*, so that Q_n is the same as the fundamental term of the derived equation and differs from P_m only in having a suffix more convenient for our present purpose.

Let Q_n be expanded in a series of powers of p_n: thus

$$Q_n = \phi_0 + \phi_1 p_n + \phi_2 p_n^2 + \ldots$$

where ϕ_0, ϕ_1, ϕ_2, &c., are all functions of p_0, p_1, &c., which functions have to be found. Let the roots of $f(x) = 0$ with their signs changed be a, b, $c \ldots$, then

$$Q_{n-1} = (a+b)(a+c)\ldots$$

Let us introduce a new root, which, when its sign is changed, we shall call r. Then

$$Q_n = (a+b)(a+c) \ldots (r+a)(r+b)\ldots$$

$$= \frac{Q_{n-1}}{p_0} (p_0 r^{n-1} + p_1 r^{n-2} + \ldots + p_{n-1}).$$

This value of Q_n must be the same as that given by the series when we write

$$p_0, \quad p_1 + rp_0, \quad p_2 + rp_1, \quad \&c., \quad p_{n-1} + rp_{n-2}, \quad rp_{n-1},$$

respectively, for p_0, p_1, p_2, &c., p_{n-1}, p_n. Equating the coefficients of the terms independent of r we have

$$\phi_0 = Q_{n-1} \frac{p_{n-1}}{p_0}.$$

Equating the terms containing the first power of r we have

$$p_{n-1}\phi_1 + \left(p_0 \frac{d}{dp_1} + p_1 \frac{d}{dp_2} + \ldots + p_{n-2}\frac{d}{dp_{n-1}}\right)\phi_0 = Q_{n-1}\frac{p_{n-2}}{p_0}.$$

Substituting for ϕ_0 we have, by a known theorem in the Differential Calculus,

$$\phi_1 = -\left(p_0 \frac{d}{dp_1} + p_1 \frac{d}{dp_2} + \ldots + p_{n-2}\frac{d}{dp_{n-1}}\right)\frac{Q_{n-1}}{p_0}.$$

Equating the terms containing the second power of r we have

$$\frac{1}{2}\left\{p_0^2 \frac{d^2}{dp_1^2} + 2p_0 p_1 \frac{d^2}{dp_1 dp_2} + \ldots\right\}\phi_0$$

$$+ \left(p_0 \frac{d}{dp_1} + p_1 \frac{d}{dp_2} + \ldots\right)\phi_1 \cdot p_{n-1}$$

$$+ \phi_2 p^2{}_{n-1} = Q_{n-1}\frac{p_{n-3}}{p_0},$$

and so on. Thus we have

$$Q_n = Q_{n-1}\frac{p_{n-1}}{p_0} - p_n\left(p_0 \frac{d}{dp_1} + p_1 \frac{d}{dp_2} + \ldots + p_{n-2}\frac{d}{dp_{n-1}}\right)\frac{Q_{n-1}}{p_0} + \&c.$$

If we examine this process, we see that when Q_{n-1} is known, we may at once write down the terms independent of p_n and the coefficient of p_n. The process to find the coefficient of p_n^2 is longer, but it may be much shortened by the consideration that when $p_0 = 1$ the result must be an integral function of the coefficients. We may therefore omit all terms as soon as they make their appearance, which do not contain the factor $p^2{}_{n-1}$, for we know that such terms must disappear from the result.

This method is not so convenient as the one which will be presently given to find the coefficients of the higher powers of p_n. But it is useful as showing that Q_n contains the term

$$\frac{p_1 p_2 \ldots p_{n-1}}{p_0^{n-1}},$$

with a positive integral coefficient equal to unity. This will be clear from the consideration that the term independent of p_n in Q_n is obtained from Q_{n-1} by multiplying by $\frac{p_{n-1}}{p_0}$. If therefore Q_{n-1} contains $\frac{p_1 p_2 \ldots p_{n-2}}{p_0^{n-2}}$, Q_n must contain the term $\frac{p_1 p_2 \ldots p_{n-1}}{p_0^{n-1}}$. No other term can be formed which is equal to this with an opposite sign, for the terms which enter by the other processes to be performed on Q_{n-1} all contain p_n as a factor.　Now $Q_2 = \dfrac{p_1}{p_0}$; therefore

Q_3 contains the term $\dfrac{p_1 p_2}{p_0^{\,2}}$, Q contains $\dfrac{p_1 p_2 p_3}{p_0^{\,3}}$, and so on.

It has been shown that every term in $p_0^{\,n-1} Q_n$ has the same number of factors (Art. 8).　It follows from this reasoning that this number of factors is $n-1$.

11.　*To find the fundamental term of the derived equation by means of a differential equation.*

[Third Method.]

The fundamental term required is a factor of the eliminant of

$$\left.\begin{array}{l} p_0 x^n + p_2 x^{n-2} + \ldots = 0 \\ p_1 x^{n-1} + p_3 x^{n-3} + \ldots = 0 \end{array}\right\}.$$

Let $x^2 = y$, then we have

$$\left.\begin{array}{l} p_0 y^{\frac{n}{2}} + p_2 y^{\frac{n}{2}-1} + p_4 y^{\frac{n}{2}-2} + \ldots = 0 \\ p_1 y^{\frac{n}{2}-1} + p_3 y^{\frac{n}{2}-2} + \ldots\ldots\ldots = 0 \end{array}\right\} n \text{ even},$$

$$\left.\begin{array}{l} p_0 y^{\frac{n-1}{2}} + p_2 y^{\frac{n-3}{2}} + \ldots\ldots\ldots = 0 \\ p_1 y^{\frac{n-1}{2}} + p_3 y^{\frac{n-3}{2}} + \ldots\ldots\ldots = 0 \end{array}\right\} n \text{ odd}.$$

If we write $y + dy$ for y the result of the elimination must be the same.　Hence if we make

$$\left.\begin{array}{ll} \dfrac{dp_2}{dy} = \dfrac{n}{2} p_0, & \dfrac{dp_4}{dy} = \left(\dfrac{n}{2}-1\right) p_2, \&c. \\[2mm] \dfrac{dp_3}{dy} = \left(\dfrac{n}{2}-1\right) p_1, & \dfrac{dp_5}{dy} = \left(\dfrac{n}{2}-2\right) p_3, \&c. \end{array}\right\} n \text{ even},$$

$$\left.\begin{array}{ll} \dfrac{dp_2}{dy} = \dfrac{n-1}{2} p_0, & \dfrac{dp_4}{dy} = \dfrac{n-3}{2} p_2, \&c. \\[2mm] \dfrac{dp_3}{dy} = \dfrac{n-1}{2} p_1, & \dfrac{dp_5}{dy} = \dfrac{n-3}{2} p_3, \&c. \end{array}\right\} n \text{ odd},$$

and if E be the eliminant, we have

$$\frac{dE}{dy} = 0.$$

It follows that whether n be even or odd, E must satisfy the equation

$$\left.\begin{array}{c} p_{n-2}\dfrac{dE}{dp_n} + p_{n-3}\dfrac{dE}{dp_{n-1}} \\[2mm] + 2\left(p_{n-4}\dfrac{dE}{dp_{n-2}} + p_{n-5}\dfrac{dE}{dp_{n-3}}\right) \\[2mm] + 3\left(p_{n-6}\dfrac{dE}{dp_{n-4}} + p_{n-7}\dfrac{dE}{dp_{n-5}}\right) \\[2mm] + \ldots\ldots\ldots\ldots\ldots\ldots\ldots \end{array}\right\} = 0.$$

We may make the elimination by multiplying the two equations by y, y^2..., until we have as many equations as we have powers to eliminate. If in the determinant thus formed, we multiply out the terms in the diagonal joining the right-hand top corner to the left bottom corner, we get when n is even $p_n^{\frac{n}{2}-1} p_1^{\frac{n}{2}+1}$ and when n is odd $p_n^{\frac{n-1}{2}} p_0^{\frac{n-1}{2}}$. Now Q_n must contain $n-1$ factors and be of the $n\dfrac{n-1}{2}$ th degree. Hence when n is even $E = cp_1 Q_n$ and when n is odd $E = cQ_n$, where c is some constant.

Now $\dfrac{d}{dp_1}$ does not occur in the above differential equation. Hence treating p_1 as a constant, we see that Q_n must satisfy the differential equation

$$\left(p_{n-2}\frac{dQ_n}{dp_n} + p_{n-3}\frac{dQ_n}{dp_{n-1}}\right) + 2\left(p_{n-4}\frac{dQ_n}{dp_{n-2}} + p_{n-5}\frac{dQ_n}{dp_{n-3}}\right)$$
$$+ 3\left(p_{n-6}\frac{dQ_n}{dp_{n-4}} + p_{n-7}\frac{dQ_n}{dp_{n-5}}\right) + \&c. = 0.$$

12. We may show that $p_0^{n-1} Q_n$ is a symmetrical function of the coefficients p_0, p_1..., p_n and the same coefficients read backwards. Let $a, b, c...$ be the roots of $f(x) = 0$ with their signs changed, then $Q_n = (a+b)(a+c)...$.

If now we read the coefficients in the opposite order, the roots of the equation thus formed will, when their signs are changed, be $\dfrac{1}{a}, \dfrac{1}{b}...$. If Q'_n be the fundamental term of the equation derived from this, we have

$$Q'_n = \left(\frac{1}{a} + \frac{1}{b}\right)\left(\frac{1}{a} + \frac{1}{c}\right)\ldots.$$

Since $\dfrac{p_n}{p_0} = abc...$ we see that

$$p_0^{n-1} Q_n = p_n^{n-1} Q'_n.$$

We may therefore infer that $p_0{}^{n-1}Q_n$ also satisfies the differential equation

$$\left(p_2\frac{dE}{dp_0}+p_3\frac{dE}{dp_1}\right)+2\left(p_4\frac{dE}{dp_2}+p_5\frac{dE}{dp_3}\right)+3\left(p_6\frac{dE}{dp_4}+p_7\frac{dE}{dp_5}\right)+\&\text{c.}=0.$$

13. *We may use either of these differential equations to find* Q_n *when* Q_{n-1} *is given.*

Let the first differential equation be represented by

$$\nabla Q_n = 0,$$

and let

$$Q_n = A_0 + A_1 p_n + A_2 p_n{}^2 + \dots,$$

where A_0, A_1, ... are functions of p_0, p_1, &c. The value of A_0 has been proved in Art. 10 to be

$$A_0 = Q_{n-1}\frac{p_{n-1}}{p_0}.$$

To find the other coefficients of the powers of p_n substitute this value of Q_n in the differential equation ; we have

$$0 = \nabla A_0 + p_n \nabla A_1 + p_{n-2} A_1$$
$$+ p_n{}^2 \nabla A_2 + 2p_{n-2}p_n A_2$$
$$+ \&\text{c.}$$

Equating the several powers of p_n to zero, we find

$$A_1 = -\frac{1}{p_{n-2}}\nabla A_0,$$

$$2A_2 = -\frac{1}{p_{n-2}}\nabla A_1,$$

$$3A_3 = -\frac{1}{p_{n-2}}\nabla A_2,$$

$$\&\text{c.} = \&\text{c.}$$

Thus by one regular and easy process each term may be derived from the other.

In performing this process we may omit every term in the subject of operation which does not contain p_{n-2}. For p_{n-2} can be introduced only by performing $\dfrac{d}{dp_n}$, and since p_n is absent from the coefficients, this operation yields nothing.

In this way we find

$$p_0 Q_2 = p_1,$$
$$p_0^2 Q_3 = p_1 p_2 - p_0 p_3,$$
$$p_0^3 Q_4 = p_1 p_2 p_3 - p_0 p_3^2 - p_1^2 p_4,$$
$$p_0^4 Q_5 = p_1 p_2 p_3 p_4 - p_0 p_3^2 p_4 - p_1^2 p_4^2$$
$$\qquad - p_5 \left(- p_0 p_2 p_3 + p_1 p_2^2 - 2 p_0 p_1 p_4 \right)$$
$$\qquad + \frac{p_5^2}{1 \cdot 2} \left(- 2 p_0^2 \right).$$

To illustrate this process, consider how Q_5 is obtained from Q_4. The first line is formed by multiplying the line above by p_4, this is A_0. To find the coefficient of $- p_5$ we operate with

$$\left(p_3 \frac{d}{dp_5} + p_2 \frac{d}{dp_4} \right) + 2 \left(p_1 \frac{d}{dp_3} + p_0 \frac{d}{dp_2} \right)$$

on such of the terms in the line above as contain p_3 and then divide by p_3. Performing the same operation on the coefficient of $(-p_5)$ we obviously obtain the coefficient of $\dfrac{p_5^2}{1 \cdot 2}$.

In M. Serret's *Cours d'Algèbre Supérieure*, Note III., there will be found a method of forming the last term of the equation to the squares of the differences, which suggested the method used in Art. 13, of substituting in a differential equation, if only a differential equation could be found. [See also Dr Salmon's *Higher Algebra*, Arts. 60, 64, and 72.]

CHAPTER III.

1.   It has been shown in the first Chapter that the stability of a dynamical system with n co-ordinates oscillating about a state of steady motion depends on the nature of the roots of a certain equation of the $2n^{\text{th}}$ degree which we may call

$$f(z) = 0.$$

The system is stable if the real roots and the real parts of the imaginary roots are all negative.   Now Cauchy has given the following theorem of which we shall make some use.

Let $z = x + y\sqrt{-1}$ be any root, and let us regard x and y as co-ordinates of a point referred to rectangular axes.   Substitute for z and let

$$f(z) = P + Q\sqrt{-1}.$$

Let any point whose co-ordinates are such that P and Q both vanish be called a radical point.   Describe any contour, and let a point move round this contour in the positive direction and notice how often $\dfrac{P}{Q}$ passes through the value zero and changes its sign. Suppose it changes α times from $+$ to $-$ and β times from $-$ to $+$. Then Cauchy asserts that the number of radical points within the contour is $\frac{1}{2}(\alpha - \beta)$. It is however necessary that no radical point should lie *on* the contour.

2. Let us choose as our contour the infinite semicircle which bounds space on the positive side of the axis of y. Let us first travel from $y = -\infty$ to $y = +\infty$ along the circumference.

If
$$f(z) = p_0 z^n + p_1 z^{n-1} + \ldots + p_n,$$

we have changing to polar co-ordinates

$$f(z) = p_0 r^n (\cos n\theta + \sin n\theta \sqrt{-1}) + \ldots$$

Hence
$$\left.\begin{array}{l} P = p_0 r^n \cos n\theta + p_1 r^{n-1} \cos (n-1)\,\theta + \ldots \\ Q = p_0 r^n \sin n\theta + p_1 r^{n-1} \sin (n-1)\,\theta + \ldots \end{array}\right\}.$$

In the limit, since r is infinite,

$$\frac{P}{Q} = \cot n\theta;$$

$\dfrac{P}{Q}$ vanishes when $n\theta = (2\kappa + 1)\dfrac{\pi}{2}$, *i.e.*

$$\theta = \pm \frac{1}{n}\frac{\pi}{2}, \quad \pm \frac{3}{n}\frac{\pi}{2}, \quad \pm \frac{5}{n}\frac{\pi}{2} \ldots\ldots\ldots\ldots (A);$$

$\dfrac{P}{Q}$ is infinite when $n\theta = 2\kappa\dfrac{\pi}{2}$, *i.e.*

$$\theta = 0, \quad \pm \frac{2}{n}\frac{\pi}{2}, \quad \pm \frac{4}{n}\frac{\pi}{2}, \quad \pm \frac{6}{n}\frac{\pi}{2} \ldots\ldots\ldots\ldots (B).$$

The values of θ in series (B) it will be noticed *separate* those in series (A).

When θ is small and very little greater than zero, $\dfrac{P}{Q}$ is positive, and therefore changes sign from $+$ to $-$ at every one of the values of θ in series (A). If n be even there will be n changes of sign. If n be odd there will be $n - 1$ changes excluding $\theta = \pm \dfrac{\pi}{2}$, in this case $\dfrac{P}{Q}$ is positive when θ is a little less than $\dfrac{\pi}{2}$, and negative when θ is a little greater than $\dfrac{\pi}{2}$.

Let us now travel along the axis of y still in the positive direction, viz. from $y = +\infty$ to $y = -\infty$. Since $x = 0$ it will be more convenient to use Cartesian co-ordinates, we have, since

$$f(z) = p_0 z^n + p_1 z^{n-1} + \ldots + p_{n-1} z + p_n,$$

and

$$z = y\sqrt{-1},$$

$$P = p_n - p_{n-2} y^2 + p_{n-4} y^4 - \ldots$$

$$Q = y(p_{n-1} - p_{n-3} y^2 + \ldots),$$

and

$$\therefore \frac{P}{Q} = \frac{p_n - p_{n-2} y^2 + p_{n-4} y^4 - \ldots}{y(p_{n-1} - p_{n-3} y^2 + \ldots)}.$$

The condition that there should be no radical point within the contour is that this expression should change sign through zero from $-$ to $+$ as often as it before changed sign from $+$ to $-$ on travelling round the semicircle. If n be even the numerator has one more term than the denominator, and when p_0 and p_1 have the same sign, $\frac{P}{Q}$ begins when y is very great by being negative. In order that it should change sign through zero n times, it is necessary and sufficient that both the equations

$$p_n - p_{n-2} y^2 + p_{n-4} y^4 - \ldots = 0,$$

$$p_{n-1} y - p_{n-3} y^3 + p_{n-5} y^5 - \ldots = 0,$$

should have their roots real, and that the roots of the latter should separate the roots of the former.

If n be odd, the numerator and denominator have the same number of terms, and when p_0 and p_1 have the same sign, $\frac{P}{Q}$ begins when y is very great by being positive. In order that it should change sign through zero from $-$ to $+$ $n-1$ times, it is necessary and sufficient that the same two equations as before should have their roots real, and that the roots of the former should separate the roots of the latter.

In order then to express the necessary and sufficient conditions, that $f(z) = 0$ *may have no radical point on the positive side of the axis of* y, *put* $z = y\sqrt{-1}$ *and equate to zero separately the real and imaginary parts. Of the two equations thus formed, the roots of the one of lower dimensions must separate the roots of the other. It is also necessary that the coefficients of the two highest powers of* z *in* f (z) *should have the same sign.*

3. It has been stated that p_0 and p_1 the coefficients of the two highest powers in $f(z)$ must have the same sign. It is easy to see

that, if they had opposite signs, $\dfrac{P}{Q}$ would change sign through zero $2n$ times as we travel round the contour. All the radical points of the equation would then lie on the positive instead of the negative side of the axis of y.

It has also been assumed that no radical point lies on the contour. It has therefore been assumed that $f(z) = 0$ has no root of the form $z = y\sqrt{-1}$. It will be more convenient to consider this exception a little further on.

4. *It is required to express in an analytical form the conditions that the roots of an equation* $f_2(x) = 0$ *may be all real, and may separate the roots of another equation* $f_1(x) = 0$ *of one degree higher dimensions.*

To effect this, let us use Sturm's theorem *reversed.* Perform the process of finding the greatest common measure of $f_1(x)$ and $f_2(x)$, changing the sign of each remainder as it is obtained. Let the series of modified remainders thus obtained be $f_3(x)$, $f_4(x)$, &c. Then it may be shown that when any one of these functions vanishes, the two on each side have opposite signs. It is also clear that no two successive functions can vanish unless $f_1(x)$ and $f_2(x)$ have a common factor. This exception will be considered presently.

Hence in passing from $x = -\infty$ to $+\infty$ no variation of sign can be lost except when $f_1(x)$ vanishes. If a variation is lost it is regained when x has the next greatest value which makes $f_1(x)$ vanish *unless* $f_2(x) = 0$ has a root between these two successive roots of $f_1(x) = 0$. Hence this rule:—

The roots of the equations $f_1(x) = 0$, $f_2(x) = 0$, *will be all real and the roots of the latter will separate those of the former, if in the series*

$$f_1(x),\ f_2(x),\ f_3(x) \ldots$$

as many variations of sign are lost in passing from $x = -\infty$ *to* $x = +\infty$ *as there are units in the degree of the equation* $f_1(x) = 0$.

We have supposed the variations of sign to be *lost* instead of *gained* in passing from $x = -\infty$ to $+\infty$. That this may be the case the *signs* of the highest powers of $f_1(x)$ and $f_2(x)$ must be the same.

These functions are alternately of an even and odd degree, the condition that the whole number of variations of sign may be lost in passing from $x = -\infty$ to $+\infty$ may be more conveniently expressed thus:—*The coefficients of the highest powers of* x *in the series*

$$f_1(x),\ f_2(x),\ f_3(x) \ldots$$

must all have the same sign.

5. The process of finding the greatest common measure of two algebraic expressions is usually rather long. We may in our case shorten it materially by omitting the quotients and performing the division in the following manner. Let

$$f_1(x) = p_0 x^n - p_2 x^{n-2} + p_4 x^{n-4} - \ldots$$
$$f_2(x) = p_1 x^{n-1} - p_3 x^{n-3} + p_5 x^{n-5} - \ldots$$

then, since p_1 is positive, it easily follows by division that

$$f_3(x) = A x^{n-2} - A' x^{n-4} + A'' x^{n-6} - \ldots$$

where
$$A = p_1 p_2 - p_0 p_3,$$
$$A' = p_1 p_4 - p_0 p_5,$$
$$\&c. = \&c.,$$

so that by remembering this simple cross-multiplication *we may write down the value of* $f_3(x)$ *without any other process than what may be performed by simple inspection.* In the same way $f_4(x)$, &c. may all be written down.

6. **Ex. 1.** Express the conditions that the real roots and real parts of the imaginary roots of the cubic

$$x^3 + px^2 + qx + r = 0$$

may be all negative.

$$f_1(x) = x^3 - qx,$$
$$f_2(x) = px^2 - r,$$
$$f_3(x) = (pq - r)\, x,$$
$$f_4(x) = (pq - r)\, r.$$

The necessary conditions are that

$$p,\ pq - r \text{ and } r$$

must all be positive.

Ex. 2. Express the corresponding conditions for the bi-quadratic

$$x^4 + px^3 + qx^2 + rx + s = 0,$$
$$f_1(x) = x^4 \qquad\qquad\qquad - qx^2 + s,$$
$$f_2(x) = px^3 \qquad\qquad\qquad - rx,$$
$$f_3(x) = (pq - r)\, x^3 \qquad\qquad - ps,$$
$$f_4(x) = \{(pq - r)\, r - p^2 s\}\, x,$$
$$f_5(x) = \{(pq - r)\, r - p^2 s\}\, ps.$$

The conditions are that

$$p, \quad pq - r, \quad (pq - r)\, r - p^2 s \text{ and } s$$

must be all positive.

These are evidently equivalent to the five conditions that

$$p, \quad q, \quad r, \quad s, \quad (pq - r)\, r - p^2 s,$$

should be all positive.

In both these examples all the numerical work has been exhibited.

7. Since the coefficients of the highest powers of x in $f_1(x)$ and $f_2(x)$ are p_0 and p_1 we see that the condition that p_0 and p_1 should have the same sign is included in the general statement that all the coefficients of the highest powers should have the same sign. If the function $f(x)$ be of n dimensions we thus obtain n necessary and sufficient conditions.

On examining these conditions in the cases of the cubic and biquadratic it will be seen that they cannot be satisfied if any one of the coefficients of the given equation should be negative.

8. Although the theorem in its present form gives n conditions as the proper number for an equation of the nth degree, yet it is important to notice that it gives other conditions also which are true and may be useful. It has been shown in the second Chapter that all the coefficients of the equation $f(x) = 0$ must be positive, hence the roots of $f_1(x) = 0$ must all be positive. It may be shown also, that the roots of each of the functions $f_1(x)$, $f_2(x)$, &c. are separated by the roots of the function next below it in order. Hence the roots of all these functions must be positive, and therefore in every one of the functions the coefficients of all the powers must be alternately positive and negative and not one can vanish. If however $f_1(x)$ and $f_2(x)$ have one or more common factors some of the functions $f_3(x)$, $f_4(x)$, &c. will wholly vanish.

9. When the degree of the equation is very considerable there is some labour in the application of the rule given in Art. 5. The objection is that we only want the terms in the first column, and to obtain these we have to write down all the other columns. *We shall now investigate a method of obtaining each term in the first column from the one above it without the necessity of writing down any expression except the one required.*

We notice that each function is obtained from the one above it by the same process. Now

$$f_1(x) = p_0 x^n - p_2 x^{n-2} + p_4 x^{n-4} - \ldots$$
$$f_2(x) = p_1 x^{n-1} - p_3 x^{n-3} + p_5 x^{n-5} - \ldots$$
$$f_3(x) = (p_1 p_2 - p_0 p_3)\, x^{n-2} - (p_1 p_4 - p_0 p_5)\, x^{n-4} + \ldots$$

The first and second lines will be changed into the second and third lines by writing for

$$p_0, \qquad p_1, \qquad p_2, \qquad p_3, \qquad \&c.$$

the values

$$p_1, \qquad p_1 p_2 - p_0 p_3, \qquad p_3, \qquad p_1 p_4 - p_0 p_5, \&c.$$

If then in any term of any function we make these changes, we obtain the corresponding term of the function next in order.

10. Example. Express the conditions of stability for the quintic

$$f(x) = p_0 x^5 + p_1 x^4 + p_2 x^3 + p_3 x^2 + p_4 x + p_5.$$

We have

$$f_1(x) = p_0 x^5 + \dots$$

$$f_2(x) = p_1 x^4 + \dots$$

$$f_3(x) = (p_1 p_2 - p_0 p_3)\, x^3,$$

$$f_4(x) = \{(p_1 p_2 - p_0 p_3) p_3 - p_1(p_1 p_4 - p_0 p_5)\}\, x^2,$$

$$f_5(x) = [\{(p_1 p_2 - p_0 p_3) p_3 - p_1(p_1 p_4 - p_0 p_5)\}\,(p_1 p_4 - p_0 p_5)$$
$$- (p_1 p_2 - p_0 p_3)^2 \cdot p_5]\, x,$$

$$f_6(x) = [\{(p_1 p_2 - p_0 p_3) p_3 - p_1(p_1 p_4 - p_0 p_5)\}\,(p_1 p_4 - p_0 p_5)$$
$$- (p_1 p_2 - p_0 p_3)^2 \cdot p_5]\,(p_1 p_2 - p_0 p_3) p_5.$$

11. On examining the conditions as given in the cases of a biquadratic and quintic it will be apparent that several contain the previous conditions as factors. Thus the analytical expressions are rendered much longer than is necessary. *It is now proposed to investigate a method of discovering and omitting these extraneous factors as they occur, and thus obtaining the required conditions in their simplest forms.*

Let the coefficients of the several powers of x in the functions be when taken positively

$$
\begin{array}{lllll}
f_1(x) = p_0, & p_2, & p_4, & p_6 \cdots \\
f_2(x) = p_1, & p_3, & p_5, & p_7 \cdots \\
f_3(x) = A, & A', & A'', & A''' \cdots \\
f_4(x) = B, & B', & B'', & B''' \cdots
\end{array}
$$

$$\&c. = \&c.$$

Let us first find which of these terms contain p_1 as a factor. Putting $p_1 = 0$ and using the rule in Art. 5, the series become

$$
\begin{array}{ccccc}
p_0, & p_2, & p_4, & p_6, & \cdots \quad \cdots \\[4pt]
0, & p_3, & p_5, & p_7, & \cdots \quad \cdots \\[4pt]
-p_0 p_3, & -p_0 p_5, & -p_0 p_7, & -p_0 p_9, & \cdots \quad \cdots \\[4pt]
-p_0 p_3^2, & -p_0 p_3 p_5, & -p_0 p_3 p_7, & -p_0 p_3 p_9, & \cdots \quad \cdots \\[4pt]
0, & 0, & 0, & 0, & \cdots \quad \cdots \\[4pt]
0, & 0, & 0, & 0, & \cdots \quad \cdots \\[4pt]
& & \&c. & &
\end{array}
$$

Hence the C's and D's all vanish and therefore contain p_1 as a factor. By the rule in Art. 5, the E's contain p_1^2, the F's contain p_1^3, the G's p_1^5, the H's p_1^8, and so on.

But since each line is formed from the preceding by a uniform rule, it follows that the D's and E's contain A as a factor, the F's contain A^2, the G's contain A^3, the H's contain A^5, and so on.

The factor A in the D's and E's has its origin in the factor p_1 which occurs in the C's and D's and would not appear if that factor had been omitted when the C's and D's were formed. The factor A in the D's and E's in the same way gives rise to the factor B in the E's and F's. So that if we take care each time we perform the process described in Art. 9 to omit the common factor p_1 whenever it occurs, all these subsequent factors will never make their appearance.

We shall now show that if these factors are omitted, the dimensions of the nth function $f_n(x)$ will be $n\,\dfrac{n-1}{2}$. First consider the actual dimensions of each function before the factors are omitted. If we examine the rule by which each function is derived from the preceding, it will become evident that, the dimensions of each letter being indicated by its suffix, the dimensions of any function are equal to the sum of the two preceding $+2$.

In the following table the first column indicates the function. In the second column will be found the dimensions of the leading coefficient of that function when calculated by the rule in Art. 5. In the third column will be found the dimensions as given by the formula $n\,\dfrac{n-1}{2}$. In the remaining columns are the dimensions of the extraneous factors p_1, A, B, &c. introduced into each term.

$f_1(x)$	0	0						
$f_2(x)$	1	1						
$f_3(x)$	3	3						
$f_4(x)$	6	6						
$f_5(x)$	11	10	1					
$f_6(x)$	19	15	1	3				
$f_7(x)$	32	21	2	3	6			
$f_8(x)$	53	28	3	6	6	10		
$f_9(x)$	87	36	5	9	12	10	15	
&c.	&c.	&c.	&c.	&c.	&c.	&c.	&c.	&c.

Each term in the second column is the sum of the two terms just above it $+2$. The nth term in the third column is equal to the term just above it $+(n-1)$. In all the other columns each term is the sum of the two terms just above it. The last term in the nth row is equal to the $(n-3)^{th}$ term in the third column. We wish to show that any term in the second column is equal to the sum of all the terms in the same row to the right of that term. It is not difficult to show from the data just given that if this be true for any two adjacent rows, it is true for all the others, and hence we may assume it to be always true.

It is clear that these extraneous factors may be omitted since by the conditions already expressed they are all positive. When omitted as they occur, the dimensions of the nth function has just been shown to be $n\dfrac{n-1}{2}$. It is easy to see that the conditions thus reduced must contain the terms

$$p_1, \qquad p_1 p_2, \qquad p_1 p_2 p_3, \qquad p_1 p_2 p_3 p_4, \text{ &c.}$$

Now if we take any one of these as

$$p_1 p_2 p_3 p_4 p_5 p_6 \dots \dots \dots \dots \dots (1),$$

and operate by the rule in Art. 9, we have

$$(p_1 p_2 - p_0 p_3) p_3 (p_1 p_4 - p_0 p_5) p_5 (p_1 p_6 - p_0 p_7) p_7,$$

which contains the term

$$\overline{p_1 p_2} p_3 \overline{p_1 p_4} p_5 \overline{p_1 p_6} p_7 \dots \dots \dots \dots (2).$$

Thus we have p_1 introduced as often as there is a factor in (1) with an odd suffix. But it should be introduced only once. These extra p_1's are the extraneous factors to be omitted. Each of these, if left, would appear as the factor $p_1 p_2 - p_0 p_3$ in the next condition, and be still more complicated in the next after that.

61

In order then to obtain the several conditions in their simplest form it is only necessary after performing the operation described in Art. 5 or Art. 9 to divide by $p_1{}^\kappa$, where κ is one less than the number of factors with odd suffixes in the condition operated on.

12. Example. Express the conditions of stability for the sextic

$$f(x) = p_0 x^6 + p_1 x^5 + p_2 x^4 + p_3 x^3 + p_4 x^2 + p_5 x + p_6 = 0.$$

We have

$$f_1(x) = p_0 x^6 + \ldots$$

$$f_2(x) = p_1 x^5 + \ldots$$

$$f_3(x) = (p_1 p_2 - p_0 p_3) x^4 + \ldots$$

$$f_4(x) = (p_1 p_2 p_3 - p_0 p_3{}^2 - p_1{}^2 p_4 + p_0 p_1 p_5) x^2 + \ldots$$

$$f_5(x) = \{ p_1 p_2 p_3 p_4 - p_0 p_3{}^2 p_4 - p_1{}^2 p_4{}^2 + 2 p_0 p_1 p_4 p_5 - p_1 p_2{}^2 p_5 + p_0 p_2 p_3 p_5$$
$$- p_0{}^2 p_5{}^2 + p_1{}^2 p_2 p_6 - p_0 p_1 p_3 p_6 \} x^2 + \ldots$$

$$f_6(x) = [p_1 p_2 p_3 p_4 p_5 - p_0 p_3{}^2 p_4 p_5 - p_1{}^2 p_4{}^2 p_5 + 2 p_0 p_1 p_4 p_5{}^2 - p_1 p_2{}^2 p_5{}^2$$
$$+ p_0 p_2 p_3 p_5{}^2 - p_0{}^2 p_5{}^3 + 2 p_1{}^2 p_2 p_5 p_6 - 3 p_0 p_1 p_3 p_5 p_6 - p_1 p_2 p_3{}^2 p_6$$
$$+ p_0 p_3{}^3 p_6 + p_1{}^2 p_3 p_4 p_6 - p_1{}^3 p_6{}^2] x + \&c.$$

$f_7(x) =$ coefficient of x in $f_6 \, x \times$ by p_6.

13. In the preceding theory two reservations have been made.

1. In applying Cauchy's theorem it has been assumed that there were no radical points on the axis of y.

2. It has been assumed that P and Q have no common factor, so that none of the functions f_1, f_2, &c. vanish absolutely.

If any radical point lie on the axis of y, it is clear that $f(z) = 0$ must have a factor of the form $(z^2 + a^2)^r$. Let $f(z) = (z^2 + a^2)^r \phi(z)$. In this case when we put $z = y \sqrt{-1}$, we have

$$f(z) = (a^2 - y^2)^r (P' + Q' \sqrt{-1});$$

$$\therefore \; \left. \begin{aligned} P &= (a^2 - y^2)^r P' \\ Q &= (a^2 - y^2)^r Q' \end{aligned} \right\}.$$

Thus P and Q have a common factor, and we are warned of the possible existence of radical points on the contour by the total vanishing of some one of the functions f_1, f_2, f_3, &c.

The two reserved cases may therefore be included in one. If $f(z) = 0$ be the equation furnished by dynamical considerations, we form the functions f_1, f_2, f_3, &c. If all these be finite, the question of the stability of the system has been answered. If any one vanish absolutely, $f_1(x)$ and $f_2(x)$ have a common measure, and we must add some further considerations. It will be convenient to examine separately the dynamical effect of the roots which do not and which do enter through the greatest common measure. Let us begin with the former.

14. Following the same notation as before, we have

$$f(z) = p_0 z^n + p_1 z^{n-1} + \ldots + p_{n-1} z + p_n,$$

$$\left. \begin{aligned} P &= \pm f_1(y) = p_n - p_{n-2} y^2 + \ldots\ldots \\ Q &= \pm f_2(y) = p_{n-1} y - p_{n-3} y^3 + \ldots \end{aligned} \right\}.$$

If then $f(z)$ have two roots, viz. $\pm(h + k\sqrt{-1})$, which are equal and opposite, then $f_1(y)$ and $f_2(y)$ must have two common roots, viz. $\pm \dfrac{h + k\sqrt{-1}}{\sqrt{-1}}$. The common measure therefore of $f_1(y)$ and $f_2(y)$ contains all the roots of $f(y\sqrt{-1})$ which are equal and opposite. Conversely the greatest common measure of P and Q is necessarily an even function of y, and if it be equated to zero, its roots are necessarily equal and opposite. These roots must also satisfy $f(y\sqrt{-1}) = 0$.

Let this greatest common measure be $\psi(y^2) = 0$, and let y^{2r} be the highest power which enters into it. Also let

$$f(z) = \psi(-z^2)\,\phi(z),$$

then $\phi(z)$ is a function which, as has just been shown, has not got two roots equal and opposite, and to this function we may apply Cauchy's theorem without fear of failure. Putting $z = y\sqrt{-1}$, let

$$\phi(z) = P' + Q'\sqrt{-1}.$$

Then we wish to express the condition that $\dfrac{P'}{Q'}$ should change sign from $-$ to $+$ through zero $n - 2r$ times if n be even and $n - 2r - 1$ times if n be odd. But

$$f(y\sqrt{-1}) = P + Q\sqrt{-1},$$

and

$$f(y\sqrt{-1}) = \psi(y^2)(P' + Q'\sqrt{-1});$$

$$\therefore \left. \begin{aligned} P &= \psi(y^2)\,P' \\ Q &= \psi(y^2)\,Q' \end{aligned} \right\}.$$

Thus the number of changes of sign in $\dfrac{P'}{Q'}$ is exactly the same as that of $\dfrac{P}{Q}$. The factor $\psi(y^2)$ will run through all the functions $f_2(y), f_3(y)$, &c. obtained from $f_1(y)$ by a process which is equivalent to that of finding the greatest common measure of $f_1(y)$ and

$f_2(y)$. The changes of sign of this factor will therefore not affect the number of variations of sign in the series f_1, f_2, f_3, &c.

The last factor which is not zero is $f_{n+1-2r}(y)$ if n be the dimensions of $f_1(y)$.

Hence *if we omit the considerations of the vanishing factors and apply the same rule as before to the* n + 1 − 2r *remaining factors, we can express the condition that the proper number of changes of sign from* − *to* + *have been lost through zero in the function* φ (z), *i.e. that the roots not given by the vanishing of* f$_{n+1-2r}$ *are all of the character to ensure stability.*

15.   Let us next consider the effect on stability of the roots indicated by the absolute vanishing of one of the subsidiary functions.   This function must be of the form

$$\psi(y^2) = q_0 y^n - q_2 y^{n-2} + \dots,$$

where n is even.   The corresponding factor of $f(z)$ is

$$F(z) = q_n + q_{n-2}z^2 + q_{n-4}z^4 + \dots.$$

The roots of this equation are two and two equal with opposite signs, it is therefore necessary for stability that no root should have any real part.   To express this condition, draw a straight line parallel to the axis of y at an indefinitely short distance from it, viz. $x = h$.   Let us apply, in the same manner as before, Cauchy's theorem to the contour formed by this straight line and the infinite semicircle on its positive side.   Putting $z = h + z'$, we have

$$F(z) = q_n + 2q_{n-2}hz' + q_{n-2}z'^2 + 4q_{n-4}hz'^3 + \dots$$

The two functions are therefore, omitting the positive factor h,

$$P = q_n - q_{n-2}y^2 + q_{n-4}y^4 - \&c.,$$
$$Q = 2q_{n-2}y - 4q_{n-4}y^3 + \&c.$$

Now $f_1(y)$ and $f_2(y)$ are what P and Q become when arranged in descending powers of y and the coefficients of their highest powers *made to have the same sign.*   Hence

$$f_2(y) = \frac{df_1(y)}{dy}.$$

The rule described in Art. 4 will now become the same as that usually called *Sturm's theorem.*   We are to seek the greatest common measure of $f_1(y)$ and its differential coefficient, and make the coefficients of the highest powers of y in these two and in the series of modified remainders all positive.

That we should have been led to Sturm's theorem in this case is just what we might have expected. For to express the conditions that the roots of

$$F(z) = q_n + q_{n-2}z^2 + q_{n-4}z^4 + \ldots$$

are all of the form $\pm r \sqrt{-1}$ is the same thing as to express the conditions that the roots of

$$q_n - q_{n-2}z^2 + q_{n-4}z^4 - \ldots = 0$$

are all real.

16. There is however another mode of proceeding. Suppose we have calculated the functions f_1, f_2, &c. for the general equation

$$f(z) = p_0 z^n + p_1 z^{n-1} + \ldots$$

and find when the values of p_0, p_1, &c. are substituted that some one function say f_r of the series absolutely vanishes, and therefore also all the functions which follow it. Then operate on each of these vanishing functions with

$$p_{n-1}\frac{d}{dp_n} + 2p_{n-2}\frac{d}{dp_{n-1}} + 3p_{n-3}\frac{d}{dp_{n-2}} + \ldots$$

repeating the operation until we obtain a result which is not zero. If we now replace these vanishing functions by these results we may apply the rule of Art. 4, just as if these were the functions supplied by the process of the greatest common measure. As this process is not so convenient as that already given it is unnecessary to consider it in detail*.

17. As a numerical example, let us examine whether the roots of

$$f(x) = x^8 + 2x^7 + 4x^6 + 4x^5 + 6x^4 + 6x^3 + 7x^2 + 4x + 2 = 0$$

satisfy the conditions of stability. In order to show the working of the method it will be necessary to exhibit all the numerical calculations. We have by Art. 5,

---

* The function $f_r(x)$ vanishes because the equation $f(z) = 0$ has two roots equal and opposite. If we put $z = z' + h$, where h is as small as we please, this peculiarity will disappear. Thus if the values of z are of the form $\pm (a \pm \beta \sqrt{-1})$ the corresponding values of z' are $-h \pm a \pm \beta \sqrt{-1}$. These values of z will indicate stability if a be zero and instability if a have any value positive or negative. If h be as small as we please and positive, the values of z' will indicate stability or instability under the same circumstances. We may therefore apply the rule of Art. 4 to the function $f(z' + h)$ instead of $f(z)$, provided we retain only the lowest powers of h which occur. Hence all the functions $f_1(x)$, $f_2(x) \ldots f_{r-1}(x)$ which do not vanish are unaltered. To find what function will replace $f_r(x)$ we must increase by h all the roots of $f(z) = 0$ when their signs have been changed. This may be effected by performing on $f(z)$ the operation represented by Δ in Art. 7. The rule in the text therefore follows from the one given in that article.

$$f_1(x) = x^8 - 4x^6 + 6x^4 - 7x^2 + 2,$$
$$f_2(x) = 2x^7 - 4x^5 + 6x^3 - 4x,$$
$$f_3(x) = 4x^6 - 6x^4 + 10x^2 - 4,$$
$$f_4(x) = 4x^5 - 4x^3 + 8x,$$
$$f_5(x) = 8x^4 - 8x^2 + 16.$$

Here we find $f_6(x)$ to be absolutely zero, accordingly by Art. 15 we replace it by the differential coefficient of $f_5(x)$, this being Sturm's rule. We have therefore

$$f_6(x) = 8\,(4x^3 - 2x),$$
$$f_7(x) = 8^2\,(2x^2 - 6),$$
$$f_8(x) = -8^3 \cdot 20 \cdot x,$$
$$f_9(x) = -8^5 \cdot 120.$$

We see that the two last of the coefficients of the highest powers are negative. The roots therefore do *not* satisfy the conditions of stability.

As another example, take the equation
$$fx = x^6 + x^5 + 6x^4 + 5x^3 + 11x^2 + 6x + 6.$$

Here

$$f_1(x) = x^6 - 6x^4 + 11x^2 - 6,$$
$$f_2(x) = x^5 - 5x^3 + 6x,$$
$$f_3(x) = x^4 - 5x^2 + 6,$$
$$f_4(x) = 0.$$

Replacing $f_4(x)$ by the differential coefficient of $f_3(x)$, we have

$$f_4(x) = 4x^3 - 10x,$$
$$f_5(x) = 10x^2 - 24x,$$
$$f_6(x) = 4x,$$
$$f_7(x) = 4 \cdot 24.$$

Here all the coefficients of the highest powers are positive, hence the roots satisfy the conditions of stability.

It is clear that when the coefficients are *numerical* the rule given in Art. 5 is the most convenient, but when the coefficients are letters, the rule in Art. 9 will be found preferable.

The process would be simplified by omitting the alternate positive and negative signs of the terms in each line.

18. It may be interesting *to express the two subsidiary functions* $f_1(x)$ *and* $f_2(x)$ *in terms of the roots of the given equation.*

Let $a_1, a_2, a_3 \ldots a_n$ be the roots of the given equation $f(x) = 0$, so that

$$f(x) = (x - a_1)(x - a_2)(x - a_3) \ldots$$
$$= x^n + p_1 x^{n-1} + p_2 x^{n-2} + \ldots$$

Then it is evident that

$$\pm f_1(x\sqrt{-1}) = x^n + p_2 x^{n-2} + p_4 x^{n-4} + \ldots$$
$$= \tfrac{1}{2}(x + a_1)(x + a_2) \ldots + \tfrac{1}{2}(x - a_1)(x - a_2) \ldots$$

It may be shown* that

$$\pm f_2(x\sqrt{-1}) = p_1 x^{n-1} + p_3 x^{n-3} + \ldots$$
$$= -\Sigma \frac{(a_1 + a_2)(a_1 + a_3) \ldots (a_1 + a_n)}{(a_1 - a_2)(a_1 - a_3) \ldots (a_1 - a_n)} a_1 (x - a_2) \ldots (x - a_n).$$

19. The following propositions are not necessary to the main argument, but as they illustrate geometrically the propositions in this chapter it has been considered proper to state them very briefly. The demonstrations will therefore be much curtailed.

The equation being

$$f(z) = p_0 z^n + p_1 z^{n-1} + \ldots + p_{n-1} z + p_n = 0,$$

we put as in Art. 1, $z = x + y\sqrt{-1}$, and thus obtain two curves, whose equations expressed in polar co-ordinates are

$$\left. \begin{array}{l} P = p_0 r^n \cos n\theta + p_1 r^{n-1} \cos (n-1)\theta + \ldots = 0 \\ Q = p_0 r^n \sin n\theta + p_1 r^{n-1} \sin (n-1)\theta + \ldots = 0 \end{array} \right\}.$$

These intersect in the radical points of the equation $f(z) = 0$.

20. If we trace these curves we find that the curve $P = 0$ has n asymptotes whose *directions* are given by $\cos n\theta = 0$, *i.e.*

$$\theta = \frac{1}{n}\frac{\pi}{2}, \quad \frac{3}{n}\frac{\pi}{2}, \quad \frac{5}{n}\frac{\pi}{2}, \ldots \ldots$$

---

* Let us assume

$$p_1 x^{n-1} + p_3 x^{n-3} + \&c. = A_1 (x - a_2) \ldots (x - a_n) + A_2 (x - a_1) \ldots (x - a_n) + \&c.,$$

where $A_1, A_2,$ &c. are constants whose values have to be found. Putting $x = a_1$, we have
$$p_1 a_1^{n-1} + p_2 a_1^{n-3} + \&c. = A_1 (a_1 - a_2) \ldots (a_1 - a_n).$$
But since
$$x^n + p_1 x^{n-1} + \ldots = (x - a_1)(x - a_2) \ldots (x - a_n),$$
we have by putting $x = a_1$ and $x = -a_1$
$$a_1^n + p_1 a_1^{n-1} + \ldots = 0,$$
$$a_1^n - p_1 a_1^{n-1} + \ldots = 2a_1 (a_1 + a_2) \ldots (a_1 + a_n).$$
Subtracting the second of these results from the first we find A_1 to have the value given in the text.

These asymptotes all pass through the same point on the axis of x, viz. $x = -\dfrac{p_1}{np_0}$. It is also clear that only one branch of the curve can go to each end of an asymptote. Similar remarks apply to the curve $Q = 0$, the directions of its asymptotes being given by $\sin n\theta = 0$, i.e.

$$\theta = 0, \quad \frac{2}{n}\frac{\pi}{2}, \quad \frac{4}{n}\frac{\pi}{2}, \quad \frac{6}{n}\frac{\pi}{2}, \ldots\ldots$$

21. From these simple propositions we might, if it were worth while, deduce that every equation must have a root. The asymptotes of the two curves $P = 0$, $Q = 0$ are *alternate*, and no two branches of the same curve can approach the same end of an asymptote. By sketching a figure, it may be easily shown that some branch of the P curve must cut some branch of the Q curve.

22. Let us next consider the intersections of the curves $P = 0$, $Q = 0$.

If we transform the origin to h, k, we put $x = h + \xi$, $y = k + \eta$. This is the same as expanding $f(h + k\sqrt{-1} + \xi + \eta\sqrt{-1})$, and collecting into two parcels the real and imaginary terms. Let the expansion be

$$A_0 + A_1(\xi + \eta\sqrt{-1}) + A_2(\xi + \eta\sqrt{-1})^2 + \ldots$$

where $A_0 A_1 \ldots$ are of the form

$$c(\cos \alpha + \sin \alpha\sqrt{-1}).$$

If we put $\xi + \eta\sqrt{-1} = r(\cos\theta + \sin\theta\sqrt{-1})$, we have

$$\left.\begin{array}{l} P = c_0\cos\alpha_0 + c_1 r\cos(\theta + \alpha_1) + c_2 r^2\cos(2\theta + \alpha_2) + \ldots \\ Q = c_0\sin\alpha_0 + c_1 r\sin(\theta + \alpha_1) + c_2 r^2\sin(2\theta + \alpha_2) + \ldots \end{array}\right\}.$$

If the point (h, k) be a point of intersection $c_0 = 0$. If the intersection be a double point on either curve, the terms of the first degree must be zero, therefore $c_1 = 0$, and the origin is therefore a double point on the other curve also.

It is not difficult to show that if the intersection be a multiple point of any degree of multiplicity on one curve, it is a point of the same degree of multiplicity on the other curve. The tangents to these branches all make equal angles with each other, the tangents to the P and Q curves being *alternate* as we travel round the point of intersection. If the intersection be not a multiple point on either curve, the branches cut at right angles.

Let us travel round a point of intersection along the circumference of a small circle whose centre is the point of intersection in the direction in which θ is measured. Then it may be shown that as we pass from a P curve to a Q curve, P and Q have opposite signs, and as we pass from a Q curve to a P curve the same sign. This is in fact merely Cauchy's rule for the changes of sign of $\dfrac{P}{Q}$ when we travel round a radical point.

23. Let us express the condition that there is no radical point on the positive side of the axis of y. This is the geometrical illustration of Art. 2.

Draw a circle of infinite radius, and let it cut the asymptotes of the P curve in P_1, P_2, P_3,...P_{2n} and the asymptotes of the Q curve in Q_1, Q_2,... Q_{2n}. These points alternate with each other. Taking only those points which lie on the positive side of the axis of y, the P and Q curves may be said to begin at these points and are to intersect each other only on the negative side of the axis of y. The branches of the two curves must therefore remain alternate with each other throughout the space on the positive side of the axis of y. Their points of intersection with the axis of y must be also alternate, and hence if we put $x = 0$, in the equations $P = 0$, $Q = 0$, and regard them as equations to find y the roots of each must separate the roots of the other.

Conversely, we may show that if the intersections of the two branches are alternate on the axis of y, they cannot have intersected on that side of the axis of y on which the common intersection of all the asymptotes is not. This is the result arrived at in Art. 2.

24. The following diagrams exhibit the forms of the curve $P = 0$, $Q = 0$ for a biquadratic. The dotted lines represent the asymptotes.

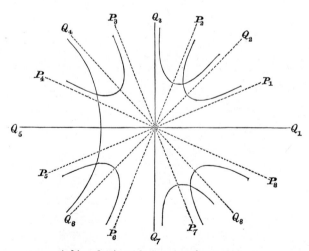

A biquadratic with four imaginary roots.

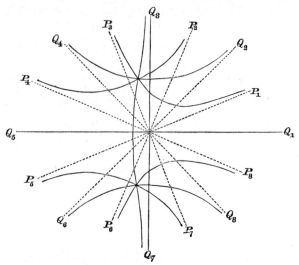

A biquadratic with equal imaginary roots.

25. [If $z = x + y\sqrt{-1}$, we have

$$f(z) = P + Q\sqrt{-1}.$$

Differentiating with respect, firstly to x and secondly to y, we find

$$\left. \begin{aligned} f'(z) &= \frac{dP}{dx} + \frac{dQ}{dx}\sqrt{-1} \\ f'(z) &= \frac{dQ}{dy} - \frac{dP}{dy}\sqrt{-1} \end{aligned} \right\}.$$

It easily follows that $\dfrac{dP}{dx} = \dfrac{dQ}{dy}$ and $\dfrac{dQ}{dx} = -\dfrac{dP}{dy}$; so that both the functions P and Q satisfy the equation

$$\frac{d^2V}{dy^2} + \frac{d^2V}{dx^2} = 0.$$

The equation $f(z) = 0$ gave us two curves which we have called $P = 0$ and $Q = 0$. In the same way the derived equation $f'(z) = 0$ will give us two other curves, which we may represent by $P' = 0$ and $Q' = 0$. These we may call the *derived* P and Q curves.

If as in Art. 22 we transform the origin to the point (h, k) we have

$$P' = c_1 \cos \alpha_1 + 2c_2 r \cos(\theta + \alpha_2) + 3c_3 r^2 \cos(2\theta + \alpha_3) + \dots$$
$$Q' = c_1 \sin \alpha_1 + 2c_2 r \sin(\theta + \alpha_2) + 3c_3 r^2 \sin(2\theta + \alpha_3) + \dots$$

If the origin be at a point of intersection of the curves $P = 0$, $P' = 0$ which is not a double point on the first of these curves, we have $c_0 \cos \alpha_0 = 0$ and $\cos \alpha_1 = 0$. Hence the tangent to the curve $P = 0$ at the point of intersection is parallel to the axis of x. Conversely if we move the origin to any point on the curve $P = 0$ at which the tangent is parallel to the axis of x, we find that the curve $P' = 0$ passes through the origin. Hence the derived P curve passes through all those points on the curve $P = 0$ at which the tangent is parallel to the axis of x, and all those points on the curve $Q = 0$ at which the tangent is parallel to the axis of y. In the same way the derived Q curve passes through those points on the curve $Q = 0$ at which the tangent is parallel to the axis of x, and those points on the curve $P = 0$ at which the tangent is parallel to the axis of y.

If $c_0 \cos \alpha_0 = 0$, and $c_1 = 0$, the origin is a double point on the curve $P = 0$ and the origin also lies on both the curves $P' = 0$, $Q' = 0$. So that both the derived curves cut the curves $P = 0$ and $Q = 0$ in their double points. In other words, these double points are radical points for the derived equation $f'(z) = 0$. In the same way, any multiple point on either curve is a multiple point of one degree less multiplicity on both the derived curves.

If a finite straight line AB be drawn parallel to the axis of x joining two points A, B on the same or on different branches of the curve $P = 0$, this finite straight line must cut one or more branches of the derived P curve. For it is clear that if P vanishes at A and B, P' which is equal to $\dfrac{dP}{dx}$ cannot keep one sign between A and B, and must therefore vanish somewhere between A and B. If A and B be adjacent points, *i.e.* if there be no other points between A and B belonging to the curve $P = 0$, then the straight line AB must cut an *odd* number of branches of the derived P curve. In the same way if a straight line CD be drawn parallel to the axis of y joining two adjacent points on a derived Q curve, this straight line must also cut an odd number of branches of a derived P curve between C and D.

By considering a tangent as the limit of secant, it again follows that if a tangent be drawn to the curve $P = 0$ parallel to the axis of x, the derived P curve must pass through the point of contact.

Let R be a radical point on the derived curve $f'(z) = 0$, and let it not be a double point on either of the curves $P = 0$, $Q = 0$. Let a straight line be drawn from R in any direction cutting the branches of either of the curves $P = 0$, $Q = 0$ in the points A_1, A_2, &c. Then we may show that

$$\frac{1}{RA_1} + \frac{1}{RA_2} + \frac{1}{RA_3} + \&c. = 0,$$

so that the polar line of R with regard to either of the curves $P = 0$, $Q = 0$ is at infinity.

The positions of the radical points of the derived equation $f'(z) = 0$ relatively to any branch or branches of the curves $P = 0$, $Q = 0$ may be found by the use of Cauchy's theorem. If the point spoken of in Art. 1 travel along a branch of the curve $P=0$, it is easy to see that $\dfrac{P'}{Q'} = \dfrac{dy}{dx}$. If it travel along a branch of the curve $Q = 0$ we have $\dfrac{P'}{Q'} = -\dfrac{dx}{dy}$. If then any contour be partly bounded by branches of these curves, the simplest inspection of the points at which the tangents are parallel to the axis will determine the changes of sign of $\dfrac{P'}{Q'}$ as it passes through zero. If another part of the contour be an arc of a circle of infinite radius whose centre is the origin, the changes of sign through zero will be from $+$ to $-$ and their number will be indicated by the number of asymptotes of the derived P curve which cut the arc.]

26. The use of Watt's Governor in the steam engine is too well known to need description. It has however, as commonly used, a great defect. It is sometimes of importance that the engine should continue to work at the same rate notwithstanding great changes in the resistances. Suppose the load suddenly diminished, the engine works quicker, the balls diverging cut off the steam, and the engine, after a time, again works uniformly, but at *a different rate from before*. The balls as they open out or close in are usually made to describe circles. Let them now be constrained to describe some other curve which we may afterwards choose so as to correct the above defect. If this curve be a parabola and the balls be treated as particles, it is clear from very elementary considerations that these will be in relative equilibrium only when the engine works at a given rate. This principle is due to Huyghens, see *Astronomical Notices*, December, 1875. It is now proposed to determine the condition of stable oscillation about a state of steady motion.

Two equal rods AB, AB' are attached at A by hinges to a small ring which can slide smoothly along a vertical axis. The ring is attached by a rod to the valve and can thus govern the amount of steam admitted. Two equal balls are attached at B and B', and the centre of gravity G of the rod AB and the ball B is constrained to describe some curve. To represent the inertia of the engine we shall suppose a horizontal fly-wheel attached to the vertical axis whose moment of inertia about the axis is I. Let the excess of the action of the steam over the resistance of the load be represented by some couple whose moment about the vertical axis is $f(\theta)$, where θ is the inclination of the rod AG to the vertical, and f is a function which depends on the construction of the engine.   Since the steam is cut off when the balls open out, it is clear that $\dfrac{df(\theta)}{d\theta}$ is negative.

There may be also some resistances which vary with the velocity.   Let these be represented by a couple $B\dfrac{d\phi}{dt}$ tending to retard the motion round the vertical axis and a couple round A in the plane BAB' equal to $mC\dfrac{d\theta}{dt}$, where ϕ is the angle the vertical plane BAB' makes with a fixed vertical plane.

Let m be the mass of either sphere and rod; k the radius of gyration about an axis through G perpendicular to the rod, and k' that about the rod, let $l = AG$.   Then the equation of angular momentum gives

$$\frac{d}{dt}\left\{I\frac{d\phi}{dt} + 2m\,(\overline{k^2 + l^2}\sin^2\theta + k'^2\cos^2\theta)\,\frac{d\phi}{dt}\right\} = f(\theta) - B\frac{d\phi}{dt}.$$

Let the steady motion be given by $\theta = \alpha$, $\dfrac{d\phi}{dt} = n$, and let the oscillations be represented by $\theta = \alpha + x$, $\dfrac{d\phi}{dt} = n + y$.   We have then

$$f(\theta) = f(\alpha) + f'(\alpha)\,x,$$
$$f(\alpha) = Bn.$$

The equation then reduces to

$$\{I + 2m\,(\overline{k^2 + l^2}\sin^2\alpha + k'^2\cos^2\alpha)\}\,\frac{dy}{dt} + 2m\,(l^2 + k^2 - k'^2)\sin 2\alpha n\,\frac{dx}{dt}$$
$$= f'(\alpha)\,x - By.$$

This equation may be briefly written

$$A\frac{dy}{dt} + By + E\frac{dx}{dt} + Fx = 0.$$

Let z be the altitude of G above some fixed horizontal plane. Then if T be the semi vis viva

$$2T = I\phi'^2 + 2m\,\{(k^2 + l^2)\sin^2\theta + k'^2\cos^2\theta\}\,\phi'^2 + 2mk^2\theta'^2$$
$$+ 2m\left\{\left(\frac{dz}{d\theta}\right)^2 + l^2\cos^2\theta\right\}\theta'^2.$$

If U be the force function, omitting the couple of resistance, we have $U = -2mgz$.   The virtual moment of the couples of resistance being $2mC\theta'\delta\theta$, the Lagrangian equation of motion becomes

$$\frac{d}{dt}\frac{dT}{d\theta'} - \frac{dT}{d\theta} = \frac{dU}{d\theta} - 2mC\theta'.$$

73

Substituting for T and U we have when the motion is steady

$$\frac{n^2}{g} (l^2 + k^2 - k'^2) \sin \theta \cos \theta = \frac{dz}{d\theta},$$

$$\therefore \frac{n^2}{2g} (l^2 + k^2 - k'^2) \sin^2 \theta = z.$$

Since $l \sin \theta$ is the distance of G from the vertical axis, we see that the path of G must be a parabola. The semi latus rectum is

$$\frac{gl^2}{n^2 (l^2 + k^2 - k'^2)},$$

which, we notice, is independent of the radius of the balls. The length of this latus rectum must of course be adjusted to suit the particular rate at which the engine is intended to work.

When the system is oscillating about the state of steady motion we have, putting

$$a^2 = l^2 + \frac{n^4}{g^2} (l^2 + k^2 - k'^2)^2 \sin^2 \alpha,$$

and rejecting the squares of x and y,

$$(k^2 + a^2 \cos^2 \alpha) \frac{d^2 x}{dt^2} + C \frac{dx}{dt} - (l^2 + k^2 - k'^2) \sin 2\alpha n y = 0.$$

The term x, it will be noticed, has disappeared from the equation. This equation may be briefly written in the form

$$H \frac{d^2 x}{dt^2} + C \frac{dx}{dt} - Ly = 0.$$

Eliminating y from the equations of motion we have

$$AH \frac{d^3 x}{dt^3} + (AC + BH) \frac{d^2 x}{dt^2} + (BC + EL) \frac{dx}{dt} + FLx = 0.$$

The coefficients are all positive, the necessary and sufficient condition of stability is therefore

$$(AC + BH)(BC + EL) > AFHL.$$

In some clocks to which Watt's Governor is applied, there is a special arrangement which causes C to be much greater than B. See the *Astronomical Notes*, XI., 1851, and the *Memoirs of the Astronomical Society*, Vol. XX. Neglecting therefore B, we have

$$CE > FH.$$

$$\therefore 2 Cmn (l^2 + k^2 - k'^2) \sin 2\alpha > F(k^2 + a^2 \cos^2 \alpha).$$

CHAPTER IV.

Formation of the equations of steady motion and of small oscillation where Lagrange's method may be used. Arts. 1—5.

The equations being all linear the conditions of stability are expressed by the character of the roots of a determinantal equation of an even order. Art. 6.

Mode of expanding the determinant. Art. 7.

A method of finding the proper co-ordinates to make the coefficients of the Lagrangian function constant. Arts. 8—10.

How the Harmonic oscillations about steady motion differ from those about a position of equilibrium. The forces which cause the difference are of the nature of centrifugal forces produced by an imaginary rotation about a fixed straight line. Arts. 11—19.

Reduction of the fundamental determinant to one of fewer rows by the elimination of all co-ordinates which do not appear except as differential coefficients in the Lagrangian function; with an example. Arts. 20—23.

Formation of the equations of Motion and of the determinant when the geometrical equations contain differential coefficients, so that Lagrange's method cannot be used ; with an example. Arts. 24—27.

1. Let the system be referred to any co-ordinates ξ, η, ζ, &c. The general expression for the kinetic energy is

$$T = \tfrac{1}{2} P\xi'^2 + Q\xi'\eta' + \dots$$

where P, Q, &c. are known functions of ξ, η, ζ, &c. and accents have their usual meaning. Let us suppose the system to have some motion represented by

$$\xi = f(t), \quad \eta = F(t), \quad \&c.$$

and when disturbed, we wish to find the oscillations about this motion. To effect this, we put

$$\xi = f(t) + \theta, \quad \eta = F(t) + \phi, \quad \&c.$$

where θ, ϕ, &c. are all small quantities. Substituting and expanding T in powers of θ, ϕ, &c., we find

$$
\begin{aligned}
T = {} & T_0 + A_1\theta + A_2\phi + \dots \\
& + B_1\theta' + B_2\phi' + \dots \\
& + \tfrac{1}{2}\,(A_{11}\theta^2 + 2A_{12}\theta\phi + \dots) \\
& + \tfrac{1}{2}\,(B_{11}\theta'^2 + 2B_{12}\theta'\phi' + \dots) \\
& + C_{11}\theta\theta' + C_{12}\theta\phi' + C_{21}\theta'\phi + \dots \\
& + \&c.
\end{aligned}
$$

In the same way we may make an expansion for the Potential Energy of the forces, viz.

$$
\begin{aligned}
V = {} & E_0 + E_1\theta + E_2\phi + \dots \\
& + \tfrac{1}{2}\,(E_{11}\theta^2 + 2E_{12}\theta\phi + \dots),
\end{aligned}
$$

when these two functions are given the whole dynamical system and the forces are known; and we may form the equations of motion by Lagrange's method.

2. We shall here however limit the question by supposing that the motion about which the system is oscillating is what has been called in Chap. I. *steady*. The analytical peculiarity of such a motion is that when referred to proper co-ordinates, every coefficient in each of these two series is constant, i.e. independent of t. As already explained the physical peculiarities are that the vis viva is constant throughout the steady motion and the same oscillations follow from the same disturbance at whatever instant it may be applied to the motion. A method of discovering the proper co-ordinates, if unknown, will be given a little further on.

3. In order to form the equations of motion we must now substitute in Lagrange's equations

$$
\frac{d}{dt}\frac{d\dot{T}}{d\theta'} - \frac{dT}{d\theta} + \frac{dV}{d\theta} = 0,
$$

$$
\&c. = 0,
$$

rejecting all the squares of small quantities. The steady motion being given by θ, ϕ, &c. all zero, each of these must be satisfied when we omit the terms containing θ, ϕ, &c. We thus obtain the equations of steady motion, viz.

$$
\begin{aligned}
A_1 &= E_1, \\
A_2 &= E_2, \\
\&c. &= \&c.
\end{aligned}
$$

These equations may be simply formed in any case by the following rule. Putting $L = T - V$, so that L is the difference between the kinetic and potential energies, expand L in powers of the co-ordinates θ, ϕ, &c. regarding θ', ϕ', &c. as zero. The required relations are obtained by equating the coefficients of the first powers to zero. This rule may be also expressed thus. *Let* L *be the general expression for the excess of the kinetic energy over the potential energy of a dynamical system in terms of its* n *co-ordinates* ξ, η, &c. *Let this system be moving in steady motion with constant values of* $\dfrac{d\xi}{dt}, \dfrac{d\eta}{dt}$, &c.* *Then substituting these constant values in the general expression for* L. *the relations between the constants of steady motion are given by*

$$\frac{dL}{d\xi} = 0, \quad \frac{dL}{d\eta} = 0, \quad \&c.$$

In this way we obtain in general as many equations as there are co-ordinates. Usually the coefficients in the expression for T are constant because some of the co-ordinates are constant in the state of steady motion, and the other co-ordinates appear in the expressions for T and V only as differential coefficients. In such cases we have clearly fewer equations than co-ordinates to connect the constants of steady motion. We have then a system of possible steady motions which we may conveniently term *parallel steady motions.*

4. To obtain the equations to the oscillatory motion, we retain the first powers of θ, ϕ, &c. We thus obtain a series of equations of which the following is a specimen :

$$\left(B_{11} \frac{d^2}{dt^2} - A_{11} + E_{11} \right) \theta$$

$$+ \left\{ B_{12} \frac{d^2}{dt^2} + (C_{21} - C_{12}) \frac{d}{dt} - A_{12} + E_{12} \right\} \phi$$

$$+ \left\{ B_{13} \frac{d^2}{dt^2} + (C_{31} - C_{13}) \frac{d}{dt} - A_{13} + E_{13} \right\} \psi$$

$$+ \dots\dots\dots = 0.$$

To solve these we write

$$\theta = M_1 e^{mt}, \quad \phi = M_2 e^{mt}, \quad \psi = M_3 e^{mt}, \quad \&c.$$

Substituting we obtain on eliminating the ratios $M_1 : M_2 : M_3$ &c. a determinantal equation, viz.

---

* Since we may in Art. 1 change the co-ordinates from ξ, η, ζ, &c. to ξ_1, η_1, ζ_1, &c., where $\xi = f(\xi_1)$ $\eta = F(\eta_1)$ &c., it is clear that the steady motion can be always expressed by *constant* values of the differential coefficients of the co-ordinates.

$$
\begin{vmatrix}
B_{11}m^2 - A_{11} + E_{11} & \begin{array}{l} B_{12}m^2 - A_{12} + E_{12} \\ + (C_{21} - C_{12})\, m \end{array} & \begin{array}{l} B_{13}m^2 - A_{13} + E_{13} \\ + (C_{31} - C_{13})\, m \end{array} & \text{\&c.} \\
\begin{array}{l} B_{12}m^2 - A_{12} + E_{12} \\ - (C_{21} - C_{12})\, m \end{array} & B_{22}m^2 - A_{22} + E_{22} & \begin{array}{l} B_{23}m^2 - A_{23} + E_{23} \\ + (C_{32} - C_{23})\, m \end{array} & \text{\&c.} \\
\begin{array}{l} B_{13}m^2 - A_{13} + E_{13} \\ - (C_{31} - C_{13})\, m \end{array} & \begin{array}{l} B_{23}m^2 - A_{23} + E_{23} \\ - (C_{32} - C_{23})\, m \end{array} & B_{33}m^2 - A_{33} + E_{33} & \text{\&c.} \\
\text{\&c.} & \text{\&c.} & \text{\&c.} & \text{\&c.}
\end{vmatrix} = 0.
$$

This equation will be referred to as the *Determinantal equation*.

5. If we refer to the equation formed by this determinant and read it in horizontal lines, we have of course the several equations of motion, each term being the coefficient of θ, ϕ, ψ, &c. in order. In this form the equations may be reproduced by the following easy rule.

Taking the expression for $T - V$ as given in Art. 1, let us consider only the terms of the second order, those of the first having been already used to determine the steady motion as explained in Art. 3. Separate from the rest, the even powers of θ, θ', ϕ, ϕ', &c. and write for θ'^2, $\theta'\phi'$, &c. $-D^2\theta^2$, $-D^2\theta\phi$, &c., so that D will stand either for $\dfrac{d}{dt}$ or for the m in the determinant of Art. 4, when we write $\theta = M_1 e^{mt}$, $\phi = M_2 e^{mt}$, &c. Let the sum of these terms be called P, so that

$$P = \tfrac{1}{2}\left(A_{11} - E_{11} - B_{11}D^2\right)\theta^2 + \left(A_{12} - E_{12} - B_{12}D^2\right)\theta\phi + \text{\&c.}$$

Let the remaining portion of the terms of $T - V$, viz. those containing both θ, ϕ, &c. and θ', ϕ', &c., be called Q, so that

$$Q = C_{11}\theta\theta' + C_{12}\theta\phi' + C_{21}\phi\theta' + \cdots$$

Then the several equations may be formed from the rule

$$
\left.
\begin{aligned}
\frac{dP}{d\theta} + \frac{dQ}{d\theta} - D\,\frac{dQ}{d\theta'} &= 0 \\
\frac{dP}{d\phi} + \frac{dQ}{d\phi} - D\,\frac{dQ}{d\phi'} &= 0 \\
\text{\&c.} &= 0
\end{aligned}
\right\}.
$$

In applying this rule no accented letters will occur except in the second term of each equation. If we wish D to stand for m

in the determinant, we must regard θ', ϕ', &c. as abbreviations for $D\theta$, $D\phi$, &c. If we wish to use the equations themselves, we replace $D\theta$, $D\phi$, &c. by θ', ϕ', &c.

[The determinant may also be found by another rule. Taking as before only the terms of the second order in the Lagrangian function $L = T - V$, let us separate the terms of the form

$$Q = C_{11}\theta\theta' + C_{12}\theta\phi' + C_{21}\theta'\phi + \&c.$$

In the remaining terms put $\theta' = \theta m \sqrt{-1}$, $\phi' = \phi m \sqrt{-1}$, and so on, and write down the *discriminant*. If the system oscillates about a position of equilibrium the terms represented by Q are absent and the discriminant thus formed will be the determinantal equation giving the required values of m. But if the system oscillate about a state of steady motion we must modify the discriminant by adding some quantity derived from Q to each term. To find this, write above the columns θ', ϕ', &c. and before the rows θ, ϕ, &c. Consider any term, say the term in the column ϕ' and row θ. We must add to that term $(C_{12} - C_{21})\, m$, where $C_{12} - C_{21}$ is the excess of the coefficient of $\phi'\theta$ above the coefficient of $\phi\theta'$ in the expression for Q. Since the determinant is unchanged by writing $- m$ for m, we may, if preferred, add the excess of the coefficient of $\theta'\phi$ above the coefficient of $\theta\phi'$ provided we adhere to one order throughout.]

6. If in the determinantal equation we write $- m$ for m, the rows of the new determinant are the same as the columns of the old, so that the determinant is unaltered. When expanded, we shall have an equation which contains only *even* powers of m.

The condition of dynamical stability is that the roots of this equation should be all of the form

$$m = \pm \beta \sqrt{-1}.$$

If we write $m^2 = - p^2$, the roots of the transformed equation must be all real.

In the case of equal roots of the form $m = \pm \beta \sqrt{-1}$, it has been shown in Art. 5 of Chap. I. that it is necessary for stability that the proper number of minors in this determinant should vanish. If there be two equal roots, these roots must make all the first minors zero; if three equal roots, all the first and second minors must vanish, and so on.

7. When the system depends on many co-ordinates the labour of expanding this determinant is often considerable. Methods of evading this in certain cases will be given in the following chap-

ters. But when the development is necessary we may proceed in the following manner. Let the determinant be written

$$\begin{vmatrix} B_{11}m^2 + a_{11} & B_{12}m^2 + a_{12} & B_{13}m^2 + a_{13} \\ & \quad + F_{12}m & \quad + F_{13}m \\ B_{12}m^2 + a_{12} & B_{22}m^2 + a_{22} & B_{23}m^2 + a_{23} \\ \quad + F_{21}m & & \quad + F_{23}m \\ \&c. & \&c. & \&c. \end{vmatrix},$$

and let

$$B = B_{11}\frac{\theta^2}{2} + B_{12}\theta\phi + \dots,$$

$$a = a_{11}\frac{\theta^2}{2} + a_{12}\theta\phi + \dots,$$

$$F_{pq} = - F_{qp}.$$

We know that the determinant when expanded is of an even order, hence all odd powers of m must finally vanish. Let us expand the determinant in powers of the F's. The first term is the discriminant of $Bm^2 + a$, this term is independent of the F's. The terms which contain the first powers of the F's are obtained by erasing any one line of this discriminant and replacing it by the corresponding F terms. But these terms all vanish and we need not describe them minutely. The terms containing the products and squares of the F's may be obtained by erasing every two lines of the discriminant and replacing them by the corresponding F terms. Thus if we erase the two first lines we have the determinant

$$\begin{vmatrix} 0 & F_{12}m & F_{13}m & \&c. \\ -F_{12}m & 0 & F_{23}m & \&c. \\ B_{13}m^2 + a_{13} & B_{23}m^2 + a_{23} & B_{33}m^2 + a_{33} & \&c. \\ \&c. & \&c. & \&c. \end{vmatrix},$$

and so on for all the other rows taken two and two. The terms which contain the cubes and all odd powers of the F's vanish, while the terms which contain the fourth powers may be obtained by erasing four lines of the discriminant and replacing them by the corresponding F's.

When the determinant has been expanded, we have an equation of an *even* order to find the values of m. We may therefore employ the short method of Art. 5, Chap. III., to obtain the Sturmian functions.

8. Necessary and sufficient tests of the stability of the motion of a system of bodies are given in the preceding pages. But it

is assumed, as explained in Art. 2, that the co-ordinates have been properly chosen. They are supposed to have been so chosen that the coefficients in the expanded Lagrangian function are all constants. When this is not the case we must discover the proper co-ordinates to which the system must be referred before we can apply the test of stability. But when the motion is steady this is not difficult.

There are obviously many such systems of co-ordinates, and one set may generally be found by a simple examination of the steady motion. If there are any quantities which are constant during the steady motion, they will often serve for some of the co-ordinates. Others may be found by considering what quantities appear only as differential coefficients or velocities. Practically these will be the most convenient methods of discovering proper co-ordinates, since no further change will then be necessary and we may at once form the determinant of stability. But if these methods fail we may adopt the following analytical method of transforming (where possible) the general Lagrangian function with variable coefficients into one with constant coefficients.

9. Let the Lagrangian function be

$$L = L_0 + A_1\theta + A_2\phi + \&c. + B_1\theta' + B_2\phi' + \&c.$$
$$+ \tfrac{1}{2} A_{11}\theta^2 + A_{12}\theta\phi + \ldots$$
$$+ \tfrac{1}{2} B_{11}\theta'^2 + B_{12}\theta'\phi' + \ldots$$
$$+ C_{11}\theta\theta' + C_{12}\theta\phi' + C_{21}\phi\theta' + \ldots$$

where the coefficients are all functions of t and the co-ordinates θ, ϕ, &c. have been so chosen as to vanish along the steady motion. We have therefore for the steady motion

$$\frac{d}{dt}B_1 - A_1 = 0,$$
$$\&c. = 0.$$

The oscillations about the steady motion are given by the terms of the second order. Our present object is to transform these to others with constant coefficients by the following substitutions :

$$\theta = p_1 x + p_2 y + p_3 z + \&c.,$$
$$\phi = q_1 x + q_2 y + q_3 z + \&c.,$$
$$\&c. = \&c.,$$

where the p's, q's, &c. are functions of the time at our disposal.

Substituting and equating the coefficients of x'^2, y'^2, &c. to unity, we have as many equations of the form

$$\tfrac{1}{2} B_{11}p^2 + \tfrac{1}{2} B_{22}q^2 + B_{12}pq + \ldots = 1 \ldots\ldots\ldots\ldots (1)$$

81

as there are co-ordinates. Equating the coefficients of the products $x'y'$, $x'z'$, &c. to zero we get $n\dfrac{n-1}{2}$ equations of the form

$$B_{11}\,p_1p_2 + B_{22}q_1q_2 + B_{12}\,(p_1q_2 + p_2q_1) + \ldots = 0 \ldots\ldots\ldots (2),$$

supposing that there are n co-ordinates.

Equating to the constants α_1, α_2, $\ldots$ the coefficients of xx', yy', &c. having subtracted the differential coefficients of (1) we have n equations of the form

$$(C_{11} - \tfrac{1}{2}B_{11}')\,p^2 + (C_{22} - \tfrac{1}{2}B_{22}')\,q^2 + (C_{12} + C_{21} - B_{12}')\,pq + \ldots = \alpha\ldots(3).$$

Adding the coefficients of xy' and $x'y$ and subtracting the differential coefficients of (2) we have $n\dfrac{n-1}{2}$ equations of the form

$$\left.\begin{array}{l}(2C_{11} - B_{11}')\,p_1p_2 + (2C_{22} - B_{22}')\,q_1q_2 \\ + (C_{12} + C_{21} - B_{12}')\,(p_1q_2 + p_2q_1) + \ldots\end{array}\right\} = 0 \ldots\ldots (4).$$

Equations (1), (2) and (4) give n^2 equations to find the n^2 quantities p_1p_2, &c., q_1q_2, &c. The solution of these equations is a purely geometrical problem. If we construct the two quadrics

$$\tfrac{1}{2}B_{11}\theta^2 + \tfrac{1}{2}B_{22}\phi^2 + B_{12}\theta\phi + \ldots = 1,$$

$$(C_{11} - \tfrac{1}{2}B'_{11})\,\theta^2 + (C_{22} - \tfrac{1}{2}B'_{22})\,\phi^2 + (C_{12} + C_{21} - B'_{12})\,\theta\phi + \ldots = 1,$$

and refer them to their common conjugate diameters, by writing

$$\theta = p_1x + p_2y + \ldots$$

$$\phi = q_1x + q_2y + \ldots$$

$$\&c. = \&c.,$$

making the first quadric to become what we may call a sphere by projection; the values of p_1p_2, &c., q_1q_2, &c. thus found are the values required to make some of the coefficients in the Lagrangian function become constant. These values must of course make all the other coefficients of the second order in the Lagrangian function constants also, and thus we have $n(n+1)$ analytical conditions that the motion should be steady.

It might be supposed that greater generality would be obtained by replacing the zero's of equations (2) and (4) or the unities of (1) by arbitrary constants. This may be convenient in practice, but as we know that by a subsequent real change with constant values of p_1p_2, &c., q_1q_2, &c., we can render them zero or unity, it simplifies the argument to perform the two transformations at once.

10. The geometrical problem just alluded to admits of a real solution whenever one quadric can be projected by a real projection into a sphere. The problem then becomes that of finding the principal axes of the other. This is just our case, since the expression

$$\tfrac{1}{2}B_1\,\theta'^2 + \beta_{12}\theta'\phi' + \ldots$$

is necessarily positive for all values of $\theta'\phi'$.

It is unnecessary to describe here the mode of solving this problem. It is sufficient to say that it may be reduced to the solution of the symmetrical determinantal equation

$$\begin{vmatrix} B_{11} - \lambda D_{11}, & D_{12} - \lambda D_{12} \ldots \\ B_{12} - \lambda D_{12}, & D_{22} - \lambda D_{22} \ldots \\ \cdots\cdots & \cdots\cdots \end{vmatrix} = 0,$$

where D_{11}, D_{12}, &c. are the coefficients of θ^2, $\theta\phi$, &c. in the second of the quadrics. The roots of this equation are known to be real when the suppositions just mentioned are satisfied.

11. In order to examine the fundamental determinant in Art. 4 a little more closely, let us suppose it reduced to depend on three co-ordinates. We may then have the advantage of a geometrical analogy. Let the co-ordinates be ξ η, ζ, and let the equations of motion be written

$$\left(B_{11}\frac{d^2}{dt^2} - A_{11}\right)\xi + \left(\begin{matrix} B_{12}\dfrac{d^2}{dt^2} - A_{12} \\ - G\dfrac{d}{dt} \end{matrix}\right)\eta + \left(\begin{matrix} B_{13}\dfrac{d^2}{dt^2} - A_{13} \\ + F\dfrac{d}{dt} \end{matrix}\right)\zeta = 0,$$

$$\left(\begin{matrix} B_{12}\dfrac{d^2}{dt^2} - A_{12} \\ + G\dfrac{d}{dt} \end{matrix}\right)\xi + \left(B_{22}\frac{d^2}{dt^2} - A_{22}\right)\eta + \left(\begin{matrix} B_{23}\dfrac{d^2}{dt^2} - A_{23} \\ - E\dfrac{d}{dt} \end{matrix}\right)\zeta = 0,$$

$$\left(\begin{matrix} B_{13}\dfrac{d^2}{dt^2} - A_{13} \\ - F\dfrac{d}{dt} \end{matrix}\right)\xi + \left(\begin{matrix} B_{23}\dfrac{d^2}{dt^2} - A_{23} \\ + E\dfrac{d}{dt} \end{matrix}\right)\eta + \left(B_{33}\frac{d^2}{dt^2} - A_{33}\right)\zeta = 0.$$

Let a geometrical point P move in space so that its co-ordinates referred to any axes are ξ, η, ζ. Then the position and motion of the point exactly give us the position and motion of the system.

12. Looking at the equations of motion just written down we see that they are similar to those which give the oscillations of a

system about a position of equilibrium, but that there are in addition terms $E\dfrac{d\eta}{dt}$, $F\dfrac{d\zeta}{dt}$, &c. The general effect of these terms, as will appear from what follows in the subsequent chapter, is to increase the stability. If we transpose these terms to the other sides of the equations, we may regard them as impressed forces acting on the system, whose resolved parts in the directions of the axes ξ, η, ζ, are

$$\left.\begin{aligned} X &= G\frac{d\eta}{dt} - F\frac{d\zeta}{dt}\\ Y &= E\frac{d\zeta}{dt} - G\frac{d\xi}{dt}\\ Z &= F\frac{d\xi}{dt} - E\frac{d\eta}{dt} \end{aligned}\right\}.$$

We see at once that

$$\left.\begin{aligned} EX+FY+GZ &= 0\\ \frac{d\xi}{dt}X + \frac{d\eta}{dt}Y + \frac{d\zeta}{dt}Z &= 0 \end{aligned}\right\}.$$

so that these forces are at once orthogonal to the path of the representative point P and also orthogonal to the straight line whose direction cosines are proportional to E, F, G. These forces are therefore of the nature of *centrifugal forces*, as if they were produced by the rotation of the system about this straight line.

13. We may show that the straight line (E, F, G) is fixed in space. To prove this, let us transform our co-ordinates from ξ, η, ζ to x, y, z, where x, y, z are connected with ξ, η, ζ by any linear relations, such as

$$\left.\begin{aligned} \xi &= a_1x + b_1y + c_1z\\ \eta &= a_2x + b_2y + c_2z\\ \zeta &= a_3x + b_3y + c_3z \end{aligned}\right\}.$$

Let the portion of the Lagrangian function under consideration (Art. 1) be

$$C_{11}\xi\xi' + C_{12}\xi\eta' + C_{21}\eta\xi' + \dots$$

then $G = C_{12} - C_{21}$, $E = C_{23} - C_{32}$, $F = C_{31} - C_{13}$.

Substituting for ξ, η, ζ their values in terms of x, y, z, we find that the difference between the coefficients of xy' and $x'y$ is

$$G' = G\begin{vmatrix} a_1 & a_2\\ b_1 & b_2 \end{vmatrix} + E\begin{vmatrix} a_2 & a_3\\ b_2 & b_3 \end{vmatrix} + F\begin{vmatrix} a_3 & a_1\\ b_3 & b_1 \end{vmatrix},$$

with similar equations for E' and F'. But if μ be the determinant of transformation

$$\mu z = \zeta \begin{vmatrix} a_1 & a_2 \\ b_1 & b_2 \end{vmatrix} + \xi \begin{vmatrix} a_2 & a_3 \\ b_2 & b_3 \end{vmatrix} + \eta \begin{vmatrix} a_3 & a_1 \\ b_3 & b_1 \end{vmatrix},$$

with similar equations for x and y. The *ratios* of E, F, G are therefore transformed as if they were co-ordinates. If the transformation be a real transformation of Cartesian co-ordinates, let lengths each equal to unity be measured from the origin along the axes $O\xi$, $O\eta$, $O\zeta$, thus forming a tetrahedron whose volume is V. Let a similar construction be made for the new axes, forming a tetrahedron of volume V'. Then* $\mu = \dfrac{V'}{V}$. Hence the quantities $\dfrac{E}{V}$, $\dfrac{F}{V}$, $\dfrac{G}{V}$ may be transformed as if they were lengths measured along the axes and become $\dfrac{E'}{V'}$, $\dfrac{F'}{V'}$, $\dfrac{G'}{V'}$. If both systems of co-ordinates are rectangular we have $V = \dfrac{1}{3}$, $V' = \dfrac{1}{3}$.

Let ω be the resultant of $\dfrac{E}{V}$, $\dfrac{F}{V}$, $\dfrac{G}{V}$, *then ω may be regarded as a fixed length measured from the origin along a straight line fixed in space.*

Let v be the velocity of the representative particle, θ the angle between the direction of this velocity and the axis whose direction cosines are proportional to E, F, G. Then the resultant of the forces X, Y, Z is easily seen to be $2vV\omega \sin \theta$ acting perpendicular to the axis and to the direction of the motion. We might call the straight line (EFG) the axis of the centrifugal forces.

[* Let $(\xi_1 \eta_1 \zeta_1)$, $(\xi_2 \eta_2 \zeta_2)$, $(\xi_3 \eta_3 \zeta_3)$ be the co-ordinates of three points A, B, C referred to any *oblique* co-ordinates. Let us find the volume V' of the tetrahedron of which these and the origin are the angular points. Since the volume vanishes when any angular point as C lies in the plane containing the origin and the other two A, B, the expression for the volume must contain the factor

$$\mu = \begin{vmatrix} \xi_1 & \xi_2 & \xi_3 \\ \eta_1 & \eta_2 & \eta_3 \\ \zeta_1 & \zeta_2 & \zeta_3 \end{vmatrix}.$$

The volume is evidently an integral rational function of the co-ordinates when the axes are rectangular and the plane AOB is taken as the plane of xy, it easily follows that this is true for all axes. Since this function cannot be of more than the third order, we have $V' = M\mu$, where M is independent of the co-ordinates of A, B, C. When the points A, B, C are on the axes at unit distances from the origin, let V be the volume of the tetrahedron. In this case $\mu = 1$, and $\therefore M = V$. We have therefore in all cases $V' = V\mu$.

In the text, let the extremities of the unit lengths measured along the axes of x, y, z be called A, B, C. Then the $(\xi \eta \zeta)$ co-ordinates of A, B, C are (a_1, a_2, a_3), (b_1, b_2, b_3), (c_1, c_2, c_3), respectively. Hence by what has just been said $V' = V\mu$.]

14.   The expressions for the co-ordinates in terms of the time will in general contain as many periodic functions as there are co-ordinates.   If the initial conditions are such that each contains one and the same periodic function, the motion recurs after a constant interval and the system is said to be performing a *simple* or *harmonic oscillation.*

If the system be oscillating about a position of equilibrium, with a Lagrangian function

$$A_{11}\xi^2 + 2A_{12}\xi\eta + \dots$$
$$+ B_{11}\xi'^2 + 2B_{12}\xi'\eta' + \dots$$

we know* that the harmonic oscillations are represented by *rectilinear* motions of the representative particle, and that these are along the common conjugate diameters of the two quadrics whose equations are

$$\left. \begin{aligned} A_{11}\frac{\xi^2}{2} + A_{12}\xi\eta + \dots = a \\ B_{11}\frac{\xi^2}{2} + B_{12}\xi\eta + \dots = b \end{aligned} \right\},$$

where a and b are two constants chosen to make the quadrics real. Let us consider what are the harmonic paths of the representative point when the system is oscillating about a state of steady motion.

In any harmonic vibration we have $\xi = L \cos (\lambda t + a)$ with similar equations for η and ζ.   Hence

$$\frac{d^2\xi}{dt^2} = -\lambda^2\xi, \quad \frac{d^2\eta}{dt^2} = -\lambda^2\eta, \quad \frac{d^2\zeta}{dt^2} = -\lambda^2\zeta.$$

Substitute these in the equations of Art. 11.   Differentiate and substitute again.   Multiply by ξ, η, ζ, add and integrate, we obtain

$$\left(B_{11}\frac{\xi^2}{2} + B_{12}\xi\eta + \dots \right)\lambda^2 + \left(A_{11}\frac{\xi^2}{2} + A_{12}\xi\eta + \dots \right) = c,$$

where c is some constant.   The harmonic path lies on this quadric, which has a common set of conjugate diameters with the two quadrics a and b.

If we resume the result of the substitution of $\dfrac{d^2\xi}{dt^2}$, &c. in the equations of Art. 11, and multiply by E, F, G respectively and add, we obtain

$$[(B_{11}E + B_{12}F + B_{13}G)\,\xi + \&\text{c.}]\,\lambda^2 + [(A_{11}E + \dots)\,\xi + \&\text{c.}] = 0,$$

---

* A short paragraph in Thomson and Tait's *Natural Philosophy*, page 273, is the only notice of this which the author has discovered.

which is a plane, and is diametral to the straight line (EFG) with regard to the quadric c.

The harmonic paths are therefore ellipses. The three harmonic planes are diametral to the same straight line and this straight line is fixed in space, being the axis of the centrifugal forces.

If we eliminate λ between the equations to the plane and the quadric c, we get a cubic surface on which the three harmonic conics lie.

If E, F, G are zero, which is the case when the system oscillates about a position of equilibrium, the quadric c becomes a cylinder. This may be conveniently shown by referring the system to such co-ordinates that the coefficients $B_{12}, B_{13}, B_{23}, A_{12}, A_{13}, A_{23}$ are all zero. In this case the diametral plane of every straight line passes through the axis of the cylinder. The harmonic oscillations are therefore rectilinear.

If R be the length of that semidiameter of the quadric (c) which is parallel to the fixed straight line (E, F, G), it may be shown that the

$$\left.\begin{array}{r}\text{Product of the axes}\\ \text{of the quadric } c\end{array}\right\} = \frac{R}{\sqrt{E^2+F^2+G^2}} \cdot \frac{2c}{\lambda}.$$

If E, F, G are all zero, and their ratio is indeterminate, R is any diameter. Hence one of the axes of the quadric (c) must be infinite and the quadric will be a cylinder.

[If the quadric (c) be a cylinder and E, F, G are not all zero, we must have either λ zero or R infinite. In the latter case the axis of the cylinder will coincide with the axis of the centrifugal forces.]

The quadric (c) has also the following geometrical property. Let the lengths of semidiameters of the quadrics (a) and (b) drawn parallel to the axis of the centrifugal forces be ρ and ρ'. Through the intersection of these quadrics describe a quadric so that the

$$\left.\begin{array}{r}\text{Product of}\\ \text{its axes}\end{array}\right\} = \frac{2\sqrt{ab}}{\sqrt{E^2+F^2+G^2}} \cdot \frac{\left(\frac{1}{\rho'^2}-\frac{1}{\rho^2}\right)R}{\sqrt{\left(\frac{1}{\rho'^2}-\frac{1}{R^2}\right)\left(\frac{1}{R^2}-\frac{1}{\rho^2}\right)}}.$$

This quadric is similar to the quadric (c).

15. The introduction of the representative point to exhibit the motion of a system may appear somewhat artificial. If however we properly choose the co-ordinates the particle moves exactly as a free particle, and we might reduce the problem of finding the

oscillations of a system to a problem in Dynamics of a particle. Refer the quadric

$$B_{11}\frac{\xi^2}{2} + B_{12}\xi\eta + \ldots = b$$

to its principal axes and let the equation thus changed be

$$B_{11}'\frac{\xi_1^2}{2} + B_{22}'\frac{\eta_1^2}{2} + \ldots = b.$$

Since B_{11}', B_{22}', &c. are positive quantities, we may put

$$\sqrt{B_{11}'}\xi_1 = x, \quad \sqrt{B_{22}'}\eta_1 = y, \quad \&c.$$

The quadric has thus been "projected" into a sphere. Let x, y, z be now chosen as the co-ordinates of the system and let the Lagrangian function be expressed in the form

$$L = x'^2 + y'^2 + z'^2 + \tfrac{1}{2}A_{11}x^2 + A_{12}xy + \ldots$$
$$+ C_{11}xx' + \ldots$$

the terms of the first degree being omitted as not necessary to our present purpose. The three equations of motion at the beginning of Art. 11 take the form

$$\left(\frac{d^2}{dt^2} - A_{11}\right)x + \left(-A_{12} - G\frac{d}{dt}\right)y + \left(-A_{13} + F\frac{d}{dt}\right)z = 0,$$
$$\&c. = 0,$$

which are the three equations of motion of a free single particle whose co-ordinates are x, y, z under the action of forces whose force function is

$$\tfrac{1}{2}A_{11}x^2 + A_{12}xy + \ldots$$

and a force acting perpendicular to the path and also perpendicular to a fixed straight line, the force being proportional to the velocity.

16. As an illustration of this theory, let us here make a short digression. However the particles of light may oscillate, whether in a rotatory or linear manner, we know the motion is related to a certain plane called the plane of polarization. It may be shown that any harmonic oscillation about a position of *equilibrium* may be represented by a *rectilinear* oscillation of the representative particle. Let us represent the motion at any point of the ether by a rectilinear oscillation in a direction perpendicular to the plane of polarization. This would be Fresnel's Vibration. The representative particle, as just shown, would not necessarily move as if it were a free single particle. But let us assume (and a proof is not necessary to our present purpose) that when the oscillation is drawn as above described the motion in the plane of the front

is the same as that of a free particle, while that perpendicular is not free. On this assumption we see that Fresnel in his theory of double refraction is justified in taking actual instead of relative displacements, for it is the representative particle he is considering. He also neglects the force normal to the front, for the particle moves as a free particle only in the plane of the front. These general remarks are not meant to explain Fresnel's theory, but merely to show how the representative particle may be used to replace a complicated motion.

17. [When a system is performing a harmonic oscillation about a state of steady motion or about a position of equilibrium, the motion repeats itself continually at a constant period, that is to say, the values of the co-ordinates recur at this interval. This is the chief peculiarity of a harmonic oscillation. When the oscillation is about a position of equilibrium, the representative particle oscillates in a straight line whose middle point represents the position of equilibrium. Thus the system passes through the position of equilibrium twice in each complete oscillation. When the oscillation is about a state of steady motion the path of the representative particle is an ellipse whose centre is at the point occupied by the system in steady motion at the same instant. Thus the system does not in general ever coincide with the simultaneous position of the system in the undisturbed or steady motion. When a system is disturbed by a small impulse from a state of steady motion, it will in general describe a compound oscillation made up of at least two harmonic oscillations, at the instant of disturbance these two neutralize each other so that in the disturbed and undisturbed motions two simultaneous positions are coincident. But it is clear that this cannot occur again unless either the periods of the two harmonics are commensurable or the period of one of them is infinite.]

18. [In some cases the ellipse degenerates into a straight line. Thus if the quadric (c) be a cylinder the diametral plane of the axis of the centrifugal forces will pass through the axis of the cylinder, and thus the harmonic oscillation corresponding to this particular value of λ will be rectilinear. In this case the system twice in each oscillation passes through the position it would have occupied at the same instant in the undisturbed motion.

The quadric (c) has a common set of conjugate diameters with the quadrics (a) and (b). Hence if (c) be a cylinder, its axis must be parallel to one of the three common conjugate diameters of (a) and (b). If we refer the quadrics (a) and (b) to their common conjugate diameters, they take the form

$$\left.\begin{array}{l} A_{11}{}'\xi^2 + A_{22}{}'\eta^2 + A_{33}{}'\zeta^2 = 2a \\ B_{11}{}'\xi^2 + B_{22}{}'\eta^2 + B_{33}{}'\zeta^2 = 2b \end{array}\right\}.$$

The cylinder which passes through their intersection and has its axis parallel to the diameter ζ is found by eliminating ζ^2 between these equations. We see therefore that $B_{33}'\lambda^2 + A_{33}' = 0$. If then the axis of the cylinder cut the quadrics (a) and (b) in D and D' respectively, we find that for this oscillation

$$\lambda^2 = \frac{OD'^2}{OD^2} \cdot \frac{-a}{b}$$

It has already been shown that when this value is finite, the direction of ODD' is along the axis of the centrifugal forces.]

19. [In some cases two or more of the values of λ are zero. In these cases the co-ordinates will have terms of the form $nt + \epsilon$, where n and ϵ are two small constants. When, as explained in Art. 3 of this Chapter, there are several *parallel* states of steady motion, these terms imply that the motion is stable about a state of steady motion very nearly the same as the undisturbed motion but not coincident with it. The actual undisturbed motion, unless n is zero, is unstable in the sense that if a proper disturbance be given to the system, the system will depart widely from the positions it would have simultaneously occupied in the undisturbed motion.]

20. In many cases of small oscillations it will be found that the Lagrangian function $T - V$ is not a function of some of the co-ordinates as θ, ϕ, &c. though it is a function of their differential coefficients θ', ϕ', &c. In such cases the steady motion will be usually given by constant values of these differential coefficients, while the other co-ordinates as ξ, η, &c. are also constant. It is evident that the determinantal equation of Art. 4 is needlessly complicated. It is clear that there will be as many pairs of roots equal to zero as there are co-ordinates θ, ϕ, &c. It will be an advantage to eliminate θ', ϕ', &c. altogether from the Lagrangian function, and to find the remaining roots by operating only with the co-ordinates ξ, η, &c. We shall thus obtain a determinant with just as many rows as there are co-ordinates of the kind ξ, η, &c.

Let L_1 be the Lagrangian function expressed as a function of $\theta'\phi'$, &c. $\xi\eta$, $\xi'\eta'$, &c. Let L_2 be its value when $\theta'\phi'$ are eliminated, so that L_2 is a function of $\xi\eta$, $\xi'\eta'$, &c. only. To effect this elimination we have the integrals

$$\frac{dT}{d\theta'} = c_1, \quad \frac{dT}{d\phi'} = c_2, \text{ &c.}$$

where c_1, c_2, &c. are constants. Then

$$\frac{dL_2}{d\xi'} = \frac{dL_1}{d\xi'} + \frac{dL_1}{d\theta'} \cdot \frac{d\theta'}{d\xi'} + \frac{dL_1}{d\phi'} \cdot \frac{d\phi'}{d\xi'} + \text{&c.}$$

$$= \frac{dL_1}{d\xi'} + c_1 \frac{d\theta'}{d\xi'} + c_2 \frac{d\phi'}{d\xi'} + \cdots$$

$$\frac{dL_2}{d\xi} = \frac{dL_1}{d\xi} + c_1\frac{d\theta'}{d\xi} + c_2\frac{d\phi'}{d\xi} + \dots$$

$$\therefore \frac{d}{dt}\frac{dL_2}{d\xi'} - \frac{dL_2}{d\xi} = \frac{d}{dt}\frac{dL_1}{d\xi'} - \frac{dL_1}{d\xi} + c_1\left(\frac{d}{dt}\frac{d\theta'}{d\xi'} - \frac{d\theta}{d\xi}\right) + \&c.$$

But
$$\frac{d}{dt}\frac{dL_1}{d\xi'} - \frac{dL_1}{d\xi} = 0.$$

Hence if we take
$$L' = L - c_1\theta' - c_2\phi' - \&c.$$
and eliminate θ', ϕ' *by help of the integrals* $\dfrac{dT}{d\theta'} = c_1$, $\dfrac{dT}{d\phi'} = c_2$, *we may treat* L' *just as we do the Lagrangian function* L. *The equations giving the small oscillations about the steady motion will be*

$$\frac{d}{dt}\frac{dL'}{d\xi'} - \frac{dL'}{d\xi} = 0, \ \&c. = 0.$$

The function L' may be called the *modified Lagrangian function.*

[It should be noticed that this is equivalent to a partial use of Hamilton's transformation of Lagrange's equations. Sir W. R. Hamilton eliminates *all* the differential coefficients θ', ϕ', &c. by the help of equations of the form $\dfrac{dT}{d\theta'} = u$, $\dfrac{dT}{d\phi'} = v$, &c. where u, v, &c. are made to be new variables*. In our transformation only

* The Hamiltonian transformation of Lagrange's equations bears a remarkable analogy to the transformation of Reciprocation in Geometry. This may be shown in the following manner.

When the system has three co-ordinates θ, ϕ, ψ, we may regard θ', ϕ', ψ' as the Cartesian co-ordinates of a representative point P. The position and path of P will exhibit to the eye and will determine the motion of the system. Let u, v, w be the Hamiltonian variables, so that
$$u = \frac{dT_1}{d\theta'}, \quad v = \frac{dT_1}{d\phi'}, \quad w = \frac{dT_1}{d\psi'},$$
where T_1 is the semi vis viva expressed as a function of θ, ϕ, ψ, θ', ϕ', ψ'. Then u, v, w may be regarded as the co-ordinates of another point Q whose position and path will also determine the motion of the system.

If the semi vis viva be given by the general expression
$$T_1 = \tfrac{1}{2}A_{11}\theta'^2 + A_{12}\theta'\phi' + \dots$$
it is clear that the point P always lies on the quadric $T_1 = U$ where U is the force function and the co-ordinates θ, ϕ, ψ have their instantaneous values. The point Q must therefore lie on another quadric which is the polar reciprocal of the first with regard to a sphere whose centre is at the origin and whose radius is equal to $\sqrt{2U}$. The equation to the reciprocal quadric is therefore

$$T_2 = -\frac{1}{2\Delta}\begin{vmatrix} 0 & u & v & w \\ u & A_{11} & A_{12} & A_{13} \\ v & A_{12} & A_{22} & A_{23} \\ w & A_{13} & A_{23} & A_{33} \end{vmatrix} = U,$$

those new variables are introduced which would be constants in Sir W. R. Hamilton's transformation.

This remark suggests an extension of the process. If L be a function of θ, ϕ, &c. as well as of θ', ϕ', &c. the quantities c_1, c_2, &c. will not be constants. We express this by writing u, v, &c. instead of c_1, c_2, &c. Suppose we wish to eliminate *some* of the differential coefficients, viz. θ', ϕ', &c. and to retain the remaining ones, viz. ξ', η', &c. If we put

$$L' = L - u\theta' - v\phi' - \&c.$$

we may easily show as in the preceding page that

$$\frac{d}{dt}\frac{dL'}{d\xi'} - \frac{dL'}{d\xi} = 0, \quad \&c. = 0.$$

where Δ is the determinant, called the discriminant, which may be formed from the determinant just written down by omitting the first row and the first column.

This is a general expression for the Hamiltonian function and agrees with that which may be deduced from the result in Art. 21, when *all* the variables are transformed by the Hamiltonian process.

Since the polar reciprocal of the polar reciprocal is the original quadric, it follows that

$$\theta' = \frac{dT_2}{du}, \quad \phi' = \frac{dT_2}{dv}, \quad \psi' = \frac{dT_2}{dw},$$

which are three of the six Hamiltonian equations.

We may also show geometrically that if the coefficients of T_1 be functions of any quantity θ, then $\dfrac{dT_1}{d\theta} = -\dfrac{dT_2}{d\theta}$. To prove this we notice that if x, y, z be the co-ordinates of a point P, situated on a radius vector OP' of a quadric $\phi\,(x,\,y,\,z) = 1$ referred to its centre O, then $\phi\,(x,\,y,\,z) = \left(\dfrac{OP}{OP'}\right)^2$. The quadrics $T_1 = 1$ and $T_2 = 1$ may be regarded as polar reciprocals of each other with regard to a sphere whose radius is $\sqrt{2}$ and whose centre is the common centre of the two quadrics. Let P be any point on the quadric $T_1 = 1$, and let the radius vector be produced to Z so that $OP \cdot OZ = 2$, then the quadric $T_2 = 1$ touches a plane drawn through Z perpendicular to OP and Q is the point of contact. Let these quadrics be slightly altered in consequence of a variation of θ, so that their equations are now $T_1 + dT_1 = 1$ and $T_2 + dT_2 = 1$. Let OP and OQ produced cut these quadrics respectively in P' and Q'. Then

$$T_1 + dT_1 = \left(\frac{OP}{OP'}\right)^2, \quad T_2 + dT_2 = \left(\frac{OQ}{OQ'}\right)^2.$$

Now if Z' be a point on OP produced so that $OP' \cdot OZ' = OP \cdot OZ$, the quadric $T_2 + dT_2$ will touch the plane drawn through Z' in some point q near Q'. The point Q' will therefore lie very nearly in the tangent plane, so that by similar triangles

$$\frac{OQ}{OQ'} = \frac{OZ}{OZ'} = \frac{OP'}{OP}.$$

Since each of these ratios is indefinitely nearly equal to unity, it follows that $dT_1 = -dT_2$.

If we put $L = T_1 + U$ and $H = T_2 - U$, Lagrange's equations may be written in the forms $u' = \dfrac{dL}{d\theta}$, $v' = \dfrac{dL}{d\phi}$, $w' = \dfrac{dL}{d\psi}$. Hence we have

$$-u' = \frac{dH}{d\theta}, \quad -v' = \frac{dH}{d\phi}, \quad -w' = \frac{dH}{d\psi},$$

which are the remaining three of the Hamiltonian equations.

We have thus as many equations of the Lagrangian form as there are variables ξ, η, &c. Also since $u = \dfrac{dL}{d\theta'}$, &c. we have by differentiation

$$\frac{dL'}{du} = \left(\frac{dL}{d\theta'} - u\right)\frac{d\theta'}{du} - \theta' + \&c. = -\theta',$$

with similar equations for ϕ', &c. By Lagrange's equations we obtain

$$\frac{dL'}{d\theta} = u', \&c.$$

Thus we have as many sets of equations of the Hamiltonian form as there are variables θ, ϕ, &c.]

21. We may effect this elimination once for all and find a definite expression for L'.

Let the kinetic energy be

$$T = T_{\theta\theta}\frac{\theta'^2}{2} + T_{\theta\phi}\,\theta'\phi' + \ldots$$

Then the integrals used will be

$$T_{\theta\theta}\theta' + T_{\theta\phi}\phi' + \ldots = c_1 - T_{\theta\xi}\xi' - T_{\theta\eta}\eta' - \ldots$$
$$T_{\theta\phi}\theta' + T_{\phi\phi}\phi' + \ldots = c_2 - T_{\phi\xi}\xi' - T_{\phi\eta}\eta' - \ldots$$
$$\&c. = \&c.$$

For the sake of brevity let us call the right-hand members of these equations $c_1 - X$, $c_2 - Y$, &c. Since T is a homogeneous function, we have

$$\left.\begin{aligned}T = T_{\xi\xi}\frac{\xi'^2}{2} + T_{\xi\eta}\xi'\eta' + \ldots\\ + \tfrac{1}{2}\theta'(c_1 + X) + \tfrac{1}{2}\phi'(c_2 + Y) + \&c.\end{aligned}\right\},$$

$$\therefore\; \left.\begin{aligned}L' = T_{\xi\xi}\frac{\xi'^2}{2} + T_{\xi\eta}\xi'\eta' + \&c. - V\\ - \tfrac{1}{2}\theta'(c_1 - X) - \tfrac{1}{2}\phi'(c_2 - Y) - \&c.\end{aligned}\right\}.$$

If we substitute in the second line the values of θ', ϕ', &c. found by solving the integrals just written down, we have

$$L' = T_{\xi\xi}\frac{\xi'^2}{2} + T_{\xi\eta}\xi'\eta' + \&c. - V$$

$$+ \frac{1}{2\Delta}\begin{vmatrix} 0 & c_1 - X & c_2 - Y & \ldots \\ c_1 - X & T_{\theta\theta} & T_{\theta\phi} & \ldots \\ c_2 - Y & T_{\theta\phi} & T_{\phi\phi} & \ldots \\ \ldots & \ldots & \ldots & \ldots \end{vmatrix},$$

where Δ is the discriminant of the terms in T, which contain only θ', ϕ', &c., and may be derived from the determinant just written down by omitting the first row and the first column.

We may expand this determinant and write it in the form

$$L' = T_{\xi\xi}\frac{\xi'^2}{2} + T_{\xi\eta}\xi'\eta' + \&c. - V$$

$$+\frac{1}{2\Delta}\begin{vmatrix} 0 & c_1 & c_2 & \cdots \\ c_1 & T_{\theta\theta} & T_{\theta\phi} & \cdots \\ c_2 & T_{\theta\phi} & T_{\phi\phi} & \cdots \\ \cdots & \cdots & \cdots & \cdots \end{vmatrix} + \frac{1}{2\Delta}\begin{vmatrix} 0 & X & Y & \cdots \\ X & T_{\theta\theta} & T_{\theta\phi} & \cdots \\ Y & T_{\theta\phi} & T_{\phi\phi} & \cdots \\ \cdots & \cdots & \cdots & \cdots \end{vmatrix}$$

$$-\frac{1}{\Delta}\begin{vmatrix} 0 & X & Y & \cdots \\ c_1 & T_{\theta\theta} & T_{\theta\phi} & \cdots \\ c_2 & T_{\theta\phi} & T_{\phi\phi} & \cdots \\ \cdots & \cdots & \cdots & \cdots \end{vmatrix},$$

where X, Y, &c. stand for

$$\left.\begin{array}{l} X = T_{\theta\xi}\xi' + T_{\theta\eta}\eta' + \cdots \\ Y = T_{\phi\xi}\xi' + T_{\phi\eta}\eta' + \cdots \\ \&c. = \&c. \end{array}\right\} .$$

The first of these three determinants will contain only the constants c_1, c_2, &c., and the co-ordinates ξ, η, &c. The second will not contain c_1, c_1, &c. but will be a quadratic function of ξ', η', &c. The last determinant will contain terms of the form ξ', η' with variable coefficients which may also be functions of c_1, c_2...

Since $\xi\xi'$, $\eta\eta'$, &c. are all small quantities, it is clear that this expression for L' when expanded will take a form precisely similar to that given in Art. 2, only that we have fewer variables to deal with.

22.   As an example, let us consider the following problem.

A body has a point O which is in one of the principal axes at the centre of gravity G fixed in space. The body is in steady motion rotating with angular velocity n about OG which is vertical. Find the conditions that the motion may be stable.

Let OA, OB, OC be the principal axes at O and let OC co-incide with the vertical OZ in steady motion. Let ξ, η be the direction cosines of the vertical OZ referred to OA, OB. Let ω_1, ω_2, ω_3 be the angular velocities about the principal axes at O. Then to the first order

$$\left.\begin{array}{l} \omega_1 = \quad \eta' + \omega_3\xi \\ \omega_2 = -\xi' + \omega_3\eta \end{array}\right\} .$$

Let θ be the angle ZOC, ψ the angle the plane ZOC makes with a plane ZOX fixed in space and ϕ the angle it makes with the plane AOC fixed in the body.   Then

$$\left. \begin{array}{l} \xi = -\sin\theta\cos\phi \\ \eta = \sin\theta\sin\phi \end{array} \right\}.$$

$$\omega_3 = \phi' + \psi'\cos\theta$$

$$= \phi' + (\chi' - \phi')\left(1 - \frac{\theta^2}{2}\right),$$

putting $\chi = \phi + \psi$.   We easily find

$$\omega_3 = \chi' - \chi'\frac{\xi^2 + \eta^2}{2} - \tfrac{1}{2}(\xi\eta' - \xi'\eta).$$

If then A, B, C be the principal moments of inertia at O, the Lagrangian function is

$$L = \frac{C}{2}\left\{ \chi'\left(1 - \frac{\xi^2 + \eta^2}{2}\right) - \tfrac{1}{2}(\xi\eta' - \xi'\eta) \right\}^2$$

$$+ \frac{A}{2}(\eta' + \chi'\xi)^2 + \frac{B}{2}(-\xi' + \chi'\eta)^2$$

$$- Mgh\left(1 - \frac{\xi^2 + \eta^2}{2}\right),$$

where M is the mass of the body, and $h = OG$.

Since χ is absent from the equation we have the integral

$$\frac{dL}{d\chi'} = c_1,$$

which gives

$$\chi' = n + \text{terms of second order.}$$

Hence

$$L' = L - Cn\chi'$$

$$= \text{const} + \frac{A}{2}\eta'^2 + \frac{B}{2}\xi'^2$$

$$+ \{(A - C)n^2 + Mgh\}\frac{\xi^2}{2} + \{(B - C)n^2 + Mgh\}\frac{\eta^2}{2}$$

$$+ \left(A - \frac{C}{2}\right)n\xi\eta' - \left(B - \frac{C}{2}\right)n\xi'\eta.$$

Using this as the Lagrangian function we easily find

$$\left| \begin{array}{ll} (A - C)n^2 + Mgh - Bm^2, & (A + B - C)nm \\ -(A + B - C)nm, & (B - C)n^2 + Mgh - Am^2 \end{array} \right| = 0.$$

The roots of this equation to find m must for stability be of the form $\pm \beta \sqrt{-1}$. Putting $m^2 = -\lambda^2$ we have a quadratic to find λ^2. The roots of this quadratic must be real and positive.

If $A = B$, as in the case of a top spinning with its axis vertical, we have

$$\lambda = \pm \left\{ \frac{2A - C}{2A} n \pm \sqrt{\frac{C^2 n^2 - 4AMgh}{2A}} \right\}.$$

The motion is stable or unstable according as $C^2 n^2$ is greater or less than $4AMgh$. If $C^2 n^2 = 4AMgh$, the equation has equal roots and as the first minors are not zero the motion is unstable.

23. [As another example of the use of the modified Lagrangian function, let us consider a case discussed by Prof. Ball in the *Notices of the Royal Astronomical Society for March*, 1877. In a problem in Physical Astronomy, we want the *relative* co-ordinates of the system, while its *absolute* motion in space does not concern us. Lagrange's equations involve both the relative and absolute co-ordinates, and are therefore not particularly well adapted for such problems. By using the modified Lagrangian function, we may eliminate the absolute co-ordinates.

Let the system have n co-ordinates, let us choose as three of them the co-ordinates of the centre of gravity of the whole system, viz. θ, ϕ, ψ. There will then remain $n - 3$ co-ordinates which are independent of these. Let T' be the kinetic energy of the system relative to its centre of gravity, V the potential energy, M the whole mass. Then the Lagrangian function is

$$L = \frac{1}{2} M (\theta'^2 + \phi'^2 + \psi'^2) + T' - V.$$

In problems in Physical Astronomy the potential energy is a function only of the *relative* positions of the bodies, and is therefore independent of θ, ϕ, ψ and their differential coefficients. We have therefore

$$\frac{dL}{d\theta'} = c_1, \quad \frac{dL}{d\phi'} = c_2, \quad \frac{dL}{d\psi'} = c_3.$$

Hence the modified Lagrangian function is

$$L' = T' - V - \text{a constant.}$$

It is independently clear that we might take this as the Lagrangian function, for the first three terms of L do not enter into any one of the Lagrangian equations, except the three formed by differentiating with regard to θ', ϕ', ψ'.

The function T' is made up of two parts, (1) the kinetic energies of the rotations of the bodies about their centres of gravity, which we may call T_1', and (2) the relative kinetic energies of the several bodies, each collected at its centre of gravity, which we may call T_2'. Let m_1, m_2, &c. be these masses; x_1, x_2, &c. the abscissæ of their centres of gravity referred to the centre of gravity of the whole as origin. Then, accents denoting differential coefficients with regard to the time, we have

$$m_1 x_1' + m_2 x_2' + \&c. = 0.$$

Let us square this and write

$$2 x_1' x_2' = x_1'^2 + x_2'^2 - (x_1' - x_2')^2.$$

If we examine the coefficient of any power as $x_1'^2$ we see that it is

$$m_1^2 + m_1(m_2 + m_3 + \&c.) = m_1 \Sigma m.$$

Hence the square becomes

$$\Sigma m \, \Sigma m x'^2 - \Sigma m_1 m_2 (x_1' - x_2')^2 = 0.$$

Similar expressions hold for the y and z co-ordinates. Hence on the whole we see that the relative kinetic energies of the several bodies collected at their respective centres of gravity is

$$T_2' = \frac{\Sigma m_1 m_2 v^2}{2 \Sigma m},$$

where v is the relative velocity of the centres of gravity of the masses m_1, m_2. If we express this in any kind of co-ordinates, we may use the Lagrangian function L' to find the relative motion.

The expression for T_2' agrees with that given by Prof. Ball, but his demonstration is quite different. Prof. Cayley has given another demonstration in the same number of the Astronomical Notices.

The Lagrangian function thus found may be still further "modified." To avoid symbols of summation, let us consider the case of three particles moving in one plane under their mutual attractions. Let the separate masses be m_1, m_2, m_3, and let μ be their sum. Referring the system to m_1 as a central mass, let the distances of m_2, m_3 from m_1 be respectively r and ρ, and let the opposite side of the triangle be R. Let the interior angle between r and ρ be ϕ and the exterior angle between r and R be χ. Let θ be the angle r makes with some fixed straight line in space. We easily find

$$\mu T_2' = \frac{1}{2} A \theta'^2 + B \theta' + C,$$

where

$$A = m_1 m_2 r^2 + m_1 m_3 \rho^2 + m^2 m_3 R^2,$$

$$B = m_3 (m_1 \rho^2 \phi' + m_2 R^2 \chi'),$$

$$C = \frac{1}{2\mu} \Sigma m m' v^2,$$

and v is the relative velocity of the masses m, m' calculated on the supposition that m_1 is fixed, and that the straight line r has no rotation round m_1. Thus A, B, C are all functions of r, ρ, ϕ and their differential coefficients with regard to the time.

If we only want the changes in the form and magnitude of the triangle joining the three particles, we may eliminate θ' by means of the equation

$$A\theta' + B = c_1.$$

We then find as our modified Lagrangian function

$$L'' = \frac{1}{\mu}\left\{ C - \frac{1}{2}\frac{(C_1 - B)^2}{A} \right\} - V,$$

which contains only the *three* co-ordinates r, ρ and ϕ].

24. When the geometrical equations contain differential coefficients of the co-ordinates ξ, η, ζ, &c. of the system with regard to the time, we cannot express the co-ordinates x, y, z of any element of a body in terms of ξ, η, ζ, &c. by means of equations of the form

$$x = f_1(\xi, \eta, \zeta, \&\text{c.}, t),$$
$$y = f_2(\xi, \eta, \zeta, \&\text{c.}, t),$$
$$z = f_3(\xi, \eta, \zeta, \&\text{c.}, t).$$

It follows, as is pointed out in our books on Rigid Dynamics, that Lagrange's equations cannot be employed in the form

$$\frac{d}{dt}\frac{dT}{d\xi'} - \frac{dT}{d\xi} = -\frac{dV}{d\xi}.$$

In many of the most interesting problems in Rigid Dynamics, it so happens that the geometrical equations do contain $\dfrac{d\xi}{dt}$, $\dfrac{d\eta}{dt}$, &c. For example, let a sphere be set rotating about a vertical diameter and be on the summit of a perfectly rough surface of any form. If a small disturbance be now given to it, the sphere may roll round and round the summit. During this motion the velocity of the point of contact is zero, and our mode of representing this analytically in terms of the co-ordinates will give us two equations of the form

$$A\xi' + B\eta' + C\zeta' + \ldots = 0.$$

To include such cases the equations of motion must be modified. If L be the difference between the kinetic and potential energies, all the Lagrangian equations may be written in the form

$$\left(\frac{d}{dt}\frac{dL}{d\xi'} - \frac{dL}{d\xi}\right)\delta\xi + \left(\frac{d}{dt}\frac{dL}{d\eta'} - \frac{dL}{d\eta}\right)\delta\eta + \&\text{c.} = 0,$$

where $\delta\xi$, $\delta\eta$, &c. are any small arbitrary displacements consistent with the geometrical equations. But if these geometrical equations be given in the form

$$G = G_1\xi' + G_2\eta' + \ldots = 0$$
$$H = H_1\xi' + H_2\eta' + \ldots = 0$$
$$\text{&c.} = 0$$

these arbitrary displacements must satisfy

$$G_1\,\delta\xi + G_2\delta\eta + \ldots = 0$$
$$\text{&c.} = 0$$

If this were not the case, the geometrical displacement of the body given in applying Virtual Velocities would not be such as to cause the unknown frictional forces, &c. to disappear. Using the principle of Indeterminate Multipliers, we get

$$\frac{d}{dt}\frac{dL}{d\xi'} - \frac{dL}{d\xi} + \lambda G_1 + \mu H_1 + \ldots = 0$$
$$\frac{d}{dt}\frac{dL}{d\eta'} - \frac{dL}{d\eta} + \lambda G_2 + \mu H_2 + \ldots = 0$$
$$\text{&c.} = 0$$

These joined to the geometrical equations

$$G_1\xi' + G_2\eta' + \ldots = 0$$
$$\text{&c.} = 0$$

are sufficient to determine the unknown co-ordinates ξ, η, &c. and the multipliers λ, μ, &c.

It will be more convenient to write these equations in the form

$$\frac{d}{dt}\frac{dL}{d\xi'} - \frac{dL}{d\xi} + \lambda\frac{dG}{d\xi'} + \mu\frac{dH}{d\xi'} + \ldots = 0,$$

$$\frac{d}{dt}\frac{dL}{d\eta'} - \frac{dL}{d\eta} + \lambda\frac{dG}{d\eta'} + \mu\frac{dH}{d\xi'} + \ldots = 0,$$

$$\text{&c.} = 0,$$

the geometrical equations being

$$G = 0, \quad H = 0, \quad \text{&c.}$$

It is of course obvious that these indeterminate coefficients λ, μ, &c. are merely the frictions or other resistances introduced into the equations in a convenient form.

25. In order to apply these equations to the oscillations of a system about a state of steady motion, it will be convenient to

change the co-ordinates ξ, η, &c. into others θ, ϕ, &c. which vanish in the steady motion. Let L be thus expanded in powers of θ, ϕ, &c. as explained in Art. 1, and let P and Q have the meaning given to them in Art. 5.

Let us then put

$$\xi' = \alpha + \theta', \quad \eta' = \beta + \phi', \quad \&c.$$

$$\lambda = \lambda_0 + \lambda_1, \quad \mu = \mu_0 + \mu_1, \quad \&c.$$

where α, β, λ_0, μ_0, &c. are the values of ξ', η', λ, μ, &c. in steady motion. The geometrical equations will then take the form

$$G = G_1 (\alpha + \theta') + G_2 (\beta + \phi') + \&c. = 0 \Big\}_{\&c. = 0},$$

and the equations connecting $\delta\theta$, $\delta\phi$, &c. will be

$$G_1 \delta\theta + G_2 \delta\phi + \&c. = 0 \Big\}_{\&c. = 0}.$$

In these equations G_1, G_2, &c. are functions of θ, ϕ, &c. Let a square bracket indicate that the value of the inscribed quantity in steady motion is to be taken. Thus $[G_1]$ means the value of G_1 when θ, ϕ, &c. have all been put zero.

The equations of steady motion may then, exactly as in Art. 3, be written

$$-\left[\frac{dL}{d\theta}\right] + \lambda_0 \left[\frac{dG}{d\theta'}\right] + \mu_0 \left[\frac{dH}{d\theta'}\right] + \&c. = 0$$
$$-\left[\frac{dL}{d\phi}\right] + \lambda_0 \left[\frac{dG}{d\phi'}\right] + \mu_0 \left[\frac{dH}{d\phi'}\right] + \&c. = 0$$
$$\&c. = 0$$

From these the relations which exist between α, β, &c., λ_0, μ_0, &c. may be found.

The equations of the oscillatory motion may be written

$$\frac{d (P + Q)}{d\theta} - D \frac{dQ}{d\theta'} - \lambda_0 G_1 - \lambda_1 \left[\frac{dG}{d\theta'}\right] - \mu_0 H_1 - \mu_1 \left[\frac{dH}{d\theta'}\right] - \&c. = 0,$$

with similar equations for ϕ, ψ, &c.

26. The final determinant written for two variables θ, ϕ, and two geometrical equations G and H in the notation of Art. 19, will be

$$\begin{vmatrix} B_{11}m^2 - A_{11} + E_{11} \\ + \lambda_0\left[\dfrac{dG_1}{d\theta}\right] + \mu_0\left[\dfrac{dH_1}{d\theta}\right] & \begin{matrix} B_{12}m^2 - A_{12} + E_{12} \\ + (C_{21} - C_{12})m \\ + \lambda_0\left[\dfrac{dG_1}{d\phi}\right] + \mu_0\left[\dfrac{dH_1}{d\phi}\right] \end{matrix} & \left[\dfrac{dG}{d\theta'}\right] & \left[\dfrac{dH}{d\theta'}\right] \\[3em] \begin{matrix} B_{12}m^2 - A_{12} + E_{12} \\ - (C_{21} - C_{12})m \\ + \lambda_0\left[\dfrac{dG_2}{d\theta}\right] + \mu_0\left[\dfrac{dH_2}{d\theta}\right] \end{matrix} & B_{22}m^2 - A_{22} + E_{22} + \lambda_0\dfrac{dG_2}{d\phi} + \mu_0\dfrac{dH_2}{d\phi} & \left[\dfrac{dG}{d\phi'}\right] & \left[\dfrac{dH}{d\phi'}\right] \\[3em] \left[\dfrac{dG}{d\theta}\right] + \left[\dfrac{dG}{d\theta'}\right]m & \left[\dfrac{dG}{d\phi}\right] + \left[\dfrac{dG}{d\phi'}\right]m & 0 & 0 \\[2em] \left[\dfrac{dH}{d\theta}\right] + \left[\dfrac{dH}{d\theta'}\right]m & \left[\dfrac{dH}{d\theta}\right] + \left[\dfrac{dH}{d\phi'}\right]m & 0 & 0 \end{vmatrix} = 0.$$

It will be noticed how very much this determinant is simplified if the values of λ, μ in steady motion are zero.

27. Let us apply these equations to the solution of the following problem.

A heavy sphere rotating about a vertical diameter rests in equilibrium on the summit of a perfectly rough surface and being slightly disturbed makes small oscillations, find the periods.

As the sphere moves about, its centre always lies on a surface which may be called parallel to the given surface. Let the highest point of this surface be taken as the origin and let the axes of x and y be the tangents to its lines of curvature at O, so that the equation to the surface in the neighbourhood of O is

$$z = -\tfrac{1}{2}\left(\frac{x^2}{\rho_1} + \frac{y^2}{\rho_2}\right).$$

Let P be the centre of the sphere, PC that diameter which is vertical when the sphere is in equilibrium on the summit. Let PA, PB be two other diameters forming with PC a system of rectangular axes fixed in the sphere. Let the inclination of PC to the axis of Z, which is vertical, be θ, and let the vertical plane through PC make with the plane xz an angle ψ, and with the plane CPA an angle ϕ. The vis viva $2T$ of the sphere will then be given by

$$T = \tfrac{1}{2}\left(x'^2 + y'^2\right) + \tfrac{1}{2}k^2\left\{(\phi' + \psi'\cos\theta)^2 + \theta'^2 + \sin^2\theta\,\psi'^2\right\}.$$

Let $\sin \theta \cos \psi = \xi$, $\sin \theta \sin \psi = \eta$, then we have to the necessary degree of approximation

$$\left. \begin{aligned} \theta^2 \psi' &= \xi \eta' - \eta \xi' \\ \theta'^2 + \sin^2 \theta \, \psi'^2 &= \xi'^2 + \eta'^2 \end{aligned} \right\}.$$

Also let $\phi + \psi = \chi$. These transformations of co-ordinates are all permissible, because they do not involve any differential coefficients with regard to the time. We thus find if L be the difference between the kinetic and potential energies

$$L = \tfrac{1}{2} (x'^2 + y'^2) + \frac{k^2}{z} \{ \chi'^2 - \chi' \, (\xi \eta' - \eta \xi') + \xi'^2 + \eta'^2 \} + \frac{g}{2} \left(\frac{x^2}{\rho_1} + \frac{y^2}{\rho_2} \right).$$

If ω_x, ω_y, ω_z are the angular velocities of the sphere about parallels to the axes, the geometrical conditions are

$$\left. \begin{aligned} x' - a \left(\omega_y - \omega_z \frac{y}{\rho_2} \right) &= 0 \\ y' + a \left(\omega_x - \omega_z \frac{x}{\rho_1} \right) &= 0 \end{aligned} \right\},$$

where a is the radius of the sphere. These equations by well-known rules reduce to

$$\left. \begin{aligned} -\frac{x'}{a} + \phi' \sin \psi \sin \theta + \theta' \cos \psi - (\psi' + \phi' \cos \theta) \frac{y}{\rho_2} &= 0 \\ -\frac{y'}{a} - \phi' \cos \psi \sin \theta + \theta' \sin \psi + (\psi' + \phi' \cos \theta) \frac{x}{\rho_1} &= 0 \end{aligned} \right\};$$

expressing these in terms of our new co-ordinates we have

$$\left. \begin{aligned} G &= -\frac{x'}{a} + \chi' \eta + \xi' - \chi' \frac{y}{\rho_2} = 0 \\ H &= -\frac{y'}{a} - \chi' \xi + \eta' + \chi' \frac{x}{\rho_1} = 0 \end{aligned} \right\}.$$

The position of the system has now been expressed in terms of such co-ordinates, that the coefficients in the governing functions L, G, H are all constant. See Art. 2.

The steady motion is given by x, y, ξ, η all zero, and $\chi' = n$. To find λ_0, μ_0 we may use the equations of steady motion

$$- \left[\frac{dL}{dq} \right] + \lambda_0 \left[\frac{dG}{dq} \right] + \mu_0 \left[\frac{dH}{dq} \right] = 0,$$

where q stands for any one of the co-ordinates. Taking $q = x$ and $q = y$, we see that $\lambda_0 = 0$ and $\mu_0 = 0$.

To find the oscillation we may substitute in the determinant and thus form the equation which gives the periods. As most of the constituents of the determinants are zero, it will be more convenient to form each equation directly from the standard formula

$$\frac{d\,(P+Q)}{dq} - D\,\frac{dQ}{dq'} - \lambda_1\left[\frac{dG}{dq'}\right] - \mu_1\left[\frac{dH}{dq'}\right] = 0,$$

where q stands for any one of the co-ordinates. Taking q in turn to be $x,\ y,\ \chi,\ \xi,\ \eta$ we find

$$\left.\begin{aligned}
x'' - g\,\frac{x}{\rho_1} - \frac{\lambda_1}{a} &= 0 \\
y'' - g\,\frac{y}{\rho_2} - \frac{\mu_1}{a} &= 0 \\
k^2\chi'' &= 0 \\
k^2\,(\xi'' + \chi'\eta') + \lambda_1 &= 0 \\
k^2\,(\eta'' - \chi'\eta') + \mu_1 &= 0
\end{aligned}\right\}.$$

Putting $\chi' = n$ these with the two geometrical equations are all linear and ready for elimination.

Eliminating $\lambda_1,\ \mu_1$ we have

$$\left.\begin{aligned}
\xi'' + n\eta' + \frac{a}{k^2}\,x'' - \frac{ga}{k^2}\,\frac{x}{\rho_1} &= 0 \\
\eta'' - n\xi' + \frac{a}{k^2}\,y'' - \frac{ga}{k^2}\,\frac{y}{\rho_2} &= 0
\end{aligned}\right\}.$$

Substituting for $\xi,\ \eta$ from the two geometrical equations, we have

$$\left.\begin{aligned}
\frac{k^2+a^2}{a^2}\,x'' - g\,\frac{x}{\rho_1} &= -\frac{nk^2}{a^2\rho_2}\,y' \\
\frac{k^2+a^2}{a^2}\,y'' - g\,\frac{y}{\rho_2} &= +\frac{nk^2}{a^2\rho_1}\,x'
\end{aligned}\right\}.$$

To solve these put $x = X\cos\,(pt + q)\ y = Y\sin\,(pt + q)$ so that p is the quantity required. We obviously have

$$\left(p^2 + \frac{a^2}{a^2+k^2}\,\frac{g}{\rho_1}\right)\left(p^2 + \frac{a^2}{a^2+k^2}\,\frac{g}{\rho_2}\right) = \frac{k^4}{(a^2+k^2)^2}\,\frac{a^2n^2}{\rho_1\rho_2}\,p^2,$$

which is a quadratic to find p^2.

If $\rho_1,\ \rho_2$ have opposite signs the roots cannot be real, and the steady motion must be unstable. If $\rho_1,\ \rho_2$ are both positive, so that the sphere is on the *summit*, the motion is stable only if

$$n^2 > \frac{a^2+k^2}{k^4}\,g\,(\sqrt{\rho_1} + \sqrt{\rho_2})^2.$$

CHAPTER V.

Certain subsidiary determinants are formed from the dynamical determinant, and it is shown that there must be at least as many roots indicating stability as there are variations of sign lost in these subsidiary determinants, and must exceed the number lost by an even number. Arts. 1—5, and 9.

This is equivalent to a maximum and minimum criterion of stability with similar limitations. Arts. 6—8.

Effect of equal roots on this test of the stability of the system. Arts. 10, 11.

Example. Art. 12.

1. In order to test the nature of the roots of the determinantal equation, let us apply a method analogous to that by which Dr Salmon in his Higher Algebra proves the reality of the roots of the equation which occurs in the determination of the secular inequalities of the planets.

2. Let Δ be the determinant which forms the left-hand side of the fundamental equation, let Δ_{pq} be the determinant formed by omitting the pth row and q^{th} column. Let Δ_r be the determinant formed by omitting the first r rows and r columns. Thus $\Delta_1 = \Delta_{11}$. We then have by a known theorem in determinants

$$\Delta\Delta_2 = \Delta_{11}\Delta_{22} - \Delta_{12}\Delta_{21}.$$

It has already been noticed that if we change m into $-m$, the determinant Δ is changed into another determinant whose columns and rows are the same as the rows and columns of the first determinant. It easily follows that the minor $-\Delta_{12}$ is changed into the minor $-\Delta_{21}$ by changing m into $-m$. Hence if

then
$$\begin{aligned}
\Delta_{12} &= \phi\,(m^2) + m\psi\,(m^2) \\
\Delta_{21} &= \phi\,(m^2) - m\psi\,(m^2)
\end{aligned}$$

Hence the product $\Delta_{12}\Delta_{21}$ is necessarily positive for all negative values of m^2.

It also follows that if Δ_{12} vanishes for any negative value of m^2 then Δ_{21} also vanishes for the same value of m^2.

3.   When the determinant Δ_1 vanishes, we have

$$\Delta\Delta_2 = -\Delta_{12}\Delta_{21},$$

so that Δ and Δ_2 must have opposite signs, or one of them must be zero.   Consider then the series of determinants

$$\Delta, \ \Delta_1, \ \Delta_2, \ \Delta_3, \ \ldots\ldots$$

each one being formed from the preceding by erasing the first row and the first column.   We thus have a series of functions of m^2 whose degrees regularly diminish from the nth to the first. As we may suppose the determinant Δ to have a row and a column of zeros added on at the bottom and right-hand side, but with any positive constant in the right-hand bottom corner, we may add to this series of determinants any positive constant.   We have just proved that if any determinant of this series vanish for a negative value of m^2, the two determinants on each side have opposite signs.   The case in which two successive determinants vanish for the same value of m^2 will be considered afterwards.

We may then use these determinants in a manner somewhat similar to that in which we use Sturm's functions, provided no two successive functions vanish for the same negative value of m^2. No variation of sign can be lost as we pass from $m^2 = -\infty$ to $m^2 = 0$ except by the vanishing of the determinant Δ at the head of the series.   And when a variation of sign is lost, it will be regained again at the next root, unless a root of the determinant Δ_1 separates the two roots of the determinant Δ.   *If therefore in this passage from $-\infty$ to zero, as many variations of sign are lost as is indicated by the highest power of* m^2, *the values of* m^2 *found from the determinantal equation must be all real and negative.* It will also follow that the roots of each of the series of determinants are all real and negative, and that the roots of each separate the roots of the determinant next above it.   If, however, the proper number of variations of signs be not lost, in the passage from $m^2 = -\infty$ to $m^2 = 0$, it does not follow that the values of m^2 are not real and negative.

4.   If the proper number of variations of sign has not been lost in this passage from $m^2 = -\infty$ to $m^2 = 0$, this proposition does not leave us without information as to the nature of the roots. *We infer that the number of real negative values of* m^2 *is equal to or exceeds the number of variations of sign lost by an even number and unless the number of variations be even the system is unstable.*

If we do not object to the labour of expanding the determinants, we might extend this theorem to determine the positions of the negative values of m^2 as well as their number. The number of real negative values of m^2 between $m^2 = -\alpha$ and $m^2 = -\beta$ is equal to, or exceeds by an even number, the number of variations of sign lost in the series of determinants. In this form the theorem resembles Fourier's theorem in the Theory of Equations.

5. The converse of this proposition has not been proved. If in the passage from $m^2 = -\infty$ to $m^2 = 0$, the number of variations of signs is unaltered, it is not true that the values of m^2 cannot be real and negative. Thus in the simple case

$$\begin{vmatrix} m^2 - a_{11} & a_{12}m \\ -a_{12}m & m^2 - a_{22} \end{vmatrix} = 0,$$

where a_{11}, a_{12}, a_{22} are all positive, no variations are lost, yet if $a_{12} > \sqrt{a_{11}} + \sqrt{a_{22}}$ the values of m^2 are real and negative. And if $a_{12} = \sqrt{a_{11}} + \sqrt{a_{22}}$ the roots are equal and negative. It will be noticed that the minors in this last case are not zero.

6. In order to discover the meaning of these losses or gains of changes of sign, it will be convenient to make such changes of the co-ordinates as will simplify the dynamical determinant as much as possible. Let us write

$$V_0 = (E_{11} - A_{11}) \frac{\theta^2}{2} + (E_{12} - A_{12}) \theta\phi + \dots$$

If we now change our co-ordinates by writing for θ, ϕ, &c. linear expressions of some new co-ordinates, we know that we can clear this expression of all the terms containing the products. We know also that this can be done in an infinite number of ways. We thus have

$$V_0 = a_{11} \frac{\theta_1^2}{2} + a_{22} \frac{\phi_1^2}{2} + \dots$$

where the symbols θ_1, ϕ_1, &c. represent the new co-ordinates.

Again, let us consider the expression

$$W_0 = B_{11} \frac{\theta'^2}{2} + B_{12} \theta'\phi' + \dots\dots$$

the coefficients are here the values of P, Q, &c. in the general expression for T, Art. 1, Chap. IV. when θ, ϕ, &c. are all put zero. But since T is necessarily positive for all values of ξ, $\eta'\dots\xi$, $\eta,\dots$ it follows that W_0 is positive for all values of θ', $\phi'\dots$ Hence by a well-known theorem, we may by a *real* linear transformation of the variables clear the expression W_0 also of the terms containing the products θ', ϕ', &c. and can make the coefficients of the squares any positive constants we may please. We thus have

$$W_0 = \frac{\theta_1'^2}{2} + \frac{\phi_1'^2}{2} + \ldots\ldots$$

It may be shown that we cannot in general clear the expression for T of all the terms containing $\theta\phi'$, $\theta'\phi$, &c. unless $C_{12} - C_{21} = 0$, &c. by substituting for θ, ϕ, &c., any linear functions of other variables. As this is only a negative result of which no further use will here be made, it is unnecessary to supply the demonstration.

7. Using these simplifications the determinant Δ will now take the simpler form,

$$\Delta = \begin{vmatrix} m^2 + a_{11}, & a_{12}m, & a_{13}m, & \ldots \\ -a_{12}m, & m^2 + a_{22}, & a_{23}m, & \ldots \\ -a_{13}m, & -a_{23}m, & m^2 + a_{33}, & \ldots \\ \ldots\ldots\ldots, & \ldots\ldots\ldots, & \ldots\ldots\ldots, & \ldots \end{vmatrix} = 0,$$

where $a_{12} = C_{21} - C_{12}$, &c.

If we form from Δ the series of subsidiary determinants

$$\Delta, \Delta_1, \Delta_2 \ldots,$$

terminating with any positive constant, we see that when $m^2 = -\infty$, these subsidiary determinants are alternately positive and negative, and when $m^2 = 0$, they become

$$a_{11}a_{22}a_{33}\ldots, \quad a_{22}a_{33}\ldots, \quad a_{33}a_{44}\ldots, \quad \&c.,$$

which are all positive if a_{11}, $a_{22}\ldots$ are all positive. Hence if a_{11}, $a_{22}\ldots$ are all positive, the proper number of changes of sign has been lost, and therefore the roots of the dynamical equation $\Delta = 0$ satisfy the condition of stability.

If a_{11}, a_{22}, &c. are all positive, we see that V_0 is a minimum for all variations of θ_1, ϕ_1, &c. and therefore for all variations of the original co-ordinates. If a_{11}, a_{22}, &c. are not all positive, there will be as many variations of sign lost as there are positive quantities in the series a_{11}, a_{22}, &c. In this case V_0 is a minimum for some variations of θ, ϕ, &c. and not for others. It is shown in the appendix to Williamson's *Differential Calculus*, that n independent conditions are necessary that a quadratic expression of n variables should be always positive. These are given in the form of determinants and may be briefly summed up, in the statement that

$$A_{11}x_1^2 + 2A_{12}x_1x_2 + \ldots$$

is always positive if the roots of

$$\begin{vmatrix} A_{11}+\lambda, & A_{12}, & A_{13}, & \&c. \\ A_{12}, & A_{22}+\lambda, & A_{23}, & \&c. \\ A_{13}, & A_{23}, & A_{33}+\lambda, & \&c. \\ \&c. & \&c. & \&c. & \&c. \end{vmatrix} = 0,$$

are all real and negative.

8. We may now put the proposition of Art. 3 into another form. *Let* L *be the general expression for the excess of the kinetic energy over the potential energy of a dynamical system in terms of its* n *co-ordinates* x, y, *&c. Let this system be moving in steady motion with constant values of* $\dfrac{dx}{dt}, \dfrac{dy}{dt},$ *&c. Then if* L *be a maximum for all variations of* x, y, *&c. keeping* $\dfrac{dx}{dt}, \dfrac{dy}{dt},$ *&c. unchanged, then that steady motion is stable.*

If however only r *of the* n *conditions necessary to make* L *a maximum be satisfied, then the number of roots of the dynamical equation which satisfy the conditions of stability is equal to* r *or exceeds* r *by an even number. There cannot be stability unless* n − r *is an even number.*

If the system be oscillating about a position of equilibrium, $\dfrac{dx}{dt}, \dfrac{dy}{dt},$ &c. are all zero, and this leads at once to the condition, that the equilibrium is stable if the potential energy is a minimum.

9. In this reasoning, we have for convenience excepted the case in which two successive determinants in the series $\Delta, \Delta_1, \Delta_2 \ldots$ vanish for the same value of m^2. But this exception is of no real importance, for we may change these determinants into others whose constituents are very slightly different from those of the given determinants but which are such that no successive two of the series have a common root. In the limit, therefore, when these arbitrary changes of the constituents are indefinitely small, the roots of the series of determinants will still be real under the same circumstances as before, and the roots of each will separate, or *coincide with,* the roots of the next above it in the series.

To show that these changes are possible, let us consider the row of determinants beginning at the last. The determinant Δ_n is a positive constant, the next Δ_{n-1} is $m^2 + a_{nn}$. Proceeding thus, suppose we arrive at two determinants which we may call Δ_1 and Δ which have a common root. If we now change the constituents a_{11}, a_{12}, a_{13}, &c. into $a_{11} + \delta a_{11}, a_{12} + \delta a_{12}$, &c. we do not alter Δ_1, but, except for the root $m^2 = 0$, we *do* alter Δ in an arbitrary manner.

When for example a_{13} is altered, we alter a constituent both in the first row and in the first column.   Since

$$\Delta\Delta' = \Delta_1\Delta_{33} - \Delta_{13}\Delta_{31},$$

where Δ' is the determinant formed from Δ by omitting the first and third rows and columns, we see that when Δ and Δ_1 both vanish, the product $\Delta_{13}\Delta_{31}$ and therefore by Art. 2 both Δ_{13} and Δ_{31} must vanish.   The determinant Δ is therefore altered by $-\Delta_2 (\delta a_{13})^2$ which does not vanish, since Δ_2 is by hypothesis finite for the particular value of m^2 under consideration.

If any determinant of the series vanishes when $m^2 = 0$, it is clear that one of the quantities a_{11}, a_{22}... must be zero.   If we replace this by any small positive quantity, the argument will apply as before.

10.   It is important to consider the effect of *equal roots* on the test of stability given in Art. 8 of this chapter.

In this case we know that the roots of the minor Δ_{11} separate the roots of Δ.   If therefore Δ have two negative equal roots, it is clear that Δ_{11} must have one of them.   In the same way Δ_{22}, Δ_{33}, &c. must also all vanish for this value of m.   Since

$$\Delta\Delta' = \Delta_{pp}\Delta_{qq} - \Delta_{pq}\Delta_{qp},$$

it follows as in Art. 2 if Δ and Δ_{pp} both vanish, that Δ_{pq} and Δ_{qp} also vanish.   Hence all the first minors of the determinant Δ vanish.   This is the case considered in Art. 5 of Chap. I.   The equal roots instead of introducing into the expressions for the co-ordinates terms which contain t as a factor merely render two of the coefficients, instead of one, indeterminate.

In the same way if the equation $\Delta = 0$ is satisfied by three values of m^2 equal to the same negative quantity, the equation $\Delta_{pp} = 0$ must have two of them, and its principal minor must have one of them.   Reasoning as before we see that all the second minors of Δ must be zero.   This is again the test that there should be no terms which contain t as a factor.

The presence therefore of equal roots does not in the theorem of Art. 8 affect the stability of the motion.

When a system is disturbed from a position of equilibrium whether stable or unstable, the roots of the fundamental determinant are separated by its minors in the manner described in Art. 8 of this Chapter.   By what has just been proved, we see that if the fundamental determinant have equal roots, whether positive or negative, these do not introduce into the integrals terms which contain t as a factor.

11. The proposition in the last article may be made more general. If the fundamental determinant be reduced to the form indicated in Art. 7, we shall show that if Δ vanish for two equal negative values of m^2 which are numerically greater than the greatest negative quantity in the series a_{11}, a_{22}, a_{33}, &c., then these equal roots will not introduce any terms into the solution with t as a factor. If a_{11}, a_{22}, &c. are all positive, this reduces to the proposition proved in the last article.

Following the same notation as before, we have

$$\Delta\Delta' = \Delta_{11}\Delta_{22} - \Delta_{12}\Delta_{21}.$$

If neither Δ_{11} nor Δ_{22} are zero, they must have the same sign when Δ vanishes for a negative value of m^2. For their product is equal to $\Delta_{12}\Delta_{21}$ which has been proved in Art. 2 to be positive. Hence all the leading first minors, viz. Δ_{11}, Δ_{22}, &c. must have the same sign for any negative value of m^2 which makes Δ vanish.

By differentiation we have

$$\frac{d\Delta}{dm} = 2m\Delta_{11} + a_{12}\Delta_{12} + \dots - a_{12}\Delta_{21} + 2m\Delta_{22} + \dots - \&c.$$

But we have also

$$\Delta = (m^2 + a_{11})\,\Delta_{11} + a_{12}m\,\Delta_{12} + \dots$$
$$\Delta = -\,a_{12}m\,\Delta_{21} + (m^2 + a_{22})\,\Delta_{22} + \dots$$
$$\&c. = \&c.$$

Hence if n be the highest power of m occurring in Δ, we have

$$m\frac{d\Delta}{dm} = n\Delta + (m^2 - a_{11})\,\Delta_{11} + (m^2 - a_{22})\,\Delta_{22} - \&c.$$

If then Δ and $\dfrac{d\Delta}{dm}$ both vanish for any negative value of m^2 greater than the greatest negative quantity in the series a_{11}, a_{22}, &c., we have the sum of a number of quantities all of the same sign equal to zero. This requires that each should be zero. We have therefore $\Delta_{11} = 0$, $\Delta_{22} = 0$, &c. The rest of the proof is the same as before.

By differentiating the expression for $\dfrac{d\Delta}{dm}$ and substituting for $\dfrac{d\Delta_{11}}{dm}$, $\dfrac{d\Delta_{22}}{dm}$, &c. their values in terms of their first leading minors, we may extend this proposition to the case in which the fundamental determinant has three equal roots, and so on.

12. *A sphere is suspended by a string* OA *from a fixed point* O, *and is set rotating about a vertical diameter which is in the same straight line as the string with an angular velocity* n. *A small disturbance is given, determine if the steady motion is stable.*

Let O be the origin, and let the axis of z be vertically downwards, let lx, ly, l be the co-ordinates of A, the point at which the string is attached. Let C be the centre, and let $a\xi$, $a\eta$, a be the co-ordinates of C relative to A. Then, exactly as in Chap. iv. Art. 22, the Lagrangian function may be shown to be

$$L = \frac{k^2}{2}\left\{\chi' - \frac{\xi\eta'}{2} + \frac{\xi'\eta}{2}\right)^2 + \xi'^2 + \eta'^2\right\}$$

$$+ \tfrac{1}{2}(a\xi' + lx')^2 + \tfrac{1}{2}(a\eta' + ly')^2 - g\left\{l\frac{x^2+y^2}{2} + a\frac{\xi^2+\eta^2}{2}\right\},$$

the mass being taken unity.

Putting $\chi' = n$, ξ', η', x', y' all zero, we see that L is a maximum when x, y, ξ, η are zero, the steady motion is therefore stable for all values of n.

If we put $k^2 = \tfrac{2}{5}a^2$, and $m^2 = -\lambda^2$, so that x, y, &c. are all represented by terms of the form $\Sigma A \cos(\lambda t + \alpha)$, we may, by the methods of the last chapter, prove

$$\left(\lambda^2 - \frac{g}{l}\right)\left(\lambda^2 \pm n\lambda - \frac{5l}{2a}\right) = \frac{5g}{2l}\lambda^2.$$

This equation, whatever may be the sign of n, has two positive and two negative roots. All four give stable oscillations.

CHAPTER VI.

If the energy of the system be a maximum or minimum under certain conditions, the motion whether steady or not is stable. Arts. 1—3.

When the motion is steady, it will be also stable if a certain function of the co-ordinates called V + W *is a minimum. Art. 4.*

If there be only one co-ordinate which enters into the Lagrangian function, except as a differential coefficient, this condition is necessary and sufficient. Arts. 5, 6.

Additional conditions when there are two co-ordinates. Art. 8.

1. When a system is oscillating about a position of equilibrium, it is well known that we may determine the stability or instability of the equilibrium by what we may call the " energy criterion." This criterion may also be sometimes used when the system·is oscillating about a state of steady motion.

Let E be the sum of the kinetic and potential energies of the system. Then throughout any motion of the system we have

$$E = h,$$

where h is a constant depending on the initial conditions. If θ, ϕ, &c. are the co-ordinates of the system, E is a known function of θ, θ', ϕ, ϕ', &c. Suppose that some of the other first integrals of the equations of motion are known. Let these be

$$\left. \begin{array}{l} F_1 (\theta, \theta', \phi, \phi', \&c.) = C_1 \\ F_2 (\theta, \theta', \phi, \phi', \&c.) = C_2 \\ \qquad \&c. \end{array} \right\},$$

the time t being absent.

For the purposes of this proposition let us suppose θ, θ', ϕ, ϕ', &c. to be separate variables unconnected with each other except by the equations just written down.

If E be an absolute maximum or an absolute minimum for all variations of θ, θ', &c., those corresponding to the given motion making E constant, then that motion is stable for all displacements which do not alter the constants C_1, C_2, &c.

If this proposition be not evident, it may be proved by eliminating as many of the letters as possible. If θ, θ', &c. be the remaining co-ordinates we have

$$E = f(\theta, \theta', \&c. \; C_1, \; C_2, \ldots).$$

Let h be the value of E in the given motion, and let the
system be started in some slightly different manner so that

$$E = h + \delta h.$$

If E be a maximum along the given motion, then any change
whatever in θ, θ', &c. decreases E. Hence θ, θ', &c. cannot deviate
so much from their values along the given motion that the change
in E becomes greater than δh.

2. Let us apply this principle to a system of bodies which
moves in steady motion with some co-ordinates θ, ϕ, &c. such that
their differential coefficients θ', ϕ', &c. are constant, and the remaining co-ordinates ξ, η, &c. themselves constant. Let us further
suppose that the energy is a function of θ', ϕ', &c., but not of
θ, ϕ. By Lagrange's Equations we have the integrals

$$\frac{dT}{d\theta'} = C_1, \quad \frac{dT}{d\phi'} = C_2, \; \&c.$$

It is clear that the system can describe any one of a number
of steady motions, which we have already called parallel motions,
and which are determined by

$$\theta' = p, \qquad \phi' = q, \; \&c.$$
$$\xi = \alpha, \qquad \eta = \beta, \; \&c.$$

where p, q, &c. α, β, &c. are constants which satisfy all Lagrange's
equations.

We have thus as many relations between these constants as
there are co-ordinates ξ, η, &c. Let the system be started with
any initial conditions we please, then the constants C_1, C_2, ... are
given. These being known we have as many relations between
the constants of steady motion as there are co-ordinates θ, ϕ, &c.
The steady motion is therefore determined. If the energy of this
initial motion is nearly equal to that of this steady motion, and
if it be a maximum or minimum as explained above, then the
system will never deviate far from its corresponding position in
the steady motion, and this steady motion may be called stable.

3. Example. *A top is set spinning on its point on a perfectly
rough horizontal ground, with its axis inclined to the vertical, find
the condition of stability.*

Let θ be the inclination of the axis OC of the top to the
vertical OZ; ψ the inclination of the plane ZOC to a vertical

plane fixed in space, and ϕ the inclination to a plane through OC fixed in the body. Let O be the apex, G the centre of gravity which lies in OC, $h = OG$. Let A, A, C be the principal moments of inertia at O, and M the mass of the top. We have then

$$E = \frac{C}{2} (\phi' + \psi' \cos \theta)^2 + \frac{A}{2} (\theta'^2 + \sin^2 \theta \psi'^2) + Mgh \cos \theta.$$

By Lagrange's equations we have the integrals

$$\phi' + \psi' \cos \theta = n,$$
$$Cn \cos \theta + A \sin^2 \theta \psi' = m,$$

where n and m are two constants, the former representing the angular velocity of the top about its axis, and the latter the angular momentum about the vertical. If we now eliminate ϕ' and ψ' we find that E is a minimum when $\theta = \alpha$, if

$$C^2 n^2 > 4 MghA \cos \alpha,$$

which is the result given by other methods.

4. The theorem of Art. 2 may be put into another form. Let the kinetic energy be

$$T = T_{\theta\theta} \frac{\theta'^2}{2} + T_{\theta\phi} \theta' \phi' + \dots$$

Then since θ, ϕ, &c. are absent from the coefficients, we have the integrals

$$T_{\theta\theta} \theta' + T_{\theta\phi} \phi' + \dots = C_1 - T_{\theta\xi} \xi' - T_{\theta\eta} \eta' - \&c.$$
$$T_{\theta\phi} \theta' + T_{\phi\phi} \phi' + \dots = C_2 - T_{\phi\xi} \xi' - T_{\phi\eta} \eta' - \&c.$$
$$\&c. = \&c.$$

For the sake of brevity let us call the right-hand sides of these equations $C_1 - X$, $C_2 - Y$, &c. Since T is a homogeneous function of θ', ϕ', &c., we have, as in Chap. IV. Art. 21,

$$T = T_{\xi\xi} \frac{\xi'^2}{2} + T_{\xi\eta} \xi' \eta' + \dots$$
$$+ \tfrac{1}{2} \theta' (C_1 + X) + \tfrac{1}{2} \phi' (C_2 + Y) + \dots$$

If we substitute in the second line the values of θ', ϕ', &c. found by solving the linear equations just written down, we have the determinant

$$- \begin{vmatrix} 0, & C_1 + X, & C_2 + Y, & \&c. \\ C_1 - X, & T_{\theta\theta}, & T_{\theta\phi}, & \&c. \\ C_2 - Y, & T_{\theta\phi}, & T_{\phi\phi}, & \&c. \\ \&c. & \&c. & \&c. & \&c. \end{vmatrix} \frac{1}{2\Delta}$$

where Δ is the discriminant of the terms in T which contain θ', ϕ', &c. This determinant is unaltered by changing the signs of X, Y, &c. and is a quadratic function of C_1, C_2, &c., X, Y, &c. Hence the terms $C_1 X$, $C_2 Y$, &c. do not occur. If then we put

$$W = - \begin{vmatrix} 0 & C_1, & C_2, & \&c. \\ C_1, & T_{\theta\theta}, & T_{\theta\phi}, & \&c. \\ C_2, & T_{\theta\phi}, & T_{\phi\phi}, & \&c. \\ \&c. & \&c. & \&c. & \&c. \end{vmatrix} \frac{1}{2\Delta}$$

we have

$$T = B_{\xi\xi} \frac{\xi'^2}{2} + B_{\xi\eta} \, \xi' \eta' + \&c. + W,$$

where $B_{\xi\xi}$, &c. are independent of C_1, C_2, &c. Now T is essentially positive for all values of the variables, and therefore for such as make C_1, C_2, &c. all zero. Hence the terms involving ξ', η', &c. are together a minimum when ξ', η', &c. are all zero. The coefficients $B_{\xi\xi}$, &c. may all be treated as constants since ξ', η', &c. are all small quantities.

If V be the potential energy, we have therefore the following rule. *If* W + V *be a minimum for all variations of* ξ, η, &c. *then the steady motion is certainly stable.* It should be noticed that $W + V$ is a function only of ξ, η, &c. the co-ordinates which are constant in the steady motion.

5.　*If the energy be a function of one only of the co-ordinates, though the differential coefficients of all the others enter into its value, this condition is sufficient and necessary.*

Let ξ be this co-ordinate. Then by vis viva we have

$$B_{\xi\xi} \frac{\xi'^2}{2} + W + V = h.$$

Differentiating we have

$$B_{\xi\xi} \xi'' + \frac{d(W+V)}{d\xi} = 0.$$

This equation must be satisfied by the steady motion represented by $\xi = \alpha$. The second term $\dfrac{d(W+V)}{d\xi}$ must therefore vanish when $\xi = \alpha$, so that $W + V$ is a maximum or minimum. To find the oscillation let us put $\xi = \alpha + x$, we find

$$B_{\xi\xi} \frac{x'^2}{2} + \left[\frac{d^2(W+V)}{d\xi^2} \right] x = 0,$$

115

where the square bracket implies that ξ is to be put equal to α after differentiation. By the same reasoning as before $B_{\xi\xi}$ is necessarily positive, *and the motion will be stable or unstable according as* (W + V) *is a minimum or maximum.*

6. If we refer to Art. 21 of Chap. IV. we see that this function $W + V$ is the value of the modified Lagrangian function L' when ξ, η', &c. are all put zero, and the sign of the whole function changed. It therefore follows by Chap. V. that when $W + V$ is a minimum the steady motion is stable. The "energy criterion of stability," as far as it applies to steady motion, may therefore be deduced from that given in Chap. V. Art. 8. But the mode of demonstration adopted in that chapter gives us more information as the nature of the motion, while the modes of application to examples of the two criteria are quite different. The energy criterion may also be sometimes applied to determine the stability of a motion which is not steady.

[The relation between the theorem in this Chapter in which $E = T + V$ is made a minimum to that given in Chapters IV. and V. in which $L = T - V$ is made a maximum may be more distinctly perceived by the following statement.

Let x, y, &c. be the co-ordinates of the system, and let L be the Lagrangian function* so that $L = T - V$, then by Art. 3 of Chap. IV. the co-ordinates in steady motion satisfy the equations

$$\frac{dL}{dx} = 0, \qquad \frac{dL}{dy} = 0, \text{ &c. } \dots\dots\dots\dots\dots(1).$$

Here L is expressed as a function of x, y, &c. x', y', &c.

Suppose some of the co-ordinates as θ, ϕ, &c. are absent from the expression for L, so that L is a function of θ', ϕ', &c., the remaining co-ordinates, viz. ξ, η, &c. and their differential coefficients. Then if we form the modified Lagrangian function as in Art. 21 of Chap. IV. the equations (1) of steady motion become

$$\frac{dL'}{d\xi} = 0, \qquad \frac{dL'}{d\eta} = 0, \text{ &c.} \dots\dots\dots\dots\dots (2).$$

Here, as in the Hamiltonian equations C_1, C_2, &c. are the θ, ϕ, &c. components of momentum, and L' is expressed as a function of C_1, C_2, &c. ξ, η, &c. ξ', η', &c.

---

* Let u, v, &c. be the x, y, &c. components of momentum, so that $u = \frac{dT}{dx'}$, &c. and let H be the Hamiltonian function. Then $H = T + V$ and we easily deduce from the Hamiltonian equations that, in steady motion,

$$\frac{dH}{dx} = 0, \quad \frac{dH}{dy} = 0, \text{ &c.}$$

Here H is expressed as a function of x, y, &c. u, v, &c.

But $\qquad L' = T - C_1\theta' - C_2\phi' - \&c. - V$

$$= -T + \frac{dT}{d\xi'}\xi' + \frac{dT}{d\eta'}\eta' + \&c. - V,$$

by Euler's theorem on homogeneous functions. In steady motion ξ', η', &c. all vanish, hence the equations (2) become

$$-\frac{d(W+V)}{d\xi} = 0, \qquad -\frac{d(W+V)}{d\eta} = 0, \&c. \dots\dots\dots (3),$$

where W is the value of T when ξ', η', &c. are all put equal to zero. Here W is expressed as a function of C_1, C_2, &c. ξ, η, &c.

It is shown in Chap. v. that if the Lagrangian function expressed as required in equations (1) be a maximum the motion is stable. It is shown in this Chapter that if the function $W + V$ be a minimum the motion is stable.]

7. *To find the condition of stability when the Lagrangian function is a function of two only of the co-ordinates, though the differential coefficients of all the others enter into its value.*

Let ξ, η be these two co-ordinates, then the modified Lagrangian function as explained in Art. 20 of Chap. IV. will be a function of ξ, η, ξ', η' only.

Let the steady motion be given by $\xi = \alpha$, $\eta = \beta$, with the corresponding values of the other co-ordinates θ, ϕ, &c. Then α and β are constants. Let $\xi = \alpha + x$, $\eta = \beta + y$, and let us expand the modified Lagrangian function in powers of x, y. Neglecting the terms of the first order, as they only give the steady motion, let

$$L' = B_{11}\frac{x'^2}{2} + B_{12}x'y' + B_{22}\frac{y'^2}{2}$$

$$+ A_{11}\frac{x^2}{2} + A_{12}xy + A_{22}\frac{y^2}{2}$$

$$+ C_{11}xx' + C_{12}xy' + C_{21}yx' + C_{22}yy'.$$

Also let $E = C_{21} - C_{12}$. Then the condition of stability is that the roots of the following equation should be of the form $\beta\sqrt{-1}$.

$$\begin{vmatrix} B_{11}m^2 - A_{11}, & B_{12}m^2 - A_{12} + Em \\ B_{12}m^2 - A_{12} - Em, & B_{22}m^2 - A_{22} \end{vmatrix} = 0.$$

If $\qquad\qquad \left.\begin{array}{l} \Delta' = B_{11}B_{22} - B_{12}{}^2 \\ \Delta = A_{11}A_{22} - A_{12}{}^2 \end{array}\right\},$

and $\qquad\qquad \Theta = A_{11}B_{22} + A_{22}B_{11} - 2A_{12}B_{12}$

be the two discriminants and the other invariant, this leads at once to the conclusion that the motion is stable only when

(1) Δ is positive,

(2) $E^2 - \Theta$ is positive and $> 2\sqrt{\Delta\Delta'}$.

If $A_{11}\dfrac{x^2}{2} + A_{12}xy + A_{22}\dfrac{y^2}{2}$ is a maximum when x and y are zero, the two conditions are obviously satisfied.

This condition may be otherwise expressed; if L' be the modified Lagrangian function, a steady motion is given by

$$\frac{dL'}{d\xi} = 0, \quad \frac{dL'}{d\eta} = 0, \quad \xi' = 0, \quad \eta' = 0.$$

This motion will be stable if for the values of ξ, η thus found,

(1) $\dfrac{d^2L'}{d\xi^2}\dfrac{d^2L'}{d\eta^2} - \dfrac{d^2L'}{d\xi d\eta}$ is positive,

(2) $\left(\dfrac{d^2L'}{d\xi d\eta'} - \dfrac{d^2L'}{d\xi' d\eta}\right)^2 - \left\{\dfrac{d^2L'}{d\xi^2}\dfrac{d^2L'}{d\eta'^2} + \dfrac{d^2L'}{d\eta^2}\dfrac{d^2L'}{d\xi'^2} - 2\dfrac{d^2L'}{d\xi d\eta}\dfrac{d^2L'}{d\xi' d\eta'}\right\}$

is positive and greater than

$$2\left\{\frac{d^2L'}{d\xi^2}\frac{d^2L'}{d\eta^2} - \frac{d^2L'}{d\xi d\eta}\right\}^{\frac{1}{2}} \cdot \left\{\frac{d^2L'}{d\xi'^2}\frac{d^2L'}{d\eta'^2} - \frac{d^2L'}{d\xi' d\eta'}\right\}^{\frac{1}{2}}.$$

8. The nature of the motion when thus reduced to depend on two co-ordinates may be illustrated by geometrical reasoning. Let the position be defined by two co-ordinates x, y which are zero along the steady motion. Let these be regarded as the co-ordinates of a point P referred to any axes. Then the motion of P exactly represents that of the system.

Let us construct the conics

$$A_{11}\frac{x^2}{2} + A_{12}xy + A_{22}\frac{y^2}{2} = a,$$

$$B_{11}\frac{x^2}{2} + B_{12}xy + B_{22}\frac{y^2}{2} = b.$$

Then, exactly as in Arts. 11—14 of Chap. IV., it will be found convenient to transform the co-ordinates by writing

$$\left.\begin{array}{l} x = a_1 p + b_1 q \\ y = a_2 p + b_2 q \end{array}\right\}.$$

If μ be the modulus of transformation we have $\mu = a_1 b_2 - a_2 b_1$. It is easy to see by actual substitution, if E' be the difference of the coefficients of pq' and $p'q$, that

$$E' = \mu E.$$

If the transformation be from one set of oblique co-ordinates to another, let ω, ω' be the angles between the axes. We then have

$$\frac{E'}{\sin \omega'} = \frac{E}{\sin \omega}.$$

Transforming the axes to the common conjugate diameters, the conics become

$$\left. \begin{array}{l} A_{11}'\dfrac{p^2}{2} + A_{22}'\dfrac{q^2}{2} = a \\[2mm] B_{11}'\dfrac{p^2}{2} + B_{22}'\dfrac{q^2}{2} = b \end{array} \right\},$$

the signs of a and b being such as to make these conics real. The equation to find m becomes

$$(B_{11}'m^2 - A_{11}')(B_{22}'m^2 - A_{22}') + E'^2 m^2 = 0.$$

It is therefore necessary for stability that the conic a should be an ellipse as well as the conic b. It is also necessary that

$$\frac{E'}{\sqrt{B_{11}'B_{22}'}} > \sqrt{\frac{A_{11}'}{B_{11}'}} + \sqrt{\frac{A_{22}'}{B_{22}'}},$$

both roots having the same sign and the inequality being numerical.

Let OP, OP'; OQ, OQ' be the common conjugates of the two conics, this condition then becomes

$$\frac{E}{\sin \omega} \cdot \frac{\text{area of conic } b}{\pi \sqrt{ab}} > \frac{OQ}{OP} + \frac{OQ'}{OP'}.$$

When the system describes an oscillation with *one* period, *i.e.* an harmonic oscillation, the path of the representative particle is easily seen to be

$$(B_{11}''m^2 - A_{11}'')p^2 + (B_{22}''m^2 - A_{22}'')q^2 = \text{constant}.$$

The harmonic paths are therefore ellipses. It also appears that the two ellipses which represent the two harmonic vibrations and the two ellipses a and b have, all four, a common set of conjugate diameters.

119

CHAPTER VII.

Any small term of a high order, if its period is nearly the same as that of an oscillation of the system, may produce important effects on the magnitude of the oscillation. Art. 1.

Origin of such terms, with an example. Arts. 2—3.

Supposing the roots of the determinantal equation to satisfy the conditions of stability to a first approximation, yet if a commensurable relation hold between these roots it is necessary to examine certain terms of the higher orders to determine whether they will ultimately destroy the stability of the system. Art. 4.

If a certain relation hold among the coefficients of these terms, they will not affect the stability of the system, but only slightly alter the periods of oscillation. Arts. 5—7.

Examples, the first taken from Lagrange's method of finding the oscillations about a position of equilibrium. Arts. 8—9.

If the coefficients of the equations of motion should not be strictly constant, but only nearly so, the stability will not be affected, unless the reciprocals of their periods have commensurable relations with the reciprocals of the periods of oscillation of the system. Art. 10.

1. If we understand that a motion is called stable wh. n any small disturbance does not cause the system to deviate far fro. its undisturbed motion, it is clear that we cannot be certain of the stability without examining the terms of the second order. It is possible that some of these may have their periods so timed that their effects may accumulate until the motion is changed.

Returning to the equations of Art. 3, Chap. I. we shall have on the right hand, instead of zero, a series of small terms of orders higher than the first. To find a second approximation, we substitute the values of x, y, &c. given at the end of Art. 3, in these terms.

They will therefore take the form Ne^{nt} and will produce in x, y, &c. terms of the form $\dfrac{N'}{f(n)} e^{nt}$, where N' is of the same order at least as the term considered, and $f(m)$ has the same meaning as in Chap. I. These will have to be expressed in trigonometrical real forms, but it is unnecessary to exhibit the process, for we see at once that no small term or force (whatever it may be called) of a high order can affect the stability of the motion unless it makes $f(n)$ very nearly or exactly equal to zero. In this case its period is very nearly or exactly equal to one of the periods of the motion given by taking terms of the first order only.

A remarkable use of this principle was made by Captain Kater in his experiments on the magnitude of gravity. It was important to determine if the support of his pendulum was perfectly firm. He tells us that he had recourse to a delicate and simple instrument the sensibility of which was so great that had the slightest motion taken place in the support it must have been instantly detected. The instrument consists of a steel wire the lower part of which, inserted in the piece of brass which serves as its support, is flattened so as to form a delicate spring. On the wire a small weight slides by means of which it may be made to vibrate in the *same time* as the pendulum to which it is to be applied as a test. When thus adjusted it is placed in the material to which the pendulum is attached, and should this not be perfectly firm its motion will be communicated to the wire, which in a little time will accompany the pendulum in its vibrations. This ingenious contrivance appeared fully adequate to the purpose for which it was employed, and afforded a satisfactory proof of the stability of the point of suspension. See *Phil. Trans.*, 1818.

2. Since the term Ne^{nt} is obtained by compounding the different terms in the values of x, y, &c. it is clear that

$$n = pm_1 + qm_2 \dots$$

where p, q, &c. are positive integers whose sum is the order of the term. It is therefore only when the roots of the dynamical equation $f(m) = 0$ are such that a linear relation of the form

$$pm_1 + qm_2 + \dots = m_1 \text{ very nearly}$$

exists between them, that we may expect to find important terms among the higher orders. The order of the terms to be examined will be $p + q + \dots$, and unless this be also small, the terms will probably remain insignificant. If the root m_1 should occur twice in $f(m) = 0$ it is clear that the divisor $f(n)$ will be a small quantity of the second order, and the term may be said (as in the Lunar Theory) to rise two orders.

3. To take an example, let us suppose a particle to be describing an ellipse about a fixed centre of force in one focus. If disturbed it will describe a slightly different ellipse. Since

$$r = a\{1 - e\cos(nt + \epsilon - \omega) + \dots\},$$
$$\theta = nt + \epsilon + 2e\sin(nt + \epsilon - \omega) + \dots$$

we see that a slight change in the elements will cause variations in r and θ of the period $\dfrac{2\pi}{n}$, an additional variation in θ of the form $t\delta n + \delta \epsilon$ and an additional variation in r of the form δa. All these variations should by Art. 3 of Chap. I. be indicated by expressions of the form

$$r = \Sigma M e^{mt}, \quad \theta = \Sigma M' e^{mt},$$

where the values of m are the roots of the equation $f(m) = 0$. The roots therefore of the equation $f(m) = 0$ for δr are $m = 0$ and $\pm n \sqrt{-1}$, and for $\delta \theta$ are $m = 0$, 0 and $\pm n \sqrt{-1}$. We therefore infer that any small disturbing causes of the second order whose periods are nearly equal to that of the particle, will cause important inequalities in both δr and $\delta \theta$, and (since $f(m) = 0$ has two roots equal to zero) any term of long period will rise two orders in $\delta \theta$.

4. If the roots of the subsidiary equation are such that the relation

$$p m_1 + q m_2 + \ldots = m_1$$

holds accurately, the solution changes its character. We have now in the value of x a term of the form $t e^{m_1 t}$. Unless the real part of m_1 is negative, this indicates that the system will depart widely from the motion which we took as a first approximation. We must therefore modify our first approximation (as in the Lunar Theory) by including in it the terms which produced these important effects. We may then enquire how far this modified first approximation indicates that the motion is stable or unstable. When these terms are included the equations to be solved are in general no longer linear, and it is sometimes impossible to find a solution sufficiently accurate to serve as a first approximation throughout the whole motion.

5. In some cases, however, the oscillations may still be represented by expressions of the form

$$x = M_1 e^{n_1 t} + M_2 e^{n_2 t} + \ldots$$
$$y = M_1' e^{n_1 t} + M_2' e^{n_2 t} + \ldots$$
$$\&c.,$$

where the values of n_1, $n_2 \ldots$ differ but slightly from the roots of the equation $f(m) = 0$. Let us investigate the condition that this should be true, and also determine whether the changes in the values of m_1, $m_2 \ldots$ are sufficient to affect the stability.

Suppose that we have completed our first approximation, and find on proceeding to a higher approximation that the terms

$$N_1 e^{m_1 t} + N_2 e^{m_2 t} + \ldots$$
$$N_1' e^{m_1 t} + N_2' e^{m_2 t} + \ldots$$

present themselves on the right-hand side of the first set of equations in Art. 3, Chap. I. These terms are supposed to have arisen from several relations of the form

$$pm_1 + qm_2 + \ldots = m_1.$$

If these terms can be included in the first approximation by writing n_1, n_2, &c. for m_1, m_2, &c. we have, by substitution in the differential equations, certain equations connecting n, M, M', &c., whose left-hand sides are the same as those used in Art. 3 with n_1 written for m_1, but on the right-hand sides we have instead of zero the quantities N_1, N_1', &c. The test of the success of the process is that these modifications in the values of m must satisfy the same relations as before.

Now N_1, N_1', &c. are all at least of the second order of small quantities, hence up to terms of the first order the ratios M_1, M_1', &c. will be the same as before, so that we may put

$$M_1 = L_1 a_1, \quad M_1' = L_1 b_1, \quad \&c.,$$

following the same notation as in Art. 3, Chap. I. We also have

$$M_1 f(n_1) = N_1 a_1 + N_1' a_1' + \ldots$$

Let $n_1 = m_1 + \delta m_1$ we find

$$\delta m_1 = \frac{N_1 a_1 + N_1' a_1' + \ldots}{f'(m_1) L_1 a_1}.$$

Similarly

$$\delta m_2 = \frac{N_2 a_2 + N_2' a_2' + \ldots}{f'(m_2) L_2 a_2},$$

&c. = &c.

It is evident, by the theorem of determinants alluded to in Art. 3, that these are symmetrical expressions.

6. We may conveniently express these results in the form of a rule.

Suppose we have to a first approximation

$$x = M_1 e^{m_1 t} + M_2 e^{m_2 t} + \ldots$$

Eliminate from the differential equations all the variables except x in the usual manner. This may be done by performing on the several equations the operations represented by the minors a, a', &c., $\frac{d}{dt}$ being written for m. Let the equation thus found be

$$f\left(\frac{d}{dt}\right) x = P_1 e^{m_1 t} + P_2 e^{m_2 t} \ldots;$$

Then all these terms can be included in the first approximation, provided

$$\delta m_1 = \frac{P_1}{M_1 f'(m_1)}, \qquad \delta m_2 = \frac{P_2}{M_2 f'(m_2)} \text{ \&c.}$$

satisfy the relations

$$p\delta m_1 + q\delta m_2 + \ldots = \delta m_1,$$

$$\text{\&c.} = \text{\&c.}$$

which exist among the roots of the dynamical equation.

7. The general results we have arrived at may be summed up as follows. Though some of the terms of the higher orders may affect the magnitude of the oscillation, yet no term will arise to affect the stability of the motion unless there be some relations between the roots of the dynamical equation of the form

$$pm_1 + qm_2 + \ldots = m_1,$$

where p, q, &c. are all integers. Even if such relations occur, the lowest order of the term is $p + q + \ldots$, and if this be considerable the term will not produce any important effects until a considerable time has elapsed. If a certain relation, just found, hold among these terms, their only effect is slightly to modify the periods of oscillation, without altering the type of motion.

8. *As an example*, let us consider a system of bodies to be oscillating about a position of equilibrium. We know by Lagrange's general solution, that the equation $f(m) = 0$ is of an even order. Its roots are of the form

$$m_1 = \alpha \sqrt{-1}, \quad m_2 = -\alpha \sqrt{-1}, \quad m_3 = \beta \sqrt{-1}, \text{ \&c.}$$

Whatever the numerical values of these may be we have

$$m_1 + m_3 + m_4 = m_1, \qquad m_2 + m_3 + m_4 = m_2, \text{ \&c.}$$

so that the small terms of the third, fifth, &c. orders might affect the stability of the oscillation. But we shall now show that they only affect the periods of oscillation, and not the stability of the system.

Since both sides of Lagrange's equations must be of -2 dimensions in time and the impressed forces are also of -2 dimensions, it is clear that these terms must consist of powers of x, y, &c. $\frac{d^2x}{dt^2}$, $\frac{d^2y}{dt^2}$, &c. and products of an even number of factors of $\frac{dx}{dt}$, $\frac{dy}{dt}$, &c. We know also, by Lagrange's solution, that the co-ordinates take the form

$$x = M_1 \cos(\alpha t + \lambda_1) + \text{\&c.}$$

$$y = M_1' \cos(\alpha t + \lambda_1) + \text{\&c.}$$

The minors a, a', &c. are also all even functions of $\dfrac{d}{dt}$, hence the equation found after elimination is of the form

$$f\left(\frac{d}{dt}\right)x = P\cos(at+\lambda) + Q\cos(\beta t+\mu) + \ldots$$

Replacing $a\sqrt{-1}$, $-a\sqrt{-1}$, &c. by m_1, m_2, &c. we find by Art. 6,

$$\delta m_1 = \frac{P}{2M_1 f'(m_1)}, \quad \delta m_2 = \frac{P}{2M_1 f'(m_2)}.$$

Since $f'(m)$ is of odd dimensions, and $m_1 = -m_2$ we clearly have $\delta m_1 = -\delta m_2$, and therefore the test is satisfied.

9. [As another example let us apply the rule of Art. 6 to some very simple case which will involve no algebraical substitutions of any length.

The motion of a simple pendulum under the action of gravity may be made to depend on the equation

$$\frac{d^2 x}{dt^2} + a^2 x = \beta x^3 \quad\ldots\ldots\ldots\ldots\ldots\ldots (1),$$

where a and β are two constants and x is the inclination of the pendulum to the vertical which is supposed to be small. The first approximation to the motion is

$$x = M_1 e^{m_1 t} + M_2 e^{m_2 t} \quad\ldots\ldots\ldots\ldots\ldots\ldots (2),$$

where m_1 and m_2 are the roots of the equation $m^2 + a^2 = 0$. Our object is to ascertain by help of the rule given in Art. 6 whether the small force represented by Bx^3 renders this first approximation unstable or merely slightly alters the numerical values of m_1 and m_2.

The two roots are connected by the relation

$$m_1 + m_2 = 0 \quad\ldots\ldots\ldots\ldots\ldots\ldots\ldots (3).$$

Substituting the value of x on the right-hand side, we have

$$\left(\frac{d^2}{dt^2} + a^2\right)x = 3\beta\, M_1 M_2 \left(M_1 e^{m_1 t} + M_2 e^{m_2 t}\right) + \&c.$$

Hence by the rule in Art. 6

$$\delta m_1 = \frac{3\beta M_1^2 M_2}{2m_1 M_1}, \quad \delta m_2 = \frac{3\beta M_1 M_2^2}{2m_2 M_2}.$$

These clearly satisfy the relation

$$\delta m_1 + \delta m_2 = 0,$$

125

and therefore the first approximation taken above, so far as the disturbing force Bx^3 is concerned, is stable.

If the small force had been $\beta \left(\dfrac{dx}{dt}\right)^3$ instead of βx^3, it is easy to see in the same way that

$$\delta m_1 = \frac{3\beta M_1^2 M_2 m_1^2 m_2}{2m_1 M_1}, \qquad \delta m_2 = \frac{3\beta M_1 M_2^2 m_1 m_2^2}{2m_2 M_2},$$

so that the relation $\delta m_1 + \delta m_2 = 0$ would not have been satisfied. The first approximation taken above is therefore not sufficiently accurate to serve as a first approximation throughout the motion.

In this example we have considered the effect of a small force of the third order in disturbing the stability of the motion given by equation (1). The same equation will obviously occur in many other cases of motion. For example, let a particle describe a circular orbit about a centre of force situated in the centre. If slightly disturbed the equation giving the disturbance x in the radius vector takes the form

$$\frac{d^2x}{dt^2} + a^2 x = \beta x^2 + \gamma x^3 + \dots$$

where a, β and γ are constants. Similar remarks will therefore apply to this case also.]

10. When the coefficients of the equation of motion are not strictly constant, but yet do not vary much, then we may transpose the small variable parts of these terms to the right-hand side of the equation, and treat their products by the differential coefficients of the co-ordinates as small quantities of the second order. Suppose the variable part of one of these coefficients to be $p \sin nt$, where p is small, and let $f(m) = 0$ be the equation giving the periods of oscillation of the system when the coefficients are taken constant. Then it is clear that unless n is nearly equal to the sum or difference of two values of m, this term cannot rise into importance. On proceeding to higher orders we see that these terms cannot produce important effects unless some commensurable relation between m and the roots of the equation $f(m) = 0$ should be very nearly satisfied.

11. It should be remarked that when the coefficients are not constant it is not a sufficient test of stability that they should always satisfy the conditions of stability obtained by giving them their instantaneous constant values. Thus if the equation of motion were

$$\frac{d^2x}{dt^2} + \frac{1}{4t^2} x = 0,$$

the coefficient of x is always positive, yet as the equation is satisfied by $x = a \sqrt{t}$, x may become as great as we please.

Even if the coefficients are nearly constant, we must yet examine, by the rules just given, if their small changes are so timed as gradually to increase the oscillation until the divergence from the given motion is no longer small.

[Suppose a system to be oscillating so that its motion is determined by the equation

$$\frac{d^2x}{dt^2} + qx = 0,$$

where q is a known function of t, which during the time under consideration always lies between β^2 and β'^2 the latter being the greater. Let the system be started with an initial co-ordinate x_0 and an initial velocity x_0' in a direction tending to increase x. It may be shown that the system will begin to return, i.e. x will begin to decrease before x becomes as great as $\sqrt{x_0{}^2 + \dfrac{x_0'^2}{\beta^2}}$. If $\pm m$, $\mp m'$ be two successive maximum values of x, we may also show that m' cannot be so great as $\dfrac{\beta'}{\beta} m$, and that the time from one maximum to the next lies between $\dfrac{\pi}{\beta}$ and $\dfrac{\pi}{\beta'}$].

CHAPTER VIII.

*The Hamiltonian Characteristic or Principal functions when found deter-
mine at once the motion of the system from one given position to
another, and whether the motion is stable or unstable. Arts. 1—3.*

*Examples with a mode of effecting the integration $S = \int L dt$ in small oscil-
lations. Arts. 4—7.*

*The Characteristic function supplies the condition that the motion is stable
as to space only, while the Principal function gives the conditions that
it is stable both as to space and time. Art. 8.*

*In what sense the motion is unstable if either of the two Hamiltonian
functions is a minimum. Arts. 9—14.*

1. If we had any convenient methods of finding the Hamiltonian Characteristic or Principal function, we might determine
without difficulty the conditions of stability of a dynamical system
at the same time that we deduce the integrals of the equations of
motion. But it is very difficult to discover either of these functions by an *à priori* method. We have indeed differential equations which they must satisfy, and Jacobi has taught us what kind
of solution will serve our purpose. But the difficulty of finding
these solutions is as great as that of solving the equations of
motion. For these reasons it does not seem necessary to dwell on
the uses of these functions.

2. Suppose the Principal function S of a dynamical system to
have been found in terms of the initial co-ordinates θ_0, ϕ_0 and the
co-ordinates θ, ϕ and the time t. Let the semi-vis viva be given
by

$$T = P\frac{\theta'^2}{2} + Q\theta'\phi' + R\frac{\phi'^2}{2},$$

where P, Q, R are known functions of θ, ϕ. Let P_0, Q_0, R_0 be the values of these when θ_0, ϕ_0 are written for θ, ϕ. The final integrals of the equations of motion are then given by

$$\left.\begin{aligned}
-\frac{dS}{d\theta_0} &= P_0\theta_0' + Q_0\phi_0' \\
-\frac{dS}{d\phi_0} &= Q_0\theta_0' + R_0\phi_0'
\end{aligned}\right\}$$

Let the system receive any disturbance at the time $t = 0$, so that while starting from the same initial position, its initial velocities are slightly altered. Let x_0', y_0' be these initial changes of θ_0' and ϕ_0' and let $\theta + x$, $\phi + y$ be the co-ordinates of the system at the time t. Then we have

$$\left.\begin{aligned}
-\frac{d^2S}{d\theta_0 d\theta}\,x - \frac{d^2S}{d\theta_0 d\phi}\,y &= P_0x_0' + Q_0y_0' \\
-\frac{d^2S}{d\phi_0 d\theta}\,x - \frac{d^2S}{d\phi_0 d\phi}\,y &= Q_0x_0' + R_0y_0'
\end{aligned}\right\}$$

Here x_0', y_0' are small arbitrary quantities, hence x and y will be small if none of the ratios of $\dfrac{d^2S}{d\theta_0 d\theta}$, $\dfrac{d^2S}{d\theta_0 d\phi}$, $\dfrac{d^2S}{d\phi_0 d\theta}$, or $\dfrac{d^2S}{d\phi_0 d\phi}$ to the determinant

$$\frac{d^2S}{d\theta_0 d\theta}\,\frac{d^2S}{d\phi_0 d\phi} - \frac{d^2S}{d\theta_0 d\phi}\,\frac{d^2S}{d\phi_0 d\theta},$$

be large.

If the initial position as well as the initial motion be altered we may find, by a precisely similar process, the conditions that x and y should be small. If the system have more than two independent motions, we have more than two co-ordinates, but the conditions of stability are found in the same way.

3. If x and y be small throughout the whole motion from the one given position to the other, not only does the system not deviate far from its undisturbed course, but the system at any instant is also very nearly coincident with its undisturbed place at the same time. It is important to notice this, for the word "stability" is sometimes used in a different sense.

This condition of stability may be put under a form in which no reference is made to S. Let u and v be the components of momentum of the system corresponding to the co-ordinates θ, ϕ respectively, $i.e.$ let $u = \dfrac{dT}{d\theta'}$, $v = \dfrac{dT}{d\phi'}$, and let these be expressed as functions of θ_0, ϕ_0, θ, ϕ and t. Then the preceding equation may be written

$$\left.\begin{array}{c} \dfrac{du}{d\theta_0} x + \dfrac{dv}{d\theta_0} y = \alpha \\[2mm] \dfrac{du}{d\phi_0} x + \dfrac{dv}{d\phi_0} y = \beta \end{array}\right\},$$

where α and β are small arbitrary quantities. The condition of stability is that the values of x and y thus found should be small.

4. As an example let us consider the case of a projectile. If θ be the horizontal, and ϕ the vertical co-ordinate of the particle, we have

$$\left.\begin{array}{l} S = \dfrac{(\theta - \theta_0)^2 + (\phi - \phi_0)^2}{2t} - \tfrac{1}{2} gt (\phi + \phi_0) - \tfrac{1}{24} g^2 t^3 \\[3mm] T = \tfrac{1}{2} (\theta'^2 + \phi'^2) \end{array}\right\}.$$

The equations to find x and y are evidently

$$\left.\begin{array}{c} \dfrac{1}{t} x = x_0' \\[3mm] \dfrac{1}{t} y = y_0' \end{array}\right\}.$$

Hence the system continually deviates more and more from its undisturbed place.

5. In order to calculate the form of S when a system is oscillating about a state of motion, it is convenient to choose as co-ordinates some small quantities x, y which vanish in the given state of motion. Let the Lagrangian function be written in the form

$$L = L_0 + L_1 + L_2,$$

where L_n is a homogeneous function of x, y, x', y'. Then by a theorem of Euler's

$$L = L_0 + \Sigma \left(\frac{dL_1}{dx} x + \frac{dL_1}{dx'} x' \right) + \tfrac{1}{2} \Sigma \left(\frac{dL_2}{dx} x + \frac{dL_2}{dx'} x' \right),$$

where the Σ's imply summation for all co-ordinates.

As in Art. 9 of Chap. IV. we have

$$\frac{d}{dt} \frac{dL_1}{dx'} = \frac{dL_1}{dx},$$

and the oscillations are given by

$$\frac{d}{dt} \frac{dL_2}{dx'} = \frac{dL_2}{dx}.$$

Hence we find

$$L = L_0 + \Sigma \left(x\, \frac{d}{dt} \frac{dL_1}{dx'} + x' \frac{dL_1}{dx'} \right) + \tfrac{1}{2} \Sigma \left(x\, \frac{d}{dt} \frac{dL_2}{dx'} + x' \frac{dL_2}{dx'} \right).$$

Integrating we have

$$S = \int L_0 dt + \Sigma \left[x\, \frac{dL_1}{dx'} \right]_0^t + \tfrac{1}{2} \Sigma \left[x\, \frac{dL_2}{dx'} \right]_0^t.$$

Thus the integration has been effected, but in order to express S as a function of x_0, y_0, x, y and t, it will be necessary to find x_0', y_0', x', y' in terms of these quantities.

6. As an example, let the position of the system depend on one co-ordinate x and let

$$L = L_0 + A_1 x + B_1 x' + \tfrac{1}{2} A_{11} x^2 + \tfrac{1}{2} B_{11} x'^2 + C_{11} x x',$$

where the coefficients are all constants. We then find by the process just indicated that $A_1 = 0$ and

$$S = L_0 t + B_1 (x - x_0) + \frac{C_{11}}{2} (x^2 - x_0^{\,2})$$
$$+ \frac{m B_{11}}{2} \frac{(x^2 + x_0^{\,2})(e^{mt} + e^{-mt}) - 4 x x_0}{e^{mt} - e^{-mt}},$$

where $m^2 = \dfrac{A_{11}}{B_{11}}$. Applying the criterion of stability we find that $\dfrac{d^2 S}{dx_0 dx}$ will finally become small if m is real. The motion is therefore unstable or stable according as A_{11}, B_{11} have the same or opposite signs.

7. If the position of the system depend on two co-ordinates x, y, let

$$L = L_0 + A_1 x + A_2 y + B_1 x' + B_2 y'$$
$$+ \tfrac{1}{2} A_{11} x^2 + A_{12} xy + \tfrac{1}{2} A_{22} y^2 + \tfrac{1}{2} B_{11} x'^2 + B_{12} x' y' + \tfrac{1}{2} B_{22} y'^2$$
$$+ C_{11} x x' + C_{12} x y' + C_{21} y x' + C_{22} y y'.$$

We then find

$$S = L_0 t + B_1 (x - x_0) + B_2 (y - y_0)$$
$$+ C_{11} \frac{x^2 - x_0^{\,2}}{2} + \frac{C_{12} + C_{21}}{2} (xy - x_0 y_0) + C_{22} \frac{y^2 - y_0^{\,2}}{2} + \sigma,$$

where

$$\sigma = \frac{B_{11}}{2} (x x' - x_0 x_0') + \frac{B_{12}}{2} (x y' + x' y - x_0 y_0' - x_0' y_0) + \frac{B_{22}}{2} (y y' - y_0 y_0').$$

If we now express x', y', x_0', y_0' in terms of x, y, x_0, y_0 and t, we find for σ a fraction whose numerator is a homogeneous quadratic function of x, y, x_0, y_0, the coefficients being linear functions of exponentials of t, and whose denominator is another linear function of the same exponentials. These exponentials become sines and cosines when the motion is stable. Thus when the given motion is *steady* the simplest inspection of the form of σ will determine whether the motion is stable or not.

Referring the motion to principal co-ordinates for the sake of brevity, and writing $2G = C_{12} - C_{21}$, we find that σ must satisfy the differential equation

$$\frac{d\sigma}{dt} + \frac{1}{2B_{11}}\left(\frac{d\sigma}{dx} + Gy\right)^2 + \frac{1}{2B_{22}}\left(\frac{d\sigma}{dy} - Gx\right)^2 = \tfrac{1}{2}A_{11}x^2 + \tfrac{1}{2}A_{22}y^2.$$

This equation is obviously satisfied by such a function as that just described. The solution of this equation may be reduced to linear equations and thus σ may be found. But it is unnecessary to dwell on this, for this would be equivalent to returning to the Hamiltonian equations.

8.   If we wish to determine the condition that the general course of a dynamical system is stable without requiring it should be near its undisturbed place at any the same time, it is more convenient to use the Characteristic function. Suppose that the Characteristic function has in Jacobi's manner been expressed as a function of the co-ordinates θ, ϕ, the constant h of vis viva and two arbitrary constants a_1, a_2. Then

$$V = f(\theta, \phi, h, a_1) + a_2.$$

The relation between θ and ϕ, which may be called the equation to the path of the system, is given by

$$\frac{dV}{da_1} = b_1,$$

where b_1 is another constant. Let the system be disturbed from the same initial position so that the whole energy is unaltered. The change in ϕ corresponding to any given value of θ is found from

$$\frac{d^2V}{da_1^2}\delta a_1 + \frac{d^2V}{da_1 d\phi}\delta\phi = \delta b_1.$$

Let A be the *initial* value of $\dfrac{d^2V}{da_1^2}$, then

$$\delta\phi = -\frac{\dfrac{d^2V}{da_1^2} - A}{\dfrac{d^2V}{da_1 d\phi}} \cdot \delta a_1.$$

The condition that the path should be stable is that the coefficient of δa_1 should not be large.

We might also use the function called Q by Sir W. R. Hamilton, but it seems unnecessary to dwell more on this subject.

9. The instability of a system may be deduced from the Hamiltonian Principal or Characteristic functions, expressed as a minimum. Suppose a dynamical system to move from one position A to another B in a time t, then the motion may be found by making the first variation of $S = \int_0^t L dt$ equal to zero, the time of transit being constant. The constants of integration are determined by the conditions that the co-ordinates have given values when $t = 0$ and $t = t$. To determine whether S is a maximum or minimum or neither we must examine the second variation and here we have the assistance of Jacobi's rule. The determination of the constants will depend on the solution of equations and may lead to several different kinds of motion from A to B. One of these will be the actual motion. Let us move B along this until one of the other motions coincides or as we may say approaches indefinitely near to this actual motion. We have then reached a boundary beyond which the integration must not extend if S is to be a maximum or minimum. See Todhunter's *History of the Calculus of Variations*, page 251. Further $\frac{d^2 L}{d\theta'^2}$, if θ be a coordinate, is positive throughout the limits of integration, so that S will be a minimum and not a maximum.

10. When there are several co-ordinates θ, ϕ, &c. which are to be found as functions of the time, we may easily show that Jacobi's condition is a necessary one, and this is all that we require for the next proposition. If the system can move in two ways from A to B, then $\delta S = 0$ along each, and therefore when these two are adjacent we have both $\delta S = 0$ and $\delta (S + \delta S) = 0$. This shows that the second variation *can be made* to vanish by taking one variation through the other. This second variation will then be the same as the quadratic term of the series obtained by changing the co-ordinates θ, ϕ into $\theta + \delta\theta$, $\phi + \delta\phi$, because we can take $\delta^2\theta = 0$ and $\delta^2\phi = 0$. Hence as the sum of the terms of the third order does not, in general, vanish for this displacement, it is clear that S cannot be either a maximum or a minimum.

Let the actual motion be from A to B, and let a neighbouring motion starting from A lead the system to a position C reached in the same time along the actual motion before reaching B. Then we can show that a variation of the actual motion from A to B can be found which makes $\delta^2 S$ of any sign. Let P be any position on the neighbouring motion before reaching C, and Q, one on the actual motion after passing C. Then considering P and Q as fixed and also the time of transit, the motion along PCQ cannot make $\delta S = 0$; for this condition is known to lead to the ordinary dynamical equations, and it is clear that (impulsive forces being set aside) no actual motion can be discontinuous. But there is discontinuity at C, for otherwise when the system is started from B towards A, two courses would be open to the system on arriving at C. Hence the first variations of S for an imaginary motion along PCQ are not zero, and therefore may have any sign. But since the discontinuity at C is of the first order of small quantities, this first variation is of the second order. Now the value of S for the actual motion is equal to that along the neighbouring motion to C and then along the actual motion to B. Hence, P and Q being still fixed, variations of the actual motion from A to B can be found which make $\delta^2 S$ of any sign.

11. Let us apply this theory to determine the stability of a given state of motion. First let us suppose the given motion to be steady and to depend on only two variables. If we use the function S there will be one co-ordinate and the time, if V two co-ordinates. Let the system be disturbed at any moment by an alteration of the velocities of its several parts, so that the initial position of the disturbed motion is an undisturbed position. If the motion be stable the system will oscillate about the undisturbed motion, the oscillation repeating itself at a constant interval. It follows therefore by Jacobi's rule that S or V cannot be a minimum for a period longer than the time of a half-oscillation. If therefore S or V be a minimum for all variations, starting from A and ending at B, where B is a position on the steady motion reached by the system at an interval as long as we please, then the motion is unstable.

If we give a meaning to the word "stable" somewhat different[*] from its usual signification, we may extend this proposition to determine a test of the stability of any motion, whether steady or not. All we have assumed is, that, if the motion be not altogether unstable, there are *some* disturbances which will cause the system periodically to assume the same positions as it would have done if it had been undisturbed, but the interval of these periods may be any whatever provided the first be finite. If we use the Characteristic function, these disturbances must be such as not to alter the constant of vis viva, and if the Principal function, they must be such as to bring the system to an undisturbed position in the same time.

***

[*] This meaning does not always agree with the results of Art. 14, Chap. IV. [See also Arts. 17 and 18, Chap. IV.]

12.   Next let us suppose that as the system proceeds from the initial position A along the actual motion, S ceases to be a minimum at some position B. The conditions for a minimum are of two kinds. Suppose the system to depend on two co-ordinates θ, ϕ, and let L be the Lagrangian function, then (1) we must have $\dfrac{d^2L}{d\theta'^2}$ and $\dfrac{d^2L}{d\theta'^2}\dfrac{d^2L}{d\phi'^2} - \dfrac{d^2L}{d\theta'd\phi'}$, both positive, and (2) it must be possible to choose three arbitrary constants which enter into a very complicated expression, so that this expression may never become infinite between the limits of integration. The first condition is clearly always satisfied since the vis viva of any system is necessarily positive for all values of θ' and ϕ'. The second condition will fail if there are two neighbouring motions by which the system can proceed from A to any position between A and B. If this be the mode of failure, it is clear from the reasoning of Art. 2 that the conditions of stability are satisfied for one kind of disturbance, and that therefore some at least of the harmonic motions are stable or oscillatory, though the motion may be unstable for a different kind of disturbance.

13.   [These conditions become much simpler when the position of the system is determined by one co-ordinate, or when the Lagrangian function can be reduced to depend on one co-ordinate. Let this co-ordinate be so chosen that it vanishes along the given motion, and let us also suppose that both it and its differential coefficient with regard to t, are small for all neighbouring constrained motions. Let this co-ordinate be called θ and let the Lagrangian function be

$$L = L_0 + A_1\theta + B_1\theta' + \frac{1}{2}A_{11}\theta^2 + \frac{1}{2}B_{11}\theta'^2 + C_{11}\theta\theta'.$$

Then since the Lagrangian equation of motion is satisfied by hypothesis when $\theta = 0$, we have $A_1 = B_1'$ where the accent, as usual, denotes differentiation with regard to t.

If the system be now conducted from the initial position A to any other position B, both on the given motion, by any neighbouring mode of motion, we have

$$S = \int L_0 dt + \int\left(\frac{1}{2}B_{11}\theta'^2 + C_{11}\theta\theta' + \frac{1}{2}A_{11}\theta^2\right)dt.$$

If $\theta = u$ be any solution of the Lagrangian equation

$$\frac{d}{dt}(B_{11}\theta' + C_{11}\theta) = C_{11}\theta' + A_{11}\theta,$$

we may write the function S in the form*

$$S = \int L_0 dt + \frac{1}{2} \int B_{11} \left(u \frac{d}{dt} \frac{\theta}{u} \right)^2 dt.$$

The second term is essentially positive, since B_{11} must be positive. Hence S is a minimum along the given motion unless we can so choose the arbitrary displacement θ as to make $\dfrac{d}{dt} \dfrac{\theta}{u} = 0$. This gives $\theta = cu$ where c is some constant. But θ must vanish at the two limits A and B, hence this choice of θ is excluded unless there is some neighbouring mode of motion by which the system could move freely from the given initial position A to the position B. The result is that S cannot cease to be a minimum before the *first* instant at which some neighbouring motion will bring the system (starting from A) into coincidence with some contemporaneous position on the given motion. If the given motion be steady, it follows that S cannot cease to be a minimum before a time which is half that of a complete oscillation.

We thus have a test of stability. If the system depend on one co-ordinate and *if S be a minimum when the limits of integration are from the initial position A to all positions on the actual motion, that motion is unstable. But if S cease to be a minimum at some point C, then the actual motion is stable from A to C.*]

---

* [Following Lagrange's rule we may write the second term of S in the form

$$-\lambda\theta + \int \left\{ \frac{1}{2} B_{11} \theta'^2 + (C_{11} + 2\lambda) \theta\theta' + \left(\frac{1}{2} A_{11} + \lambda \right) \theta^2 \right\} dt.$$

The quantity outside the integral sign is to be taken between the given limits and is zero, since θ vanishes at each limit. Let us now put

$$\frac{C_{11} + 2\lambda}{B_{11}} = -\frac{u'}{u}.$$

It is clear that this value of λ cannot be infinite between the limits of integration unless u vanishes. For by hypothesis u and u' are both finite and the co-efficients B_{11} and C_{11} in the Lagrangian function are also finite. It then easily follows from the equation

$$\frac{d}{dt} (B_{11} u + C_{11} u) = C_{11} u + A_{11} u,$$

that

$$(C_{11} + 2\lambda)^2 = B_{11} (A_{11} + 2\lambda).$$

Hence the second term of S becomes

$$\frac{1}{2} \int B_{11} \left(\theta' - \theta \frac{u'}{u} \right)^2 dt,$$

which is the result in the text. This might also have been deduced from Jacobi's general transformation with one independent variable given in Prof. Jellett's *Calculus of Variations* or Prof. Price's *Differential Calculus*.

If $u = 0$ between the limits of integration this transformation fails, but, as is evident from the argument in the text, we choose $\theta = u$ to represent a neighbouring free motion such that $u = 0$ just before the system reaches A; also B is so placed that the next instant at which $u = 0$ is after the system has passed B.]

14. [We shall conclude the chapter with the application of this criterion of stability to some simple case.

A particle describes a circular orbit about a centre of force situated in the centre. It is required to deduce the conditions of stability as to space from the Characteristic function V.

Let a be the radius of the circle, n the angular velocity of the particle about the centre O. Let $\phi(a)$ be the law of force. Let A and B be two points taken on the circular orbit, and let the particle be conducted from A to B by some neighbouring path with the same energy as in the circular orbit. Let $r = a + \rho$ be the radius vector of this path, corresponding to any angle θ.

If v be the velocity at any point of this path, we easily find

$$v = an\left\{1 - \frac{\rho}{a} - \left(\frac{a\phi'(a)}{\phi(a)} + 1\right)\frac{\rho^2}{2a^2}\right\}.$$

If s be the arc of the path, we have

$$\frac{ds}{d\theta} = a + \rho + \frac{1}{2a}\left(\frac{d\rho}{d\theta}\right)^2.$$

If the angle $AOB = \beta$, we therefore have

$$V = \int v\,ds = a^2n\beta + \frac{n}{2}\int_0^\beta\left\{\left(\frac{d\rho}{d\theta}\right)^2 - p^2\rho^2\right\}d\theta,$$

where $p^2 = \dfrac{a\phi'(a)}{\phi(a)} + 3$.

If the neighbouring path be a free path described with the same energy, its equation is

$$\rho = L \sin p\theta,$$

where θ is measured from the radius vector OA, and L is an arbitrary constant. This free path will cut the circle again in some point C. If the angle $AOC = \gamma$, we have $p\gamma = \pi$.

If B coincide with C, we find by substituting this value of ρ in the expression for V, that the second term of V is zero. If B be beyond C but such that the angle COB is less than γ, draw two free paths one from A as before and the other backwards from B to meet the former in some point P. Then the angle $AOP = \frac{1}{2}\beta$. If the particle be conducted from A to P along one path and from P to B along the other, we find that the excess of the action over the action in the circular arc AB is equal to

$$\frac{np}{2}L^2 \sin p\beta.$$

Since $p\beta$ is greater than π and less than 2π, this excess is negative. The action along the circular arc is therefore not a minimum if B be beyond the first intersection of a neighbouring free path.

Lastly we may show that the action is a minimum if B lie between A and C. To prove this we write the integral in the expression for V in the form

$$\left[-\lambda\rho^2\right]_0^\beta + \int_0^\beta \left\{\left(\frac{d\rho}{d\theta}\right)^2 + 2\lambda\rho\frac{d\rho}{d\theta} + \left(\frac{d\lambda}{d\theta} - p^2\right)\rho^2\right\} d\theta.$$

The first of these two terms is zero since ρ vanishes at each limit. Following Lagrange's rule we make

$$\frac{d\lambda}{d\theta} - p^2 = \lambda^2.$$

The integral then becomes

$$\int_0^\beta \left(\frac{d\rho}{d\theta} + \lambda\rho\right)^2 d\theta.$$

This is always positive and the action along the circular arc is a minimum. The argument however requires that λ should not become infinite between the limits of integration. It is easy to see that

$$\lambda = p \tan (p\theta + E),$$

where E is a constant to be chosen at our pleasure. But if β exceed $\frac{\pi}{p}$ it is impossible to choose E so as to keep λ finite between the limits of integration. Hence the action is a minimum only if the angle AOB subtended by the limiting positions at the centre is less than $\frac{\pi}{p}$. The circular orbit is therefore stable if p^2 be positive.

If, however, p^2 be negative, the expression for λ changes its character. Writing $-q^2$ for p^2, we find

$$\frac{q+\lambda}{q-\lambda} = Ee^{-2q\theta},$$

thus the value of λ can be chosen so as not to be infinite for all positive values of θ. In this case the function V is a minimum for all arcs AB however distant B may be from A. The circular motion is therefore unstable.]

Reprinted from *Proceedings of the London Mathematical Society,* **5**
(1874), pp. 97–99

E. J. ROUTH

Stability of a dynamical system with two independent motions

Stability of a Dynamical System with two Independent Motions. By E. J. ROUTH, F.R.S.

[*Read June 11th*, 1874.]

The equations of motion of a dynamical system performing small oscillations with two independent motions are of the form

$$\left. \begin{aligned} A\frac{d^2x}{dt^2} + B\frac{dx}{dt} + Cx + F\frac{d^2y}{dt^2} + G\frac{dy}{dt} + Hy = 0 \\ A'\frac{d^2x}{dt^2} + B'\frac{dx}{dt} + C'x + F'\frac{d^2y}{dt^2} + G'\frac{dy}{dt} + H'y = 0 \end{aligned} \right\}.$$

To solve these, we eliminate either x or y, and obtain a biquadratic of the form $aD^4 + bD^3 + cD^2 + dD + e = 0.$

The whole nature of the motion depends on the forms of the roots of this equation.

Rules are given in books on the theory of equations to determine whether the roots are real or imaginary; but this is not exactly what we want to know. It is often important to ascertain whether the equilibrium about which the oscillation takes place is stable or unstable. The necessary and sufficient conditions for stability are that the real roots and the real parts of the imaginary roots should be all negative. It is proposed here to investigate a method of easy application to decide this point.

Let the biquadratic be written in the form

$$\phi(x) = ax^4 + bx^3 + cx^2 + dx + e = 0.$$

Let us form the symmetrical function of the roots which is the product of the sums of the roots taken two and two. If this be called $\dfrac{X}{a^3}$,

we find
$$X = bcd - ad^2 - eb^2$$
$$= \tfrac{1}{2} \begin{vmatrix} 2a & b & c \\ b & o & d \\ c & d & 2e \end{vmatrix}$$

Suppose we know the roots to be imaginary, say $a \pm p\sqrt{-1},\ \beta \pm q\sqrt{-1}.$

Then $\quad \dfrac{X}{a^3} = 4a\beta\{(a+\beta)^2 + (p+q)^2\}\{(a+\beta)^2 + (p-q)^2\}.$

Thus $a\beta$ always takes the sign of $\dfrac{X}{a}$, and $a+\beta$ always takes the sign of $-\dfrac{b}{a}$. Thus the signs of both a and β can be determined; and if a, b, X have the same sign, the real parts of the roots are all negative.

Suppose, next, that two of the roots are real and two imaginary. Writing $q'\sqrt{-1}$ for q, so that the roots are $a \pm p\sqrt{-1}$ and $\beta \pm q'$, we find
$$\frac{X}{a^3} = 4a\beta\{[(a+\beta)^2+p^2-q'^2]^2+4p^2q'^2\}.$$

Just as before, $a\beta$ takes the sign of $\dfrac{X}{a}$, and $a+\beta$ takes the sign of $-\dfrac{b}{a}$.

Also, $\beta^2-q'^2$ takes the sign of the last term $\dfrac{e}{a}$ of the biquadratic. This determines whether β is numerically greater or less than q'. If, then, a, b, e, and X have the same sign, the real roots and the real parts of the imaginary roots are all negative.

Lastly, suppose the roots to be all real. Then, if all the coefficients are positive, we know, by Descartes' rule, that the roots must be all negative, and the coefficients cannot be all positive unless all the roots are negative. In this case, since X is the product of the sums of the roots taken two and two, it is clear that $\dfrac{X}{a}$ will be positive.

Whatever the nature of the roots may be, yet if the real roots and the real parts of the imaginary roots be negative, the biquadratic must be the product of quadratic factors all whose terms are positive. It is therefore necessary for stability that every coefficient of the biquadratic should have the same sign.

Summing up the several results which have just been proved, we conclude that *it is necessary and sufficient for stability of equilibrium that every coefficient of the biquadratic, and also X, should have the same sign.*

If the equation on which the motion of the system depends is of the fifth degree, we may proceed in the same way. Let the equation be
$$\phi(x) = ax^5+bx^4+cx^3+dx^2+ex+f = 0.$$
Form as before the product of the sums of the roots taken two and two.

If this be $\dfrac{X}{a^4}$, we find $\quad X = \begin{vmatrix} bc-ad & be-af \\ be-af & de-cf \end{vmatrix}.$

Suppose that there are four imaginary roots $a \pm p\sqrt{-1}$, $\beta \pm q\sqrt{-1}$, and one real root γ. Then γ has the sign opposite to $\dfrac{f}{a}$, and $a\beta$ takes the sign of X, while $2(a+\beta)+\gamma = -\dfrac{b}{a}$. If then $\dfrac{f}{a}$ be positive, γ is negative. If $\dfrac{b}{a}$ be positive and $\phi\left(-\dfrac{b}{a}\right)$ negative, the root γ is numerically less than $\dfrac{b}{a}$, so that $a+\beta$ is negative. If therefore a, b, f, X, and $-\phi\left(-\dfrac{b}{a}\right)$ be all positive, a, β, γ will be all negative.

Suppose that there are two imaginary roots $a \pm p\sqrt{-1}$, and three real roots β, γ, δ. Then, if all the coefficients are positive, β, γ, δ are negative, and X takes the sign opposite to a; so that if X be also positive, a, β, γ, δ will be all negative.

Suppose all the roots to be real; then, if all the coefficients be positive, the roots will be all negative, and not otherwise; and it is also clear that X, being the product of ten negative quantities, will be positive.

In both these cases, if the real roots and the real parts of the imaginary roots be negative, it is clear that $\varphi\left(-\dfrac{b}{a}\right)$ must have the sign opposite to a.

Conversely, if all the real roots and the real parts of the imaginary roots be negative, the factors of the equation, and therefore the equation itself, must have all the coefficients of the same sign.

We therefore conclude that *it is necessary and sufficient for stability of equilibrium that every coefficient of the equation,* $-\varphi\left(-\dfrac{b}{a}\right)$, *and also* X, *should be positive.*

When the dynamical system has three independent motions, the solution in general depends on an equation of the sixth degree. The condition of stability is, as before, that the real roots and the real parts of the imaginary roots should all be negative. This case may be discussed in the same way as the biquadratic. First, we may show that all the coefficients in the equation must be of the same sign; secondly, we may then form two determinants X, Y, which are the products of the sums of the roots taken respectively two and two together, and four and four together. It may then be shown that if all the coefficients of the equation be positive, and also X and Y both negative, the above-mentioned condition of stability is satisfied. The expressions for X and Y in terms of the coefficients of the original equations may be found without difficulty. That for X may be put into the form of a determinant of three rows,

$$\begin{vmatrix} gb & af-be & bc-ad \\ f & -d & b \\ ef-dg & bg-cf & af \end{vmatrix}$$

That for Y may also be written in a determinant of the same. kind ; but the constituents are not sufficiently simple and short to render the expression of much *practical* value.

Reprinted from *Proceedings of the London Mathematical Society,* **6**
(1875), pp. 86–97

E. J. ROUTH

**On Laplace's three particles, with a supplement on the stability of
steady motion**

On Laplace's Three Particles, with a Supplement on the Stability of Steady Motion.   By E. J. Routh, F.R.S.

[*Read February 11th, 1875.*]

Laplace has shewn that, if three particles be placed at the corners of an equilateral triangle and properly projected, they will move under their mutual attractions so as always to remain at the angular points of an equilateral triangle.   He also shewed that, if they be placed in a straight line, and properly projected, they will always remain in the same straight line.   He remarks that, if the earth and moon had been originally placed in the same straight line with the sun, at distances from the sun proportional to 1 and $1 + \frac{1}{100}$, and properly projected, the moon would always have been in opposition to the sun.   The moon would have been too distant to have been in a state of continual eclipse, and thus would have been full every night.   But Liouville has shewn, in the "Additions à la Connaissance des Temps," that such a motion is unstable.

The question arises, whether the motion when the particles are at the angular points of an equilateral triangle, is also unstable.   I find, by a brief note in Jullien's Problems, that this question has been discussed by M. Gascheau in a Thèse de Mécanique, who has arrived at the result that the motion is stable when the square of the sum of the masses is greater than 27 times the sum of the products of the masses taken two and two together.   But no reference to where M. Gascheau's work can be found is given, and I have been unable to discover it.

I therefore proceeded to investigate the motion on the supposition that the law of attraction is the inverse κ^{th} power of the distance.   I found the following results:—

1. The motion cannot be stable unless κ is less than 3.

2. The motion is stable, whatever the masses may be, if the law of force be expressed by any positive power of the distance, or any negative power less than unity.   For other powers the stability will depend on the relation between the masses.

3. The motion is stable to a first approximation if

$$\frac{(M + m + m')^2}{Mm + Mm' + mm'} > 3 \left(\frac{1 + \kappa}{3 - \kappa} \right)^2,$$

where M, m, m' are the masses.   This agrees with M. Gascheau's result if $\kappa = 2$, or the law of force be the law of nature.

4. When two of the masses are much smaller than the third, the inequalities in their angular distances, as seen from the large body, have a much greater coefficient than their linear distances from the same body.

5. On proceeding to a second approximation it would seem that the form of the triangle joining the three particles is very little altered by

any disturbance, but in certain cases, depending on the nature of the disturbance, the size of the triangle may be subject to very considerable variations.

As a supplement, I have generalized the reasoning of the problem of the three bodies, so as to obtain the form of the determinantal equation, to find the periods of oscillation of any dynamical system about a state of steady motion in which the *vis viva* is constant. Two limitations have been made; first, the system must be under a conservative system of forces; and secondly, the *vis viva* can be expressed in terms of the coordinates so as not to contain the time explicitly. The equation is then shown to be always of an *even* order, and the condition of stability is that all the roots should be real and negative.

The three particles, when in motion, remain always very nearly at the angular points of an equilateral triangle. The triangles formed by joining the particles to their common centre of gravity are not marked by any simplicity of form. Instead of referring the motion to the centre of gravity, it will be more convenient to reduce one of the particles to rest, and to consider the relative motion of the other two. We have thus only one triangle to examine, and that one nearly equilateral.

Let the mass M of the particle to be reduced to rest be taken as unity, and let m, m' be the masses of the other two. Let the distances Mm, Mm' be respectively $a+x$ and $a+\xi$, where x and ξ are small; and let the angle made by these radii vectores be $\frac{\pi}{3}+\eta$. Let the angle the radius vector joining M, m makes with some fixed line in space, be $nt+y$, where y is a small quantity.

The accelerations along the radius vector, and perpendicular to it,

are
$$\frac{d^2r}{dt^2} - r\left(\frac{d\theta}{dt}\right)^2 = \frac{d^2x}{dt^2} - (a+x)\left(n+\frac{dy}{dt}\right)^2$$
$$= \frac{d^2x}{dt^2} - n^2x - 2an\frac{dy}{dt} - an^2,$$
$$\frac{1}{r}\frac{d}{dt}\left(r^2\frac{d\theta}{dt}\right) = 2n\frac{dx}{dt} + a\frac{d^2y}{dt^2}.$$

To express the forces on the particles, let r, r', R be the distances between the particles Mm, Mm', mm'; and let ϕ', ϕ, ψ be the angles opposite to these distances. Let the law of attraction be the inverse κ^{th} power.

The equations of motion are

$$\left.\begin{aligned}
\frac{d^2x}{dt^2} - n^2x - 2an\frac{dy}{dt} - an^2 + \frac{1+m}{r^\kappa} + \frac{m'\cos\psi}{r'^\kappa} + \frac{m'\cos\phi}{R^\kappa} = 0 \\
2n\frac{dx}{dt} + a\frac{d^2y}{dt^2} + \frac{m'\sin\psi}{r'^\kappa} - \frac{m'\sin\phi}{R^\kappa} = 0
\end{aligned}\right\},$$

$$\frac{d^2\xi}{dt^2} - n^2\xi - 2an\frac{d(y+\eta)}{dt} - an^2 + \frac{1+m'}{r'^\kappa} + \frac{m\cos\psi}{r^\kappa} + \frac{m\cos\phi'}{R^\kappa} = 0$$
$$2n\frac{d\xi}{dt} + a\frac{d^2(y+\eta)}{dt^2} - \frac{m\sin\psi}{r^\kappa} + m\frac{\sin\phi'}{R^\kappa} = 0$$

Putting x, y, ξ, η all zero, we have in *steady motion*

$$a^{\kappa+1}n^2 = 1 + m + m';$$

let us put $a^{\kappa+1} = b$ for brevity.

We have now to calculate these forces

$$R^2 = (a+x)^2 + (a+\xi)^2 - 2(a+x)(a+\xi)\cos\left(\frac{\pi}{3}+\eta\right)$$
$$= a^2 + ax + a\xi + a^2\sqrt{3}\,\eta\,;$$

therefore

$$R = a + \frac{x+\xi}{2} + \frac{\sqrt{3}}{2}a\eta.$$

Let us write this

$$R = a + \rho.$$

Let $\phi = \dfrac{\pi}{3} + \theta$, then we have

$$\sin\left(\frac{\pi}{3}+\theta\right) = \sin\left(\frac{\pi}{3}+\eta\right)\frac{a+\xi}{R}\,;$$

expanding and rejecting squares of small quantities,

$$\theta = \eta + \sqrt{3}\,\frac{\xi-\rho}{a}.$$

Similarly, if $\phi' = \dfrac{\pi}{3} + \theta'$, we have

$$\theta' = \eta + \sqrt{3}\,\frac{x-\rho}{a}.$$

We now have

$$\frac{\sin\phi}{R^\kappa} = \frac{\sqrt{3}}{2}\frac{1}{a^\kappa}\left(1+\frac{\theta}{\sqrt{3}}\right)\left(1-\kappa\frac{\rho}{a}\right)$$
$$= \frac{\sqrt{3}}{2}\frac{1}{a^\kappa}\left\{1 - \frac{3\kappa+1}{2\sqrt{3}}\,\eta - \frac{\kappa+1}{2}\frac{x}{a} - \frac{\kappa-1}{2}\frac{\xi}{a}\right\}.$$

Similarly, interchanging x, ξ,

$$\frac{\sin\phi'}{R^\kappa} = \frac{\sqrt{3}}{2}\frac{1}{a^\kappa}\left\{1 - \frac{3\kappa+1}{2\sqrt{3}}\,\eta - \frac{\kappa+1}{2}\frac{\xi}{a} - \frac{\kappa-1}{2}\frac{x}{a}\right\},$$

$$\frac{\cos\phi}{R^\kappa} = \frac{1}{2}\frac{1}{a^\kappa}\left(1-\sqrt{3}\,\theta\right)\left(1-\kappa\frac{\rho}{a}\right)$$
$$= \frac{1}{2}\frac{1}{a^\kappa}\left\{1 - \sqrt{3}\frac{\kappa-1}{2}\,\eta - \frac{\kappa-3}{2}\frac{x}{a} - \frac{\kappa+3}{2}\frac{\xi}{a}\right\}.$$

Similarly,

$$\frac{\cos\phi'}{R^\kappa} = \frac{1}{2}\frac{1}{a^\kappa}\left\{1 - \sqrt{3}\frac{\kappa-1}{2}\,\eta - \frac{\kappa-3}{2}\frac{\xi}{a} - \frac{\kappa+3}{2}\frac{x}{a}\right\};$$

also

$$\frac{\cos \psi}{r^{\kappa}} = \frac{1}{2} \frac{1}{a^{\kappa}} \left(1 - \sqrt{3}\, \eta - \kappa \frac{x}{a}\right),$$

$$\frac{\cos \psi}{r'^{\kappa}} = \frac{1}{2} \frac{1}{a^{\kappa}} \left(1 - \sqrt{3}\, \eta - \kappa \frac{\xi}{a}\right),$$

$$\frac{\sin \psi}{r^{\kappa}} = \frac{\sqrt{3}}{2} \frac{1}{a^{\kappa}} \left(1 + \frac{\eta}{\sqrt{3}} - \kappa \frac{x}{a}\right),$$

$$\frac{\sin \psi}{r'^{\kappa}} = \frac{\sqrt{3}}{2} \frac{1}{a^{\kappa}} \left(1 + \frac{\eta}{\sqrt{3}} - \kappa \frac{\xi}{a}\right).$$

Substituting, the four equations become, when D is written for $\frac{d}{dt}$.

$$\left\{ bD^2 - (\kappa+1)\left(1 + m + \frac{m'}{4}\right) \right\} x - 2abnDy$$
$$- m' \frac{\sqrt{3}}{4} (\kappa+1)\, a\eta - \tfrac{3}{4} m'(\kappa+1)\, \xi = 0,$$

$$\left\{ 2bnD + m' \frac{\sqrt{3}}{4} (\kappa+1) \right\} x + abD^2 y$$
$$+ m' \tfrac{3}{4} (\kappa+1)\, a\eta - \frac{\sqrt{3}}{4} m'(\kappa+1)\, \xi = 0,$$

$$\left\{ bD^2 - (\kappa+1)\left(1 + \frac{m}{4} + m'\right) \right\} \xi - 2abnDy$$
$$- \left\{ 2abnD + m \frac{\sqrt{3}}{4} (\kappa+1)\, a \right\} \eta - \tfrac{3}{4} m(\kappa+1)\, x = 0,$$

$$\left\{ -2bnD + m \frac{\sqrt{3}}{4} (\kappa+1) \right\} \xi - abD^2 y$$
$$+ \{ -abD^2 + m \tfrac{3}{4} (\kappa+1)\, a \} \eta - m \frac{\sqrt{3}}{4} (\kappa+1)\, x = 0.$$

Let us now write $\xi = x + X$. Then a variation of x, y alone, without X, η, will represent a variation of steady motion in which the particles always keep at the sides of an equilateral triangle, while a variation of X, η will represent a change from the equilateral form. One object of this transformation is, that the final determinant will have one of its roots obvious previous to expansion, and thus a great amount of numerical labour will be avoided. The four equations may be conveniently written

x	y	X	η
$bD^2 - (\kappa+1)(1+m+m')$	$-2abnD$	$-\dfrac{3}{4} m'(\kappa+1)$	$-\dfrac{\sqrt{3}}{4} m'(\kappa+1)\,a$
$2bnD$	$abD \cdot$	$-\dfrac{\sqrt{3}}{4} m'(\kappa+1)$	$\dfrac{3}{4} m'(\kappa+1)\,a$
$bD^2 - (\kappa+1)(1+m+m')$	$-2abnD$	$bD^2 - (\kappa+1)\left(1+\dfrac{m}{4}+m'\right)$	$-2abnD - \dfrac{\sqrt{3}}{4} m(\kappa+1)\,a$
$2bnD$	abD^2	$2bnD - \dfrac{\sqrt{3}}{4}(\kappa+1)\,m$	$abD^2 - \dfrac{3}{4} m(\kappa+1)\,a$

$= 0.$

To solve these equations, we put

$$x = Ae^{\lambda t}, \quad y = Be^{\lambda t}, \quad X = Ce^{\lambda t}, \quad \eta = De^{\lambda t};$$

we evidently obtain the same determinant with λ written for D. This is the equation to find λ.

We see at once that one factor is λ. This also follows from the physical consideration that a change of y without variation of x, X, or η is a possible motion.

Again, we know that a variation of x and y together without X, η is another possible motion; accordingly subtract from the x column $2n$ times the y column, these two columns then become

x	y
$b\lambda^2 - (\kappa - 3)(1 + m + m')$	$-2bn$
0	$b\lambda$
$b\lambda^2 - (\kappa - 3)(1 + m + m')$	$-2bn$
0	$b\lambda$

Clearly we have as one factor

$$b\lambda^2 - (\kappa - 3)(1 + m + m') = 0.$$

In order that the coordinates x, y, X, η may have only periodic terms, we must have κ less than 3.

To find the other factors, we divide the determinant by the factors already found. Let us also subtract the first row from the third, and the second from the fourth. We now have

1	&c.	&c.	&c.	
0	$b\lambda$	&c.	&c.	
0	0	$b\lambda^2 - (\kappa + 1)\left(1 + \dfrac{m}{4} + \dfrac{m'}{4}\right)$	$-2abn\lambda - \dfrac{\sqrt{3}}{4}(\kappa + 1)(m - m')a$	$= 0.$
0	0	$2bn\lambda - \dfrac{\sqrt{3}}{4}(\kappa + 1)(m - m')$	$ab\lambda^2 - \dfrac{3}{4}(\kappa + 1)(m + m')a$	

The expansion is now easy. We see that there is another factor λ.

Also $\quad b^2\lambda^4 + b\lambda^2(3 - \kappa)(1 + m + m') + \frac{3}{4}(1 + \kappa)^2(m + m' + mm') = 0;$

therefore $\quad b\lambda^2 = -\dfrac{3 - \kappa}{2}(1 + m + m')$

$$\pm \tfrac{1}{2}\sqrt{(1 + m + m')^2(3 - \kappa)^2 - 3(m + m' + mm')(1 + \kappa)^2}.$$

If, then, the quantity under the root be positive, and also κ less than 3, all the values of λ^2 are real and negative. In this case the motion is stable. If the quantity under the root be negative, we have λ of the form $\pm(\alpha \pm \beta\sqrt{-1})$, and hence the coordinates will have both a positive and a negative real exponent. In this case the motion is unstable.

Since $(1+m+m')^2 > 3(m+m'+mm')$,

we see that the motion is stable for all masses if
$(3-\kappa)^2 > (1-\kappa)^2$, or $(3-\kappa+1+\kappa)(3-\kappa-1-\kappa) > 0$; *i.e.*, if $1-\kappa > 0$.
The steady motion is therefore stable for any law of force expressed by
a positive power of the distance, and for any law expressed by a negative power less than unity, whatever the masses may be. For other
powers the stability will depend on the relation between the masses.

To express the coordinates in terms of the time, we must return to
the equations. Replacing the λ by D, they may be written in the form

x	y	X	η	
$b\mathrm{D}^2 - (\kappa+1)bn^2$	$-2abn\mathrm{D}$	$-\dfrac{3}{4}m'(\kappa+1)$	$-\dfrac{\sqrt{3}}{4}m'(\kappa+1)a$	
$2bn\mathrm{D}$	$ab\mathrm{D}^2$	$-\dfrac{\sqrt{3}}{4}m'(\kappa+1)$	$\dfrac{3}{4}m'(\kappa+1)a$	$= 0.$
0	0	$b\mathrm{D}^2 - \left(1+\dfrac{m}{4}+\dfrac{m'}{4}\right)(\kappa+1)$	$-2abn\mathrm{D} - \dfrac{\sqrt{3}}{4}(m-m')(\kappa+1)a$	
0	0	$2bn\mathrm{D} - \dfrac{\sqrt{3}}{4}(m-m')(\kappa+1)$	$ab\mathrm{D}^2 - \dfrac{3}{4}(m+m')(\kappa+1)a$	

The roots $\lambda^2 = 0$ give
$$x = A_1 + A_2 t, \qquad X = C_1 + C_2 t,$$
$$y = B_1 + B_2 t, \qquad \eta = D_1 + D_2 t;$$

we see at once that the C's and D's are zero. Also the second line
gives $A_2 = 0$, and the first $B_2 = -\dfrac{\kappa+1}{2}\dfrac{A_1}{a}n$.

The roots $\lambda^2 = -(3-\kappa)n^2$ give, if $\mu^2 = -\lambda^2$,
$$x = A\cos(\mu t + \mu'),$$
$$y = B\sin(\mu t + \mu'),$$
$$X = C_1\cos(\mu t + \mu') + C_2\sin(\mu t + \mu'),$$
$$\eta = D_1\cos(\mu t + \mu') + D_2\sin(\mu t + \mu').$$

The last two lines give (since these roots can be equal to the next pair
only when $\kappa = -1$) all the C's and D's zero, and the second line gives
$B = -\dfrac{2n}{a\mu}A$, except when $\kappa = -1$.

Lastly, let $-\mu^2$ and $-\nu^2$ be the values of λ^2 with the radical
$$X = C_1\cos(\mu t + \mu') + C_2\cos(\nu t + \nu').$$

Taking the first of these as a type, we get from the fourth line,
$$\eta = \frac{2bn\mu}{\Delta}C\sin(\mu t + \mu') + \frac{\dfrac{\sqrt{3}}{4}(\kappa+1)(m-m')}{\Delta}C\cos(\mu t + \mu'),$$
where
$$\Delta = ab\mu^2 + \tfrac{3}{4}(\kappa+1)(m+m')a.$$

Differentiating the first line, and adding to it $2n$ times the second, we get

$$b\left\{D^3-(\kappa-3)\,n^2D\right\}x = \frac{\sqrt{3}}{4}\,m'(\kappa+1)\left\{(\sqrt{3}\,D+2n)\,X+(D-2n\sqrt{3})\,an\right\};$$

therefore
$$x = P\sin(\mu t+\mu')+Q\cos(\mu t+\mu'),$$

where
$$P = \frac{-4an\left\{b\mu^2+\frac{3}{4}(\kappa+1)\,m'\right\}}{\Delta\Delta'\mu}\cdot\frac{\sqrt{3}}{4}\,m'(\kappa+1),$$

$$Q = \frac{-\sqrt{3}\,a\left\{b\,(\mu^2-4n^2)+\frac{1}{4}(\kappa+1)(m+2m')\right\}}{\Delta\Delta'}\cdot\frac{\sqrt{3}}{4}\,m'(\kappa+1),$$

where
$$\Delta' = b\left\{\mu^2+(\kappa-3)\,n^2\right\}.$$

In the case in which two of the particles m, m' are much smaller than the third, these results admit of some simplification. Neglecting the squares of m, m', we find

$$b\mu^2 = \frac{3}{4}\,\frac{(1+\kappa)^2}{3-\kappa}\,(m+m'),$$

$$b\nu^2 = (3-\kappa)\,bn^2 - \frac{3}{4}\,\frac{(1+\kappa)^2}{3-\kappa}\,(m+m').$$

Taking the former, we have

$$\Delta = 3\,\frac{1+\kappa}{3-\kappa}\,(m+m')\,a = \frac{4}{1+\kappa}\,ab\mu^2,$$

which is small. We then have $X = C\cos\mu t,$

$$\eta = \frac{1+\kappa}{2}\,\frac{n}{\mu}\,\frac{C}{a}\sin\mu t + \frac{3-\kappa}{4\sqrt{3}}\,\frac{m-m'}{m+m'}\,\frac{C}{a}\cos\mu t,$$

$$x = \frac{\sqrt{3}}{4}\,(1+\kappa)\,\frac{m'}{bn\mu}\,\frac{(1+\kappa)\,m+4m'}{m+m'}\,C\sin\mu t - \frac{m'}{m+m'}\,C\cos\mu t.$$

Since m' is of the order μ^2, we see that the most important term is

$$\eta = \frac{1+\kappa}{2}\,\frac{n}{\mu}\,\frac{C}{a}\sin\mu t,$$

so that there is a large inequality in the angular distance between the two smaller particles, while their distances from the central larger body are very little altered.

Taking the other value of μ, we have

$$\Delta' = -\frac{3}{4}\,\frac{(1+\kappa)^2}{3-\kappa}\,(m+m'),$$

which is small. We then have $X = C\cos\mu t,$

$$\eta = \frac{2n}{\mu}\,\frac{C}{a}\sin\mu t + \frac{\sqrt{3}}{4}\,\frac{1+\kappa}{3-\kappa}\,(m-m')\,\frac{C}{a}\cos\mu t,$$

$$x = \frac{4}{\sqrt{3}}\,\frac{3-\kappa}{1+\kappa}\,\frac{n}{\mu}\,\frac{m'}{m+m'}\,C\sin\mu t - \frac{m'}{m+m'}\,C\cos\mu t,$$

none of these terms rise to any importance.

The values of the coordinates may be written

$$x = a + A_1 \cos(n\sqrt{3-\kappa}\, t + \epsilon) + A_2 \cos \mu t$$
$$+ A_3 \sin \mu t + A_4 \cos \nu t + A_5 \sin \nu t,$$
$$y = \beta - \frac{\kappa+1}{2}\frac{a}{a} nt - \frac{2A_1}{a\sqrt{3-\kappa}} \sin(n\sqrt{3-\kappa}\, t + \epsilon) + B_2 \cos \mu t + \&c.,$$
$$X = C_2 \cos \mu t + \&c.,$$
$$\eta = D_2 \cos \mu t + \&c.$$

Since x is merely a small addition to a, we may suppose the a to be included in the a. In this case the corresponding term in y, containing t, is absorbed in the n. These two terms may therefore be omitted.

The case $\kappa = -1$ has been excepted. The law of attraction is then " directly as the distance." As this case has no special interest, we shall not further consider it.

Though the motion may be stable to a first approximation, yet it is important to examine the terms of the second order to ascertain if there be any which may ultimately disturb this stability.

If we repeat our calculation of the impressed forces, retaining now the squares and products of the small quantities, we shall evidently have additional terms of the form

$$E_1 x^2 + E_2 X^2 + E_3 \eta^2 + 2E_4 xX + 2E_5 x\eta + 2E_6 X\eta$$

in each of the four equations of motion. We must also add to the effective forces the terms

$$- a\left(\frac{dy}{dt}\right)^2 - 2nx\frac{dy}{dt}, \quad 2\frac{dx}{dt}\frac{dy}{dt} + x\frac{d^2y}{dt^2}$$

in the first two equations respectively, and similar expressions with $x + X$ and $y + \eta$ written for x, y in the two last equations.

We have now to substitute in these expressions of the second order the first approximate values of x, X, and η. We shall clearly obtain in every case an expression of the form

$$\text{constant} + \text{periodic terms.}$$

The periodic terms will none of them have the same period as those in the first approximation; because their arguments are the sums and differences of those of the first approximation, and it is easily seen that one argument cannot generally be double the other. Each periodic term will therefore give rise to a corresponding periodic term of the same period as itself. These therefore cannot affect the stability of the motion.

Thus the three roots are $b\lambda^2 = (\kappa-3)(1+m+m')$, $b\mu^2$, and $b\nu^2$. If $\lambda^2 = 4\mu^2$, or $4\nu^2$, we have $\mu^2 = \nu^2$, and the motion is unstable. If $\mu^2 = 4\lambda^2$, we get, by substituting in the equation,

$$12(\kappa-3)^2(1+m+m')^2 + \tfrac{3}{4}(1+\kappa)^2(m+m'+mm') = 0,$$

which is impossible. And if $\mu^2 = .4\nu^2$, we have

$$\frac{(1+m+m')^2}{m+m'+mm'} = \frac{25}{16} \cdot 3 \cdot \frac{(1+\kappa)^2}{(3-\kappa)^2},$$

which is possible. When this equality holds very nearly between the masses, there will be a periodic term in the disturbance which will rise from the second order to the first. If the equality hold exactly, the nature of the motion will be different from that taken as the first approximation.

Next let us consider the effect of the constant terms. Referring to the diagram on page 91, we form the equations by writing some constants e, f, g, h on the right-hand sides instead of zero. The two last equations contain only X and η, and we see that they may be satisfied by giving X and η two additional constant terms. Both of these are of the second order of small quantities, because their denominator, being of the form $\dfrac{m+m'+mm'}{am+\beta m'}$, cannot be small. The effect of these constant terms is not sensibly to alter the configuration of the particles; *i.e.*, they will still be very nearly at the angular points of an equilateral triangle.

The two first equations, on substituting for X and η their constant values just found, take the form

x	y		
$b\mathrm{D}^2 - (\kappa+1)\,bn^2$	$-2abn\mathrm{D}$	$=$	e'
$2bn\mathrm{D}$	$ab\mathrm{D}^2$		f'

These give a term $\dfrac{2f't}{(3-\kappa)\,bn}$ in the value of x, and a term $-\dfrac{1+\kappa}{3-\kappa}\dfrac{f'}{ab}\dfrac{t^2}{2}$ in the value of y. When t becomes sufficiently great to make these terms perceptible notwithstanding the smallness of f', the motion will begin to change from the character given by the first approximation. The equilateral triangle will alter in size, so that we cannot any longer consider x and y to be small.

We know, by Laplace's demonstration that the motion represented by the single type $\cos \sqrt{3-\kappa}\,nt$ must be stable. Thus, if the force be the inverse square, each of the particles m, m' will describe ellipses round M, and will always form an equilateral triangle. Let us examine what the constants e, f, g, h become when X and η are both zero. In this case the impressed forces are functions of x only, and are easily calculated. Putting $x = \mathrm{A} \cos \lambda t$, $y = \mathrm{B} \sin \lambda t$, we find the constant terms to be added to the left sides of the four equations in page 89, to be respectively

$$-a\,\frac{\mathrm{B}^2}{2}\,\lambda^2-\mathrm{AB}n\lambda+\kappa\,\frac{\kappa+1}{4}\,(1+m+m')\,\mathrm{A}^2,$$

zero,

$$-a\,\frac{\mathrm{B}^2}{2}\,\lambda^2-\mathrm{AB}n\lambda+\kappa\,\frac{\kappa+1}{4}\,(1+m+m')\,\mathrm{A}^2,$$

zero.

Hence the constants e, f, g, h on the right-hand side of the equations on page 91 become $f=0$, $g=0$, $h=0$; so that X and η have no constant additions. Also $f'=0$, and x and y, have only periodic terms, and therefore will remain small.

But this is not the case for variations of the type $\cos \mu t$ and $\cos \nu t$. The calculation of the constants e, f, g, h is very laborious. It is true that the constant terms can only arise from the product of two cosines, or two sines of the same angle, so that we may take the corresponding terms separately. But even with this simplification the arithmetic is very considerable. The want of sufficient leisure to effect this obliges me to leave the determination of these terms for a future opportunity.

Supplement.

Each of the three particles in the state of steady motion is describing a circle, so that their *vis viva* is constant, and the problem just considered was the determination of their times of oscillation. In the same way, if a dynamical system of any kind be making small oscillations about a state of steady motion in which the *vis viva* is constant, we may, by help of Lagrange's Equations, write down the determinantal equation to find the periods of oscillation.

Let the system be referred to coordinates x, y, z, &c., and be oscillating about a mean state of motion. The general value of the *vis viva* 2T is given by $2\mathrm{T} = \mathrm{A}x'^2+2\mathrm{B}x'y'+\ldots\ldots$, where A, B, &c. are functions of x, y, z, &c. Let us now put $x=a+mt+\theta$, $y=\beta+nt+\phi$, &c., where θ, ϕ, &c., will be considered small, the mean motion being given by the coordinates when $\theta=0$, $\phi=0$, &c. Then we may expand T in the form

$$\begin{aligned}
\mathrm{T} = {} & \mathrm{T}_0+\mathrm{T}_\theta\theta+\mathrm{T}_\phi\phi+\ldots \\
& +\mathrm{T}_{\theta'}\theta'+\mathrm{T}_{\phi'}\phi'+\ldots \\
& +(\mathrm{T}_{\theta\theta}\theta^2+2\mathrm{T}_{\theta\phi}\,\theta\phi+\ldots)\tfrac{1}{2} \\
& +\mathrm{T}_{\theta\theta'}\,\theta\theta'+\mathrm{T}_{\theta\phi'}\,\theta\phi'+\ldots \\
& +(\mathrm{T}_{\theta'\theta'}\theta'^2+2\mathrm{T}_{\theta'\phi'}\,\theta'\phi'+\ldots)\tfrac{1}{2}.
\end{aligned}$$

We may make a similar expansion for the potential U of the forces

$$\begin{aligned}
\mathrm{U} = {} & \mathrm{U}_0+u_\theta\theta+u_\phi\phi+\ldots \\
& +(u_{\theta\theta}\theta^2+2u_{\theta\phi}\,\theta\phi+\ldots)\tfrac{1}{2}.
\end{aligned}$$

We shall now suppose that all the coefficients are independent of t.

(1) This will happen if only some of the coordinates vary in the state of steady motion, and if the coordinates A, B, &c., in the expression for 2T, be independent of these. This is the case which generally occurs, for example in the top problem. Thus, if the steady motion be given by $x = a + mt$, $y = \beta + nt$, $z = \gamma$, then, if x and y be absent from T, the coefficients T_θ, &c. will all be constants.

(2) Even if the coefficients be functions of x, y, z, yet the relations between the quantities m, n, p, &c, given by the equations of steady motion, may cause t to disappear from the coefficients. The effect of this supposition is, that the mean motion is what is usually called "steady." The *vis viva* is constant throughout the steady motion, and the same oscillations follow from the same disturbance at whatever instant it may be applied to the system.

We must now substitute the values of T and U in Lagrange's equations

$$\frac{d}{dt}\frac{dT}{d\theta'} - \frac{dT}{d\theta} = \frac{dU}{d\theta},$$

$$\&c. = \&c.,$$

and reject the squares of small quantities. We thus get as many equations as there are independent variables. The steady motion being given by θ, ϕ, &c. all zero, each of these must be satisfied when we omit the terms containing θ, ϕ, &c. Thus we get the equations of steady motion. Omitting these, the equations may be written in the forms—

θ	ϕ	ψ	&c.	
$T_{\theta'\theta'}D^2 - T_{\theta\theta} - U_{\theta\theta}$	$T_{\theta'\phi'}D^2 - T_{\theta\phi} - U_{\theta\phi}$ $+ (T_{\theta'\phi} - T_{\theta\phi'}) D$	$T_{\theta'\psi'}D^2 - T_{\theta\psi} - U_{\theta\psi}$ $+ (T_{\theta'\psi} - T_{\theta\psi'}) D$	&c.	
$T_{\theta'\phi'}D^2 - T_{\theta\phi} - U_{\theta\phi}$ $+ (T_{\theta\phi'} - T_{\theta'\phi}) D$	$T_{\phi'\phi'}D^2 - T_{\phi\phi} - U_{\phi\phi}$	$T_{\phi'\psi'}D^2 - T_{\phi\psi} - U_{\phi\psi}$ $+ (T_{\phi'\psi} - T_{\phi\psi'}) D$	&c.	$= 0.$
$T_{\theta'\psi'}D^2 - T_{\theta\psi} - U_{\theta\psi}$ $+ (T_{\theta\psi'} - T_{\theta'\psi}) D$	$T_{\psi'\phi'} - T_{\psi\phi} - U_{\psi\phi}$ $+ (T_{\psi'\phi} - T_{\psi\phi'}) D$	$T_{\psi'\psi'}D^2 - T_{\psi\psi} - U_{\psi\psi}$	&c.	
&c.	&c.	&c.	&c.	

The operators on θ, ϕ, ψ, &c. forming the successive series of the determinant, and D standing for $\dfrac{d}{dt}$.

If we put $\theta = A e^{\lambda t}$, &c., this determinant, with λ written for D, is the equation to find λ. If we change the sign of D, the columns become rows, and the rows columns; thus the determinant is unchanged, and therefore the equation has no *odd* powers of D. We have, therefore, an equation to find D^2. If the roots be all real and negative, the motion is stable, and any simple oscillation is given by

$$\theta = A_1 \sin \mu t + B_1 \cos \mu t,$$
$$\phi = A_2 \sin \mu t + B_2 \cos \mu t, \quad \&c.$$

If any one of the roots be imaginary, or real and positive, we shall have both positive and negative real exponentials entering into the expressions for θ, ϕ, &c.; and therefore the motion will be unstable.

The chief labour in any application will be the expansion of this determinant, and the subsequent solution of the equation. Whenever, therefore, we have more than three independent variables, we should try to choose them so that some at least of the roots may be apparent without expanding the determinant.

If T and U are independent of any coordinate, say x, whose corresponding mean motion nt does not vanish, though not necessarily independent of the differential coefficients of x, we have

$$T_{\theta\theta} = 0, \ T_{\theta\phi} = 0, \ \&c., \ U_{\theta\theta} = 0, \ U_{\theta\phi} = 0, \ \&c.$$

Hence the constant terms in every constituent in the first line must vanish. We may then divide out the D from the first line and the first column, thus reducing the determinant two orders. The same argument applies to each coordinate containing nt. Thus there will be one periodic term less for every combination of coordinates which can be made constant in the steady motion, though the remaining periodic terms may occur in all the coordinates. This remark seems important, as it is often useful to know beforehand a superior limit to the number of periods of oscillation the system admits of. The zero roots may be omitted, for their effect is only to alter the mean motions of the coordinates, and these may be regarded as arbitrary in the first instance. The determinant being freed from these roots, its expansion may be simplified by methods which it is unnecessary to dwell on here.

Next suppose we know beforehand the nature of one of the harmonic oscillations, and that we can choose the coordinates so that it is produced by a variation of only one coordinate, say θ, then the equations formed by equating the first column to zero may all be satisfied by $\theta = A \sin \mu t + B \cos \mu t$. Hence the coefficients of D in that column must all be zero. The factor $\lambda^2 + \mu^2$ may then be brought out of the determinant.

So, also, if a possible oscillation can be represented by a variation of only two coordinates, say θ, ϕ; then, by adding to the first column the second column multiplied by some constant, we may again divide out by a quadratic factor, and reduce the determinant two orders.

These remarks are suggested and illustrated by the problem considered of the three particles. For, though the determinant was not deduced from Lagrange's equations, yet, however obtained, the resulting equation must be the same.

Reprinted from the sixth edition published in 1905 by Macmillan and Co. (London)

E. J. ROUTH

Chapter VI of *The advanced part of a treatise on the dynamics of a system of rigid bodies*

CHAPTER VI.

NATURE OF THE MOTION GIVEN BY LINEAR EQUATIONS AND THE CONDITIONS OF STABILITY.

Linear Differential Equations.

256. IT has been shown in Chap. III. that the problem of determining the small oscillations of a system about a state of steady motion is really the same as that of solving a corresponding system of linear differential equations. In that chapter the forces were assumed to have a potential, so that the differential equations had a certain symmetry which simplified the solution. We now propose to remove this restriction. *Taking the differential equations in their most general form, but still with constant coefficients, we shall briefly discuss any peculiarities of their solution which appear to have dynamical applications.*

The chief object of this chapter is to determine the conditions that the undisturbed motion should be stable. This resolves itself into two questions (1) *under what circumstances do positive powers of the time enter into the expressions for the coordinates, and what is the highest power which presents itself?* (2) *when the roots of the fundamental equation cannot be found, what conditions must be satisfied by the coefficients of that equation that stability may be assured?* In order to make our remarks on these two questions intelligible it will be necessary to sum up a few propositions which belong rather to the theory of differential equations than to that of dynamics. The discussion of the first question begins therefore at Art. 268 though alluded to before that article. The second question will occupy the next section.

257. Following the same notation as in Art. 111, let θ, ϕ, &c. be the co-ordinates of the system. Let the system be moving in any known manner determined by $\theta = f(t)$, $\phi = F(t)$, &c. We now suppose the system to be slightly disturbed from this state of motion. To discover the subsequent motion we put $\theta = f(t) + x$, $\phi = F(t) + y$, &c. These quantities x, y, &c. are in the first instance very small because the disturbance is small. The quantities x, y, &c. are said to be *small* when it is possible to choose some quantity numerically greater than all of them which is such that its square can be neglected. This quantity may be called the standard of reference for small quantities.

258. To determine whether x, y, &c. remain small, we substitute these new values of θ, ϕ, &c. in the equations of motion. Assuming, for the moment, that x, y, &c. remain small we may neglect their squares, and thus the resulting equations will be linear. The coefficients of x, dx/dt, d^2x/dt^2, y, dy/dt, &c. in these equations may be either constants or functions of the time. Following the definitions in Art. 111, the undisturbed motion in the former case is said to be steady.

259. We propose to consider first the case in which the system depends on two independent coordinates or (as it is sometimes called) has two degrees of freedom. This is a case which occurs very frequently, and as the results are comparatively simple it seems worthy of a separate discussion. We shall then proceed to the general case in which the system has any number of coordinates.

260. **Two degrees of freedom.** The equations of motion of a dynamical system performing its natural oscillations with two degrees of freedom may be written in the form

$$\left. \begin{aligned} A\frac{d^2x}{dt^2} + B\frac{dx}{dt} + Cx + A'\frac{d^2y}{dt^2} + B'\frac{dy}{dt} + C'y = 0 \\ E\frac{d^2x}{dt^2} + F\frac{dx}{dt} + Gx + E'\frac{d^2y}{dt^2} + F'\frac{dy}{dt} + G'y = 0 \end{aligned} \right\}.$$

To solve these equations we put

$$x = \left[A'\frac{d^2}{dt^2} + B'\frac{d}{dt} + C' \right]V, \qquad y = -\left[A\frac{d^2}{dt^2} + B\frac{d}{dt} + C \right]V,$$

these suppositions evidently satisfying the first equation whatever V may be. Substituting in the second, and using the symbol δ to represent $\frac{d}{dt}$ for the sake of brevity we find

$$\left| \begin{matrix} A\delta^2 + B\delta + C & A'\delta^2 + B'\delta + C' \\ E\delta^2 + F\delta + G & E'\delta^2 + F'\delta + G' \end{matrix} \right| V = 0.$$

This is an equation to find V in terms of t. Since δ enters into the determinant in the fourth power, the value of V when found will contain four arbitrary constants. Thence we find both x and y by means of the formulae given above. It will be observed that *these require no operation to be performed except differentiation.* Thus, no matter how complicated V may be, the values of x and y readily follow.

261. Let $\Delta(\delta)$ represent the determinant which is the operator on V. Then making $\Delta(\delta) = 0$, we have a biquadratic to find δ. If the roots of this biquadratic are m_1, m_2, m_3, m_4, we know by the rules for solving differential equations that

$$V = L_1 e^{m_1 t} + L_2 e^{m_2 t} + L_3 e^{m_3 t} + L_4 e^{m_4 t}$$

where L_1, L_2, L_3, L_4, are the four arbitrary constants.

If all the roots of the biquadratic are real and unequal, this is the proper expression to use for V. But it takes a variety of different forms when the biquadratic contains imaginary or equal roots. These however are described in the theory of differential equations, and will be summed up in Art. 264.

262. **Many degrees of freedom.** The equations which occur in Dynamics are in general all of the second order, but as this restriction is not necessary in what follows, we shall suppose the equations to contain differential coefficients of any order.

Let there be n dependent variables represented by x, y, z, &c. and one independent variable represented by t. If the symbol δ represent differentiation with regard to t, the n equations to find x, y, &c. may be written :

$$\left. \begin{aligned} f_{11}(\delta)\,x + f_{12}(\delta)\,y + f_{13}(\delta)\,z + \ldots = 0 \\ f_{21}(\delta)\,x + f_{22}(\delta)\,y + f_{23}(\delta)\,z + \ldots = 0 \\ \ldots \qquad \ldots \qquad \ldots \qquad \ldots \qquad = 0 \end{aligned} \right\} \ \ldots\ldots\ldots\ldots\ldots\ldots(1).$$

To solve these, we use the analogy which exists between the rules for combining symbols of differentiation and those of common algebra. Omitting for the moment any one equation, say the first, and proceeding to solve the remaining $n-1$ equations by the rules of common algebra, we find the ratios

$$\frac{1}{I_1(\delta)}\,x = \frac{1}{I_2(\delta)}\,y = \frac{1}{I_3(\delta)}\,z = \&c. = V \dots\dots\dots\dots(2),$$

where each of the equalities has been put equal to V. Here we have used the letter I to stand for the minors of the determinant

$$\Delta(\delta) = \begin{vmatrix} f_{11}(\delta), & f_{12}(\delta), & f_{13}(\delta),\dots \\ f_{21}(\delta), & f_{22}(\delta), & f_{23}(\delta),\dots \\ \dots & \dots & \dots \quad \dots \end{vmatrix} \quad\dots\dots\dots\dots(3).$$

The suffix of the letter I indicates the number of the column in which the constituent of the omitted equation lies whose minor is required.

Substituting these values of x, y, z, &c. in the equation previously omitted, we obtain

$$\Delta(\delta)\,V = 0 \dots\dots\dots\dots\dots\dots(4).$$

This is an equation to determine a single quantity V as a function of t. We may call V the *type of the solution.* Supposing this equation to be solved by the usual rules, the values of x, y, z, &c. are found by equations (2). Thus we have

$$x = I_1(\delta)\,V, \quad y = I_2(\delta)\,V, \ \&c\dots\dots\dots\dots(5).$$

These operators, $I_1(\delta)$, $I_2(\delta)$, &c., are all *integral and rational functions of δ*; so that, *when V is once known, all the other operations necessary for the complete solution of the equations are reduced to the one operation of continued differentiation.*

263. This arrangement of the solution of the differential equations (1) has the advantage of expressing the results by means of integral and rational functions of the symbol δ. In practice, this will be found to introduce a great simplification into the solution. The type V can always be immediately written down by the usual rules for solving equation (4). It is sometimes very complicated, and in such cases it is very convenient to be able to deduce the forms of x, y, z, &c. without having to perform any inverse operation.

264. **Different types of the solution.** If the roots of the determinantal equation $\Delta(\delta) = 0$ be m_1, m_2, &c., the type V is known to be

$$V = L_1 e^{m_1 t} + L_2 e^{m_2 t} + \dots \ \dots\dots\dots\dots(6),$$

where L_1, L_2, &c. are arbitrary constants. When a pair of imaginary roots of the form $r \pm p\sqrt{-1}$ occurs we replace the two corresponding imaginary exponentials by the terms $\quad V = e^{rt}(L \cos pt + M \sin pt) \ \dots\dots\dots\dots(7).$

If equal roots occur, the value of V thus given has no longer the full number of constants. Supposing that we have a roots each equal to m, the type of the solution which depends on these roots is

$$V = (L_0 + L_1 t + \dots + L_{a-1} t^{a-1})\,e^{mt} \dots\dots\dots\dots(8)$$

where the L's are a arbitrary constants. This may be put into the form

$$V = \left(L_0 + L_1 \frac{d}{dm} + \dots + L_{a-1} \frac{d^{a-1}}{dm^{a-1}} \right) e^{mt} \ \dots\dots\dots\dots(9).$$

If we have a equal pairs of imaginary roots of the form $r \pm p\sqrt{-1}$ we replace the a pairs of terms by

$$e^{rt}(L_0 \cos pt + M_0 \sin pt) + \frac{d}{dr}\,e^{rt}(L_1 \cos pt + M_1 \sin pt) + \&c. \ \dots\dots(10).$$

Here, if we please, we may replace the differentiation with regard to r by a differentiation with regard to p.

The peculiarity of the case of equal roots is the presence of terms containing some power of t as a factor. The occurrence of a equal roots in general indicates the presence of terms containing all the integral powers of t up to t^{a-1}.

265. In order to deduce the corresponding values of x, y, &c. from these types, we shall have, in the absence of equal roots, to operate with some integral and rational function of δ such as $I(\delta)$ on an exponential real or imaginary.

I. We have the theorem $I(\delta)\,e^{mt} = I(m)\,e^{mt}$,

so that when the roots of the equation $\Delta(\delta) = 0$ are all real and unequal we have immediately

$$x = L_1 I_1(m_1)\,e^{m_1 t} + L_2 I_1(m_2)\,e^{m_2 t} + \&c.,$$
$$y = L_1 I_2(m_1)\,e^{m_1 t} + L_2 I_2(m_2)\,e^{m_2 t} + \&c.,$$
$$z = \&c.$$

II. If X be any function of t, we have the theorem $I(\delta)\,e^{rt}X = e^{rt} I(\delta + r)\,X$, so that when a pair of imaginary roots occurs, and we have to operate on the product of a real exponential and a sine or cosine, we can immediately remove the real exponential, and reduce the operator to that of continued differentiation of the sine or cosine.

III. We have the theorem $f(\delta^2)\sin mt = f(-m^2)\sin mt$.

Hence if we have to operate with $F(\delta)$, we arrange the operator in the form $\phi(\delta^2) + \delta\psi(\delta^2)$. We then have $F(\delta)\sin mt = \phi(-m^2)\sin mt + \psi(-m^2)\,m\cos mt$.

266. When the determinantal equation $\Delta(\delta) = 0$ has equal roots we have to operate on expressions which contain some powers of t. But since the operators d/dt and d/dm or d/dr are independent we may use the theorem

$$I(\delta)\,\frac{d^\kappa}{dm^\kappa}\,e^{mt} = \frac{d^\kappa}{dm^\kappa}\{I(m)\,e^{mt}\}.$$

Thus when the equation $\Delta(\delta) = 0$ has a roots each equal to m we may write the solution given by equations (5) and (9) of Arts. 262, 264 in the form

$$x = L_0[I_1(m)\,e^{mt}] + L_1\frac{d}{dm}[I_1(m)\,e^{mt}] + \ldots + L_{a-1}\frac{d^{a-1}}{dm^{a-1}}[I_1(m)\,e^{mt}],$$
$$y = L_0[I_2(m)\,e^{mt}] + L_1\frac{d}{dm}[I_2(m)\,e^{mt}] + \ldots + L_{a-1}\frac{d^{a-1}}{dm^{a-1}}[I_2(m)\,e^{mt}],$$
$$z = \&c.$$

267. Ex. 1. If there be two roots of the determinantal equation $\Delta(\delta) = 0$ each equal to m, show by an actual comparison of the several terms that we have the same solutions for x, y, &c. whether we use as operators the minors of the first or the minors of any other row of the determinant $\Delta(\delta)$.

Ex. 2. The values of x, y, &c. are obtained from V by operating with certain functions of δ, viz. $I_1(\delta)$, $I_2(\delta)$, &c. If instead of these operators we use $\mu I_1(\delta)$, $\mu I_2(\delta)$, &c. where μ is some function of δ such as $\mu = f(\delta)$, show that the effect is merely to alter the arbitrary constants L_0, L_1, &c. Thence show that the solutions are the same, whether there be equal roots or not, whatever set of first minors of $\Delta(\delta)$ are used as operators.

268. **An indeterminate case.** If the roots of the determinantal equation $\Delta(\delta) = 0$ are m_1, m_2, &c. we have shown that the values of x, y, &c. are given by

$$x = \Sigma L I_1(m)\,e^{mt}, \quad y = \Sigma L I_2(m)\,e^{mt}, \&c.$$

But we see at once that there is a case of failure. If one of the roots of the equation $\Delta(\delta) = 0$ makes all the minors, $I_1(m)$, $I_2(m)$, &c. equal to zero, the solution becomes incomplete, for then one of the constants called L disappears from the solution. If all the minors of only one row vanished, we could find the values of x, y, z, &c. by choosing as our operators the minors of some other row. But this cannot be done *if all the minors of all the rows are zero.*

269. We shall now prove that this indeterminate case cannot occur unless the determinantal equation $\Delta(\delta) = 0$ has equal roots. To show this, we differentiate equation (3) of Art. 262. We find

$$\frac{d\Delta(\delta)}{d\delta} = I_{11}\frac{df_{11}}{d\delta} + I_{12}\frac{df_{12}}{d\delta} + \&c. + I_{21}\frac{df_{21}}{d\delta} + \&c.$$

where the letter I stands for the minor of that constituent of the determinant $\Delta(\delta)$ which is indicated by the suffix. We notice that the right-hand side of this equation vanishes when all the first minors are zero. Thus the equation $\Delta(\delta) = 0$ must have at least two equal roots. In the same way, if the second minors are all zero also, any first minor has two equal roots, and therefore the original equation has three equal roots, and so on.

270. We may notice two obvious results. (1) If all the first minors of a determinant have a root α times, the determinant has the root $\alpha + 1$ times at least. (2) If a determinant have r equal roots, and all its first, second, &c. minors vanish for these roots, then each of the first minors has the equal root $r - 1$ times, each of the second minors $r - 2$ times, and so on.

271. Let us consider, as an example, Lagrange's determinant to find the periods of the small oscillations of a system about a position of equilibrium, Art. 57. Suppose this determinant to have two equal roots, then, by Art. 266, we may expect each coordinate of the system to contain a term of the form $(A + Bt)e^{mt}$. Thus the amplitude of the oscillation will contain powers of the time.

By Art. 61 we know that every first minor of Lagrange's determinant also contains this root, so that the solution given by Art. 266 fails. Accordingly we shall find in Art. 273 that the solution does not contain any powers of the time, but that the independent constants arrange themselves in another manner which may be conveniently represented by using a double type of solution. See also Art. 281.

272. We may now consider the following general problem :—

Let the determinant $\Delta(\delta)$ have α roots each equal to m. Let β of these roots make every first minor of $\Delta(\delta)$ equal to zero. Let γ of these last make every second minor equal to zero, and so on. It is required to state the general form of the solution and to explain how the α constants in that solution are to be found.

Solution with a single type. First, let us consider the α roots which are equal to m. It has been proved in Art. 266, that the part of the solution which depends on these may be written in the form

$$x = L_0[I_1(m)e^{mt}] + L_1\frac{d}{dm}[I_1(m)e^{mt}] + \ldots + L_{\alpha-1}\frac{d^{\alpha-1}}{dm^{\alpha-1}}[I_1(m)e^{mt}],$$

with similar expressions for y, z, &c.

If these first minors are finite, these formulae contain powers of t from t^0 to $t^{\alpha-1}$, and thus supply the α constants which belong to the α equal roots. If the first minors have β roots equal to m, $I_1(m)$, $I_2(m)$, &c., and their differential coefficients up to the $(\beta-1)$th are all zero. In this case the powers of t extend only to $t^{\alpha-\beta-1}$, and thus these formulae do not supply the full number of constants.

When all the first minors have the root α times and all the second minors have the root β times, we know by Art. 270 that $\alpha - \beta - 1$ cannot be negative.

273. Solution with a double type. To find the proper forms for x, y, &c. when the first minors are all zero, we return to the analogy between operations and quantities alluded to in Art. 262. We now reject any two of the equations (1), say the first two. Solving the remaining $n-2$ equations we can express all the coordinates z, u, &c. in terms of x and y, thus obtaining a series of equations of the form

$$z = \phi(\delta)\,x + \psi(\delta)\,y,$$

where the functional symbols are really second minors of the determinant $\Delta(\delta)$. We now substitute these expressions for z, u, &c. in the two omitted equations. These two equations will be satisfied provided x and y have any values which make $I(\delta)\,x = 0$ and $I(\delta)\,y = 0$, where $I(\delta)$ is any first minor of $\Delta(\delta)$.

We notice also that these two equations are satisfied by the *separate* parts of these values of z, u, &c. which arise from x and from y. We may therefore arrange the solution so as to find these two parts separately, and then finally add the results. The following arrangement will be found convenient in practice.

When the first minors are all zero, reject some one of the given differential equations (1), say the first. We have now $n-1$ equations to determine the n coordinates. Putting $y = 0$ in these equations we find x, z, &c. in terms of a single type ξ, where ξ satisfies the equation $I_2(\delta)\,\xi = 0$. Here I_2 represents the minor of the second constituent of the first line of the determinant $\Delta(\delta)$. We write the solution thus found in the form

$$x = J_{21}(\delta)\,\xi, \qquad y = 0, \qquad z = J_{23}(\delta)\,\xi, \text{ &c.}$$

where the operators are the *second minors* of the constituents in the first two lines of $\Delta(\delta)$. Next, putting $x = 0$ instead of y in the equations after the first, we obtain another solution, by which x, z, &c. are expressed in terms of another single type η. Here η satisfies the equation $I_1(\delta)\,\eta = 0$, where I_1 is the minor of the first constituent of the first line of $\Delta(\delta)$. We write the solution thus found in the form

$$x = 0, \qquad y = J_{12}(\delta)\,\eta, \qquad z = J_{13}(\delta)\,\eta, \text{ &c.}$$

Adding these two solutions together, we have the following values of x, y, z, &c.

$$x = J_{21}(\delta)\,\xi, \qquad y = J_{12}(\delta)\,\eta, \qquad z = J_{23}(\delta)\,\xi + J_{13}(\delta)\,\eta, \text{ &c.}$$

These evidently satisfy all the equations except the one rejected. But this equation also is satisfied because by hypothesis we take those parts only of these solutions which make all the first minors equal to zero.

The types ξ, η have the same exponentials but with different constants, the operators also are different. Suppose for example the determinant $\Delta(\delta)$ had two roots only equal to m and that these make every first minor of $\Delta(\delta)$ equal to zero. The terms of x, y, z, &c. which depend on the roots other than m are found each from its own exponential by the rule given in Art. 262 for a single type. The terms of x, y, z, &c. which depend on the root m are found by putting $\xi = L_1 e^{mt}$, $\eta = L_2 e^{mt}$ where L_1 and L_2 are two different arbitrary constants. The portions of the solution due to these are respectively

$$x = L_1 J_{21}(m)\,e^{mt}, \qquad y = 0, \qquad z = L_1 J_{23}(m)\,e^{mt}, \text{ &c.}$$
$$x = 0, \qquad y = L_2 J_{12}(m)\,e^{mt}, \qquad z = L_2 J_{13}(m)\,e^{mt}, \text{ &c.}$$

where J_{ab} is a second minor which may be deduced from $\Delta(\delta)$ by rejecting the ath and bth columns and the two first rows, giving the second minor thus left its proper sign. The suffix 2 occurs in every J in the first line and the suffix 1 in every J in the second. The complete solution due to the root m is the sum of these two partial solutions. We notice that the two arbitrary constants L_1, L_2 so enter into the values of x, y, z, &c. that the exponential e^{mt} is accompanied by two arbitrary constants instead of one and these are not separated by the presence of powers of t.

274. If the minors which the types ξ and η are to satisfy contain the root $\delta = m$, β times, we have therefore

$$\xi = (G_0 + G_1 t + \ldots + G_{\beta-1} t^{\beta-1})\, e^{mt},$$

$$\eta = (H_0 + H_1 t + \ldots + H_{\beta-1} t^{\beta-1})\, e^{mt}.$$

The corresponding values of x, y, &c. are found by substitution, and may be written in the form

$$x = G_0 [J_{21}(m)\, e^{mt}] + G_1 \frac{d}{dm} [J_{21}(m)\, e^{mt}] + \ldots + G_{\beta-1} \frac{d^{\beta-1}}{dm^{\beta-1}} [J_{21}(m)\, e^{mt}],$$

with similar expressions for y, &c.

The peculiarity of the solutions which are derived from the double type ξ, η is that the corresponding terms in the expressions for x and y have *independent constants*.

If the second minors which form the operators are all finite, these formulae contain powers of t up to $t^{\beta-1}$ and supply 2β constants. But if these second minors contain γ roots equal to m, the powers of t extend only to $t^{\beta-\gamma-1}$, and thus the full number of constants has not been found.

275. **Solution with a triple type.** Thirdly, we have to find the solution when the second minors are zero as well as the first minors. In this case the solution just found becomes again insufficient. To determine the proper forms of x, y, z, &c. we now reject any three of the differential equations (1) of Art. 263, and proceed as before. We thus have $n-3$ equations to find the n coordinates. We see at once that we can express all the coordinates in terms of any three we please, say x, y, z. We thus have three times as many arbitrary constants as there are roots equal to m.

In the same way as before we can express the solution in terms of a triple type ξ, η, ζ. Putting y and z equal to zero, we find the remaining coordinates, viz. x, u, &c. in terms of a single type ξ. Putting x and z equal to zero (instead of y and z) in these $n-3$ equations we obtain a second solution depending on another single type η. Lastly, putting x and y equal to zero we obtain a third solution depending on ζ. Adding together these three solutions we find that all the coordinates may be expressed by means of operators which are really third minors of the determinant $\Delta(\delta)$. The subjects of operation are the three independent functions ξ, η, ζ. These are such that if $I(\delta)$ be any of the second minors of the constituents of the three omitted equations $I(\delta)\xi = 0$, $I(\delta)\eta = 0$, $I(\delta)\zeta = 0$. If these contain the root $\delta = m$, γ times, each of the three ξ, η, ζ will be expressed by a series of the form $\quad (K_0 + K_1 t + \ldots + K_{\gamma-1} t^{\gamma-1})\, e^{mt},$

but with independent constants.

276. **The number of constants.** Each of the sets of values of x, y, &c. given in Arts. 272, 273, and 275 is, of course, *a solution*. The complete solution is really the sum of these partial solutions, provided it has the proper number of constants. We appear, however, to have too many constants. We must therefore examine these, and determine what terms are absolutely zero and what terms are repeated in the several partial solutions.

We begin with the solution derived from the type V, Art. 272, by the help of the first minors. Since the first minors have β roots each equal to m, the first β terms of each of the expressions for x, y, &c. are easily seen to be zero. Consider the solution derived from any term L_k, where k lies between $\beta-1$ and 2β. In the case of the variables x and y they are expressions of the form

$$(A_0 + A_1 t + \ldots + A_{k-\beta} t^{k-\beta})\, e^{mt}.$$

All these are evidently included amongst the terms derived from ξ, η by the help of the second minors. The corresponding terms in z, u, &c. must be related to the terms in x, y by the formula given in Art. 273, and are therefore also included in the series derived from ξ, η. Lastly, consider the solution derived from the terms from $L_{2\beta}$ to L_{a-1}. They include powers of t from t^β to $t^{a-1-\beta}$. These $a - 2\beta$ terms are not included in the terms derived from ξ and η, and they supply $a - 2\beta$ arbitrary constants.

Secondly, we turn our attention to the solution derived from the double type ξ, η by the help of the second minors (Arts. 273 and 274). Each of these second minors has γ roots each equal to m; hence, by the same reasoning as before, the first γ terms of the series for x and y are zero, and the highest power of t is $\beta - 1 - \gamma$ instead of $\beta - 1$. In consequence of this, the terms of the series derived from the single type V, and not included in those derived from the double type ξ, η, now extend their powers of t from $t^{\beta-\gamma}$ to $t^{a-1-\beta}$. There are therefore $a - 2\beta + \gamma$ such terms instead of $a - 2\beta$.

The same reasoning applies to all the other partial solutions derived from the triple and higher types. *We therefore conclude that the partial solution derived from a single type by operating with the first minors of the first row of the fundamental determinant supplies $a - 2\beta + \gamma$ terms not included in the solutions which follow. These supply as many arbitrary constants. The partial solution derived from a double type by operating with the second minors of the two first rows of the fundamental determinant supplies $\beta - 2\gamma + \delta$ terms not included in the solutions which follow. These supply twice as many constants. The partial solution derived from a triple type by operating with the third minors of the three first rows supplies $\gamma - 2\delta + \epsilon$ terms and twice as many constants, and so on.*

Suppose (for example) that the fourth minors are not all zero; the number of constants supplied by each of the several partial solutions is indicated by the terms of the series $(a - 2\beta + \gamma) + 2(\beta - 2\gamma + \delta) + 3(\gamma - 2\delta) + 4\delta.$

If none of the terms of this series are negative, we have obtained a series of partial solutions containing the proper number of constants. This point we now proceed to discuss.

277. If a determinant contain the root just a times, if the first minors of the two first constituents of the two first rows contain the root just β times, if the second minor of these four constituents contain the root just γ times, then $a - 2\beta + \gamma$ is positive.

To prove this, let Δ be the determinant, I_1, I_2, J_1, J_2 the four first minors, Δ_2 the second minor. Then we know that $\Delta\Delta_2 = I_1 J_2 - I_2 J_1$. The left-hand side contains the root just $a + \gamma$ times, the right-hand side contains the root at least 2β times. Hence $a + \gamma - 2\beta$ is positive.

In the same way we may show, on similar suppositions, that $\beta - 2\gamma + \delta$ is positive, and so on.

278. Example. Solve the differential equations
$$\left.\begin{array}{l}(\delta - 1)^2 (\delta + 1) x - (\delta - 1)(\delta - 2) y + (\delta - 1) z = 0 \\ 3 (\delta - 1)^2 x - (\delta - 1)(\delta - 3) y + 2(\delta - 1) z = 0 \\ (\delta - 1)^2 x + (\delta - 1) y + (\delta - 1) z = 0 \end{array}\right\}.$$

The fundamental determinant (Art. 262) is $\Delta(\delta) = -(\delta - 1)^6$. This determinant (Art. 272) has six equal roots ($a = 6$), every first minor has the root three times ($\beta = 3$), and every second minor has the root once ($\gamma = 1$). The part of the solution depending on a single type (Art. 276) will supply $a - 2\beta + \gamma$ (i.e. one) constants. These accompany the highest powers of t which occur in the type, one constant for each power (Art. 272). The part of the solution depending on a double type will supply $2(\beta - 2\gamma)$ (i.e. two) constants. These accompany the highest powers of t which occur in *this* type, two constants to each power. The part of the solution depending on a triple type will supply 3γ (i.e. three) constants which again accompany the highest powers of t, three constants to each power. To obtain the full number of constants it is necessary in this example to retain only the one highest power of t which occurs in each type.

The single type is $\xi = (\&c. + At^5)\, e^t$ by Art. 264. Taking the minors of the first row of Δ (δ) we have by Art. 262 $x = -(\delta - 1)^3\,\xi$, $y = -(\delta - 1)^3\,\xi$, $z = \delta\,(\delta - 1)^3\,\xi$.

To find the part of the solution which depends on a double type we reject the first equation (Art. 273). Putting $x = 0$ we find $y = (\delta - 1)\,\xi$, $z = -(\delta - 1)\,\xi$ where $(\delta - 1)^3\,\xi = 0$. Putting $y = 0$ we find $x = (\delta - 1)\,\eta$, $z = -(\delta - 1)^2\,\eta$ where $(\delta - 1)^3\,\eta = 0$. The double type is therefore $\xi = (\&c. + Bt^2)\, e^t$, $\eta = (\&c. + Ct^2)\, e^t$. The values of the coordinates are $\qquad x = (\delta - 1)\,\eta$, $\quad y = (\delta - 1)\,\xi$, $\quad z = -(\delta - 1)\,\xi - (\delta - 1)^2\,\eta$.

To find the part of the solution which depends on a triple type we reject the two first equations (Art. 275). The three partial solutions are then *first*, $x = 0$, $y = 0$, $z = De^t$; *secondly*, $x = 0$, $y = Ee^t$, $z = 0$, *thirdly*, $x = Fe^t$, $y = 0$, $z = 0$. The sum of these is the solution derived from a triple type.

Adding up the solutions which are derived from all the different types and simplifying the constants we have

$$x = (F + Ct + At^2)\, e^t, \qquad y = (E + Bt + At^2)\, e^t, \qquad z = \{D - Bt - A\,(t^2 + 2t)\}\, e^t.$$

279. Conversely, *suppose it is given that we have such a solution as that described in Art. 276, let us enquire what minors must be zero.*

Let it be given that the solution contains terms depending on a triple type containing $(\gamma - 1)$ powers of t accompanied by independent constants in some three coordinates. Putting any two of these coordinates equal to zero the differential equations are satisfied by a solution depending on a single type. Thus we have n equations containing $n - 2$ coordinates all satisfied by values of the coordinates which contain powers of t up to the $(\gamma - 1)$th. This shows that all the second minors which can be formed from these equations must be zero and each of these minors must contain the root γ times.

From this we infer by Art. 270 that every first minor must contain the root $\gamma + 1$ times. But let us suppose that the given solution contains also terms derived from a double type which have powers of t extending up to the $(\beta - \gamma - 1)$th with independent constants in some two of the coordinates. Reasoning in the same way as before, we see that every first minor must have the root $(\beta - \gamma - 1)$ times. These must be in addition to the $\gamma + 1$ roots already counted, because we may regard the given solutions derived from the double and triple types as solutions which depend on unequal roots, and then make these roots become equal in the limit. It follows therefore that every first minor has the root β times.

We now infer by Art. 270 that the determinant (4) of Art. 262 must have the root $\beta - 1$ times. But if the given solution also contains terms derived from a single type with powers of t extending to the $(\alpha - \beta - 1)$th, we deduce by the preceding reasoning that the determinant (4) must have the root α times.

280. We may notice as a corollary of this theory that the solution cannot contain terms in which the high powers of t depend on a larger type than the low powers of t. For example, if the term $t^n e^{mt}$ occur accompanied by k independent constants, this term must be part of a solution derived from a kth type. It follows that all the lower powers of t which multiply the same exponential will be part of the same type and must be accompanied by at least k independent constants.

281. Condition that all powers of t are absent. *In some dynamical problems it is well known that, though the fundamental* *determinant has α equal roots, yet there are no terms in the solution with powers of t. We may now determine the condition that this may occur.*

We see by Art. 272 that, unless every first minor has the root $α-1$ times at least, a solution can be deduced from the first minors which has some power of t greater than zero in the coefficient. Again, unless every second minor has the root $α-2$ times at least, a solution can be deduced from the second minors with some power of t in the coefficient. *On the whole, we infer that, when α equal roots occur in the determinant, and the terms in the solution with t as a factor are to be absent, it is necessary as well as sufficient that all the first, second, &c. minors up to the $(α-1)$th should be zero.*

282. **Dynamical Meaning of the Types.** We shall now consider how the three different types of solution given in Art. 264 indicate different kinds of motion. Let us begin with a real root. In this case every coordinate has a term of the form Me^{mt}. *If m be positive* this term will become greater as time goes on, and the system may therefore depart widely from its undisturbed state, and our equations will represent only the manner in which the system begins its travels. *If m be negative* this term will gradually dwindle away and the motion will finally depend on the other terms in the solution.

Similar remarks apply whenever we have a real exponential, whether multiplied by a trigonometrical function or not. We may therefore state as a general principle, subject to some reservations in the case of equal roots which will be presently mentioned, that *the necessary and sufficient conditions of stability are that the real roots and the real parts of the imaginary roots should be all negative or zero.* A simple rule to determine whether this is the case or not will be given in another section of this chapter.

283. **Effect of equal roots on stability.** When there are equal roots in the determinantal equation we have seen that the solution in general has terms which contain powers of t as a factor. The important question for us to determine is the effect of these terms on the stability of the system. If m be positive the presence of a term $Mt^q e^{mt}$ will of course make the system unstable. But if m be negative, this term can never be numerically greater than $M\left(\dfrac{q}{em}\right)^q$. If m be very small the initial increase of the term may make the values of x, y, &c. become large, and the motion cannot be regarded as a small oscillation. But if the system be not so disturbed that $M\left(\dfrac{q}{em}\right)^q$ is large, the term will ultimately disappear and the motion may be regarded as stable. If m be wholly imaginary and equal to $n\sqrt{-1}$, this term will take the form $t^q \sin nt$ and will of course cause the system to be unstable.

Thus equal roots do not disturb the stability if their real parts are negative, but do render the system unstable if their real parts are zero or positive.

284. It is clear from this that the whole character of the motion depends on the nature of the roots of the determinantal equation $\Delta(\delta) = 0$. If we can solve this equation and find the roots, we of course know immediately the nature of the motion. But if this cannot be done, we must have recourse to the theory of equations to determine whether the roots are real or imaginary, and whether any roots are equal or not. The theorems of Fourier and Sturm will be of use in the equations of the higher orders, but in many dynamical problems we have only to deal with two coordinates. We shall therefore examine the roots of the biquadratic in Art. 260.

Rules by which the analysis of a biquadratic is made to depend on the solution of a cubic are given in most treatises on the theory of equations; but as these are not convenient in practice, a short analysis will be given here for reference. The criteria of the nature of the roots of the biquadratic are very conveniently summed up in Art. 68 of the *Theory of Equations* by Burnside and Panton, 1892.

285. **Analysis of a biquadratic.** Let the biquadratic be

$$ax^4 + 4bx^3 + 6cx^2 + 4dx + e = 0,$$

so that the invariants are $I = ae - 4bd + 3c^2$, and $J = ace + 2bcd - ad^2 - eb^2 - c^3$. This last may also be written as a determinant. It will generally be found convenient to clear the equation of the second term. Let the equation so transformed be

$$a\xi^4 - 2aH\xi^2 + aG\xi - aF = 0,$$

where $a^2H = 3(b^2 - ac)$ and $a^3G = 4(2b^3 - 3abc + a^2d)$. By using the invariants or by actual transformation it is easy to see that

$$I = \tfrac{1}{3}a^2H^2 - a^2F \quad \text{and} \quad J = \tfrac{4}{27}a^3H^3 - \tfrac{1}{16}a^3G^2 - \tfrac{1}{3}aIH.$$

Let Δ be the discriminant, i.e. $\Delta = I^3 - 27J^2$, then it is proved in all books on the theory of equations that if Δ is negative and not zero, the biquadratic has two real and two imaginary roots. If Δ is positive and not zero the roots are either all real or all imaginary.

When Δ is positive we can distinguish between the two cases by ascertaining if the biquadratic has or has not a real root. Thus if a and e have opposite signs, one root is real and therefore all the roots are real. We can also use the following criterion. Having cleared the given biquadratic of the second term we may write the resulting equation in the form $(\xi^2 - H)^2 + G\xi = K$.

If S_n be the arithmetic mean of the nth powers of the roots, we have by Newton's theorem on the sums of powers, $S_1 = 0$, $S_2 = H$, $4S_3 = -3G$ and $K = S_4 - S_2^2$. If all the roots are real we have S_2 positive and by a known theorem in "inequalities" S_4 is greater than S_2^2. Hence H and K are both positive. If all the roots are imaginary, let them be $r \pm p\sqrt{-1}$ and $-r \pm q\sqrt{-1}$. Then

$$H = S_2 = r^2 - \tfrac{1}{2}(p^2 + q^2),$$
$$K = S_4 - S_2^2 = \tfrac{1}{4}(p^2 - q^2)^2 - 2r^2(p^2 + q^2).$$

If H is positive or zero we see that K is negative. The criterion may therefore be stated thus. *If H and K are both positive the four roots are real. If either is negative or zero the four roots are imaginary.*

If the discriminant Δ is zero the biquadratic has equal roots. If two roots are real and two imaginary the equal roots must be real, and we see (by putting $q=0$) that if H is positive, K must be negative. If all the four roots are imaginary there must be two pairs of equal roots given by $r=0$, $p=q$; hence $K=0$, $G=0$. The criterion therefore is, *if H and K are both positive all the roots are real, if H or K is negative or zero, two roots are real and two are imaginary, except G=0.*

Since the equal roots satisfy the derived equation we see that *when $G=0$, the equal roots are $\xi^2=H$ or $\xi=0$.* The former makes $K=0$, $I=\frac{4}{3}a^2H^2$ and there are two pairs of equal roots given by $\xi=\pm\sqrt{H}$. In the latter case the equal roots are $\xi=0$ and the unequal roots $\pm\sqrt{2H}$.

When there are three equal roots, all the roots are real. Let the four roots be a, a, a, $-3a$, then $H=3a^2$, $G=8a^3$, $K=12a^4$. *The two necessary conditions are therefore $I=0$, $J=0$ and these give also $\Delta=0$.* If H is also zero the four roots are all equal and real.

Conditions of Stability.

286. It has been shown that the determination of the oscillation of a system can be reduced to the solution of a certain determinantal equation, which has been represented in Art. 262, by $\Delta=f(\delta)=0$. In many cases it is impracticable to solve this equation and therefore the motion cannot be properly found. If however we only wish to ascertain whether the position of equilibrium or the steady motion about which the system is in oscillation is stable or unstable we may proceed without solving the equation.

It is clear from Art. 282 that the conditions of stability are that the real roots and the real parts of the imaginary roots should all be negative. It is now proposed to investigate a method to decide whether the roots are of this character or not.

287. Taking first the case of a biquadratic; let the equation to be considered be

$$f(z) = az^4 + bz^3 + cz^2 + dz + e = 0,$$

where we have written z for δ. Let us form that symmetrical function of the roots which is the product of the sums of the roots taken two and two. If this be called X/a^3, we find*

$$X = bcd - ad^2 - eb^2 = \frac{1}{2} \begin{vmatrix} 2a & b & c \\ b & 0 & d \\ c & d & 2e \end{vmatrix}.$$

---

* The value of X may be found in several ways more or less elementary. If we substitute $z=E\pm Z$ in the given biquadratic and equate to zero the even and odd powers of Z, we have

$$aZ^4 + (6aE^2+3bE+c)Z^2 + aE^4 + bE^3 + cE^2 + dE + e = 0$$
$$(4aE+b)Z^3 + (4aE^3+3bE^2+2cE+d)Z = 0$$

Rejecting the root $Z=0$ and eliminating Z we have

$$64a^3E^6 + \ldots\ldots + bcd - ad^2 - eb^2 = 0,$$

It will be convenient to consider first the case in which X is finite. Suppose we know the roots to be imaginary, say $\alpha \pm p\sqrt{-1}$ and $\beta \pm q\sqrt{-1}$. Then

$$X/a^3 = 4\alpha\beta \left\{(\alpha+\beta)^2 + (p+q)^2\right\} \left\{(\alpha+\beta)^2 + (p-q)^2\right\}.$$

Thus, $\alpha\beta$ always takes the sign of X/a, and $\alpha+\beta$ always takes the sign of $-b/a$. The sign of both α and β can therefore be determined; and if a, b, X have the same sign, the real parts of the roots are all negative.

Suppose, next, that two of the roots are real and two imaginary. Writing $q'\sqrt{-1}$ for q, so that the roots are $\alpha \pm p\sqrt{-1}$ and $\beta \pm q'$, we find

$$X/a^3 = 4\alpha\beta \left\{[(\alpha+\beta)^2 + p^2 - q'^2]^2 + 4p^2q'^2\right\}.$$

Just as before, $\alpha\beta$ takes the sign of X/a, and $\alpha+\beta$ takes the sign of $-b/a$. Also, $\beta^2 - q'^2$ takes the sign of the last term e/a of the biquadratic. This determines whether β is numerically greater or less than q'. If, then, a, b, e, and X have the same sign, the real roots and the real parts of the imaginary roots are all negative.

Lastly, suppose the roots to be all real. Then, if all the coefficients are positive, we know, by Descartes' rule, that the roots must be all negative, and the coefficients cannot be all positive unless all the roots are negative. In this case, since X is the product of the sums of the roots taken two and two, it is clear that X/a will be positive.

Whatever the nature of the roots may be, yet if the real roots and the real parts of the imaginary roots are negative, the biquadratic must be the product of quadratic factors all whose terms are positive. It is therefore necessary for stability that every coefficient of the biquadratic should have the same sign. It is also clear that no coefficient of the equation can be zero unless either some real root is zero or two of the imaginary roots are equal and opposite.

Summing up the several results which have just been proved, we conclude that *if X and e are finite, the necessary and sufficient conditions that the real roots and the real parts of the imaginary*

---

where only the first and last terms of the equation are retained, the others not being required for our present purpose. Since $z = E \pm Z$ it is clear that each value of E is the arithmetic mean of two values of z. We have an equation of the sixth degree to find E because there are six ways of combining the four roots of the biquadratic two and two. The product of the roots of the equation in E may be deduced in the usual manner from the first and last terms, and thence the value of X is seen to be that given in the text.

If we eliminated E we should obtain an equation in Z whose roots are the arithmetic means of the differences of the roots of the given equation taken two and two. If we put $4Z^2 = \zeta$, we obtain by an easy process the equation whose roots are the squares of the differences of the roots of the given equation $f(z) = 0$.

roots should be negative are that every coefficient of the biquadratic and also X should have the same sign.

288. The case in which $X = 0$ does not present any difficulty. It follows from the definition of X, that if X vanishes two of the roots must be equal with opposite signs, and conversely if two roots are equal with opposite signs X must vanish. Writing $-z$ for z in the biquadratic and subtracting the result thus obtained from the original equation we find $bz^3 + dz = 0$. The equal and opposite roots are therefore given by $z = \pm \sqrt{-d/b}$. If b and d have opposite signs these roots are real, one being positive and one negative. If b and d have the same sign, they are a pair of imaginary roots with the real parts zero.

The sum of the other two roots is equal to $-b/a$ and their product is be/ad. We therefore conclude that, *if $X = 0$ the real roots and the real parts of the imaginary roots will be negative or zero, if every coefficient of the biquadratic is finite and has the same sign.*

289. If either a or e vanishes, the biquadratic reduces to a cubic, see note to Art. 105. Putting e zero, we have
$$X/a^3 d = bc - ad.$$

If the coefficients have all the same sign it is easy to see that it is necessary for stability that $bc - ad$ should be positive or zero.

If a and e be not zero and one of the two b, d vanish, the other must vanish also, for otherwise X could not have the same sign as a. In this case X vanishes, and the biquadratic reduces to the quadratic $\qquad az^4 + cz^2 + e = 0$.

As this equation admits of an easy solution, no difficulty can arise in practice from this case. It is necessary for stability that the roots of the quadratic should be real and negative. The conditions for this are, *firstly* the coefficients a, c, e, must all have the same sign, *secondly* that $c^2 > 4ae$.

290. **Equation of the nth degree.** When the degree of the equation is higher than a biquadratic the conditions of stability become more numerous. A very simple rule will now be proved by which these conditions can be calculated as quickly as they can be written down. Besides this we propose to give an extension of this rule by which *we may determine how many roots there are, real or imaginary, which have their real parts positive.* If there are no such roots the conditions of stability are supposed to be satisfied. The number of roots with their real parts equal to zero is also found.

291. To discover this rule we have recourse to a theorem of Cauchy. Let $z = x + y \sqrt{-1}$ be any root, and let us regard x and y as the coordinates of a point referred to rectangular axes. Substitute for z and let
$$f(z) = P + Q \sqrt{-1}.$$

Let any point whose coordinates are such that P and Q both vanish be called a radical point. Describe any contour, and let a point move round this contour in the positive direction, and notice how often P/Q passes through the value zero and changes its sign. Suppose it changes α times from $+$ to $-$ and β times from $-$ to $+$. Then Cauchy asserts that the number of radical points within the contour is $\frac{1}{2}(\alpha - \beta)$. It is however necessary that no radical point should lie on the contour.

Let us choose as our contour the infinite semicircle which bounds space on the positive side of the axis of y. Let us first travel from $y = -\infty$ to $y = +\infty$ along the circumference. If

$$f(z) = p_0 z^n + p_1 z^{n-1} + \dots + p_n \quad\dots\dots\dots\dots\dots\dots\dots(1),$$

we have, changing to polar coordinates,

$$f(z) = p_0 r^n (\cos n\theta + \sin n\theta \sqrt{-1}) + \dots$$

Hence
$$\left.\begin{array}{l} P = p_0 r^n \cos n\theta + p_1 r^{n-1} \cos (n-1)\theta + \dots \\ Q = p_0 r^n \sin n\theta + p_1 r^{n-1} \sin (n-1)\theta + \dots \end{array}\right\} \quad\dots\dots\dots\dots(2).$$

In the limit, since r is infinite, $P/Q = \cot n\theta$.

$$P/Q \text{ vanishes when } \theta = \pm\frac{1}{n}\frac{\pi}{2},\quad \pm\frac{3}{n}\frac{\pi}{2},\quad \pm\frac{5}{n}\frac{\pi}{2}\dots\dots\dots\dots(A).$$

$$P/Q \text{ is infinite when } \theta = 0,\quad \pm\frac{2}{n}\frac{\pi}{2},\quad \pm\frac{4}{n}\frac{\pi}{2}\dots\dots\dots\dots(B).$$

The values of θ in series (B), it will be noticed, *separate* those in series (A).

When θ is small and very little greater than zero, P/Q is positive and therefore changes sign from $+$ to $-$ at every one of the values of θ in series (A). If therefore n be even there will be n changes of sign.

If n be odd there will be $n-1$ changes of sign excluding $\theta = \pm\frac{1}{2}\pi$, in this case P/Q is positive when θ is a little less than $\frac{1}{2}\pi$ and negative when θ is a little greater than $\frac{1}{2}\pi$, but this result will not be wanted in the sequel.

Let us now travel along the axis of y, still in the positive direction round the contour, viz. from $y = +\infty$ to $y = -\infty$. Substituting $z = x + y\sqrt{-1}$ in (1) and remembering that $x = 0$ along the axis of y, we have, *when n is even*,

$$\left.\begin{array}{l} P = p_n - p_{n-2}y^2 + p_{n-4}y^4 - \dots + (-1)^{\frac{1}{2}n}p_0 y^n \\ Q = p_{n-1}y - p_{n-3}y^3 + \dots \quad\quad - (-1)^{\frac{1}{2}n}p_1 y^{n-1} \end{array}\right\} \quad\dots\dots\dots(3).$$

$$\therefore -\frac{P}{Q} = \frac{p_0 y^n - p_2 y^{n-2} + \dots}{p_1 y^{n-1} - p_3 y^{n-3} + \dots} \quad\dots\dots\dots\dots\dots\dots(4).$$

Let e be the excess of the number of changes of sign from $-$ to $+$ over that from $+$ to $-$ in *this* expression as we travel from $y = +\infty$ to $y = -\infty$, then by Cauchy's theorem the whole number of radical points on the positive side of the axis of y is $\frac{1}{2}(n+e)$. This of course expresses the number of roots which have their real parts positive.

292. To count these changes of sign we use Sturm's theorem. Taking

$$\left.\begin{array}{l} f_1(y) = p_0 y^n - p_2 y^{n-2} + \dots \\ f_2(y) = p_1 y^{n-1} - p_3 y^{n-3} + \dots \end{array}\right\} \quad\dots\dots\dots\dots\dots\dots(5),$$

we perform the process of finding the greatest common measure of $f_1(y)$ and $f_2(y)$, changing the sign of each remainder as it is obtained. Let the series of modified remainders thus obtained be $f_3(y)$, $f_4(y)$, &c. Then, as in Sturm's theorem, we may show that when any one of these functions vanishes the two on each side have opposite signs. It also follows that no two successive functions can vanish unless $f_1(y)$ and $f_2(y)$ have a common factor. This exception will be considered presently.

Taking then the functions $f_1(y)$, $f_2(y)$, &c., and using them as in Sturm's theorem, we see that no change of sign can be lost or gained except at *one end* of the series. Now the last is a constant and cannot change sign, hence changes of sign can be gained or lost only by the vanishing of the function $f_1(y)$ at the beginning of the series.

Consider now the beginning of the series of functions $f_1(y)$, $f_2(y)$, &c., and using them in Sturm's manner let y proceed from $+\infty$ to $-\infty$. We see that a change of sign is lost when the first two change from unlike to like signs, i.e. when the ratio of $f_1(y)$ to $f_2(y)$ changes from $-$ to $+$. In the same way a change of sign is gained when the ratio changes from $+$ to $-$. Hence e is equal to the number of variations or changes of sign lost in the series as we travel from $y = +\infty$ to $y = -\infty$.

293. When $y = \pm\infty$ we need only consider the coefficients of the highest powers in the series of functions $f_1(y)$, $f_2(y)$, &c. Let these coefficients when y is positive be called p_0, p_1, q_3, q_4,   &c.

When y is negative the signs, since n is even, will be indicated by

$$p_0, \quad -p_1, \quad q_3, \quad -q_4, \quad \text{&c.}$$

Then we have just proved that e is equal to the number of variations or changes of sign lost as we proceed from the first series to the second.

294. If every term of the series p_0, p_1, q_3, &c. have the same sign, it is evident that n changes of sign will be gained and therefore $e = -n$; and e cannot $= -n$ unless all these terms have the same sign. In this case there will be no radical point on the positive side of the axis of y. We therefore infer the following theorem. *The necessary and sufficient conditions that the real part of every root of the equation $f(z) = 0$ should be negative are that all the coefficients of the highest powers in the series $f_1(y)$, $f_2(y)$, &c. should have the same sign*.

---

* As these are the conditions of stability in dynamics (Art. 282) it is worth while to give a short summary of the argument as adapted to this special case. Putting $z = x + yi$, let $f(z) = P + Qi$. Regarding P and Q as functions of x and y, let us trace the curve $P = 0$, $Q = 0$; it is evident that each intersection corresponds to a root of $f(z) = 0$. The polar forms of these curves are given in equations (2) of Art. 291. The P curve has evidently n asymptotes whose directions are given by $\cos n\theta = 0$, the Q curve has also n asymptotes but these are given by $\sin n\theta = 0$.

We shall first show that the conditions given in Art. 294 are necessary, if there is to be no radical point on the positive side of the axis of y. Draw a circle of infinite radius, and let it cut the asymptotes of the P curve in P_1, $P_2 ... P_n$ and the asymptotes of the Q curve in Q_1, $Q_2 ... Q_n$. These points alternate with each other. Taking only those points which lie on the positive side of the axis of y, the P and Q curves may be said to begin at these infinitely distant points, and passing towards the negative side of the axis of y are not to intersect each other on the positive side of that axis. The branches of the two curves must therefore remain alternate with each other throughout the space on the positive side of the axis of y. Their points of intersection with the axis of y must also be alternate. If we put $x = 0$, in the equations $P = 0$, $Q = 0$ we have $f_1(y) = 0$, $f_2(y) = 0$, (Art. 292), and these equations must therefore be such that their roots are real and the roots of each must separate or lie between the roots of the other. It is then pointed out, in Art. 292, that the conditions that the roots of one equation should separate those of the other may practically be found by Sturm's theorem.

Conversely, we may deduce from Cauchy's theorem that the conditions given in Art. 292 are sufficient. For suppose that the intersections of the P and Q curves with the axis of y are known to be alternate. It is evident that, as we travel round the contour formed by the infinite semicircle which bounds space on the positive side of the axis of y, we pass over each P branch and each Q branch twice, crossing each in one direction on the semicircle and in the opposite direction on the axis of

295. Suppose next that these coefficients do not all have the same sign. The degree of the equation being n, there are $n+1$ functions in the series $f_1(y), f_2(y)$, &c., and therefore on the whole there are n variations and permanencies. Let there be k variations and $n-k$ permanencies of sign. Now every permanency in the series $y = +\infty$ changes into a variation in the series $y = -\infty$, and every variation into a permanency. It follows that there will be $n-k$ variations and k permanencies in this second series. Hence the number e of variations lost in proceeding from the first to the second series is $2k-n$. But the number of radical points on the positive side of the axis of y has been proved to be $= \frac{1}{2}(n+e)$; substituting for e, this becomes equal to k. We therefore infer the following theorem. *If we form the series of coefficients of the highest powers of the functions $f_1(y)$, $f_2(y)$, &c., every variation of sign implies one radical point within the positive contour, and therefore one root with its real part positive.*

296. *We require some rule to construct the series of coefficients with facility.* If we perform the process of Greatest Common Measure on the functions $f_1(y)$, $f_2(y)$ changing the signs of the remainders, we find that the first three functions are

$$f_1(y) = p_0 y^n - p_2 y^{n-2} + p_4 y^{n-4} - \&c.,$$
$$f_2(y) = p_1 y^{n-1} - p_3 y^{n-3} + p_5 y^{n-5} - \&c.,$$
$$f_3(y) = \frac{p_1 p_2 - p_0 p_3}{p_1} y^{n-2} - \frac{p_1 p_4 - p_0 p_5}{p_1} y^{n-4} + \&c.$$

Thus the *coefficients of $f_3(y)$ may be obtained from those of $f_1(y)$ and $f_2(y)$ by a simple cross-multiplication, and may therefore be written down by inspection.* The coefficients of $f_4(y)$ may be derived from those of $f_2(y)$ and $f_3(y)$ by a similar cross-multiplication, and so on. These successive functions may be called the *subsidiary functions.*

297. **First form of the Rule.** Summing up the preceding arguments, we have the following rule. The equation being

$$f(z) = p_0 z^n + p_1 z^{n-1} + p_2 z^{n-2} + \dots,$$

arrange the coefficients in two rows thus

$$\begin{array}{cccc} p_0, & p_2, & p_4, & \&c. \\ p_1, & p_3, & p_5, & \&c. \end{array}$$

Form a new row by cross-multiplication in the following manner

$$\frac{p_1 p_2 - p_0 p_3}{p_1}, \quad \frac{p_1 p_4 - p_0 p_5}{p_1}, \quad \&c.$$

Form a fourth row by operating on these two last rows by a similar cross-multiplication. Proceeding thus the number of terms in each row will gradually decrease, and we stop only when no term is left. *Then in order that there may be no roots whose real parts are positive it is necessary and sufficient that the terms in the first column should be all of one sign. If they be not all of one sign, the number of variations of sign is equal to the number of roots with their real parts positive.*

The terms which constitute the first column may be called the *test functions.*

As in forming these rows we only want their signs, we may multiply or divide any one by any positive quantity which may be convenient. We may thus often avoid complicated fractions.

298. **Equations of an odd degree.** In order to simplify the argument we have supposed the degree of the equation to be even. If n be odd, let as before

$$f(z) = p_0 z^n + p_1 z^{n-1} + \dots + p_n.$$

---

y. In Art. 293 the consequent changes of sign of P/Q are counted and it is shown that the changes of sign balance each other. It follows by Cauchy's theorem that there is no radical point within the contour.

We may regard this equation as the limit of

$$p_0 z^{n+1} + p_1 z^n + \ldots + p_n z + p_n h = 0.$$

If h be positive and indefinitely small, the additional root of this equation is real and negative, and ultimately equal to $-h$. Those roots also of the two equations which lie within the positive contour are ultimately the same.

Since $n+1$ is even we may apply to this equation the preceding rule. The two first rows are
$$p_0, \quad p_2 \ \&c., \quad p_{n-1}, \quad p_n h,$$
$$p_1, \quad p_3 \ \&c., \quad p_n.$$

We easily see by calculating a few rows that none of the coefficients in the subsequent rows contain h as a factor except the extreme coefficients on the right-hand side. Hence in the general case all the test functions, except the two last, remain finite when h is put equal to zero; and therefore have the same sign as if the rows had been calculated before the addition of the final term $p_n h$. The last two coefficients in the first column, when only the principal power of h is retained, are p_n and $p_n h$. But, since h is positive there can be no variation of sign in this sequence. We may therefore omit this final term $p_n h$ altogether as giving nothing to the number of variations of sign. The result is that the *rule to calculate the number of roots whose real parts are positive is the same whether the degree of the equation is even or odd.*

299. **Simplification of the rule when tests of stability only are required.** In a dynamical point of view it is generally more important to determine the conditions of stability than to count how many times those conditions are broken. *If we only want to discover these conditions we may in forming the successive subsidiary functions by the rule of cross-multiplication omit the divisor at every stage provided that p_0 be made positive to begin with,* for this divisor being one of the test functions must in every case be positive.

Supposing the conditions of stability to be satisfied, we see by reference to Art. 292 that the proper number of variations cannot be lost at the beginning of the series unless *the roots of the equation $f_1(y)$ are all real and the roots of $f_2(y)$ separate the roots of $f_1(y)$ and therefore are all real also.* Then, because when a subsidiary function vanishes the two on each side have opposite signs, it follows that the *roots of $f_3(y)$ are real and separate those of $f_2(y)$ and so on.*

Supposing the roots of the equation $f(z)=0$ to have their real parts negative, the real quadratic factors made up of those roots must have their terms positive. Thus every term of the equation $f(z)=0$ must be positive. It follows from the definitions of the functions $f_1(y)$ and $f_2(y)$ in Art. 292 that the signs of their terms are alternately positive and negative, and since their roots are real every one of those roots is positive. Hence all the subsequent auxiliary functions $f_3(y)$, $f_4(y)$, &c. have their roots real and positive. The signs therefore of all their terms are alternately positive and negative, and by Art. 297 the coefficient of the highest power is in every case positive.

In this way we are led to an extension of the theorem in Art. 297. Supposing p_0 to have been made positive, we see by the preceding reasoning that though it is necessary and sufficient that all the terms in the first column should be positive, yet *it is also true that the terms in every column must be positive. Hence as we perform the process indicated in that article we may stop as soon as we find any negative term,* and conclude at once that $f(z)$ has some roots with their real parts positive.

300. **Ex. 1.** Express the condition that the real roots and the real parts of the imaginary roots of the cubic $z^3 + p_1 z^2 + p_2 z + p_3 = 0$ should be all negative.

By Art. 296
$$f_1(y) = y^3 - p_2 y,$$
$$f_2(y) = p_1 y^2 - p_3.$$

Using the method of cross-multiplication given in Art. 297, and omitting the divisors as shown in Art. 299, we have

$$f_3(y) = (p_1 p_2 - p_3) y, \qquad f_4(y) = (p_1 p_2 - p_3) p_3.$$

The necessary conditions are that p_1, $p_1 p_2 - p_3$, and p_3 should be all positive.

We have retained the powers of y in order to separate the terms, and also the negative signs in the second column, but both these are unnecessary, and in accordance with Art. 297 might have been omitted. In both this and the next example all the numerical calculations are shown.

Ex. 2. Express the corresponding conditions for the biquadratic

$$z^4 + p_1 z^3 + p_2 z^2 + p_3 z + p_4 = 0,$$

$$f_1(y) = y^4 \qquad\qquad -p_2 y^2 + p_4,$$
$$f_2(y) = p_1 y^3 \qquad\qquad -p_3 y,$$
$$f_3(y) = (p_1 p_2 - p_3) y^2 \qquad -p_1 p_4,$$
$$f_4(y) = \{(p_1 p_2 - p_3) p_3 - p_1{}^2 p_4\} y,$$
$$f_5(y) = \{(p_1 p_2 - p_3) p_3 - p_1{}^2 p_4\} p_1 p_4.$$

The conditions are that p_1, $p_1 p_2 - p_3$, $(p_1 p_2 - p_3) p_3 - p_1{}^2 p_4$ and p_4 should be all positive. These are evidently equivalent to the conditions given in Art. 287.

301. Second form of the rule. When the degree of the equation is very considerable there is some labour in the application of the rule given in Art. 297. The objection is that we only want the terms in the first column and to obtain these we have to write down all the other columns. *We shall now investigate a method of obtaining each term in the first column from the one above it without the necessity of writing down any expression except the one required.*

We notice that each function is obtained from the one above it by the same process. Now the three first functions are written down in Art. 297. The first and second lines will be changed into the second and third by writing for

the values

p_0,	p_1,	p_2,	p_3,	&c.
p_1,	$p_2 - \dfrac{p_0 p_3}{p_1}$,	p_3,	$p_4 - \dfrac{p_0 p_5}{p_1}$,	&c.

......(A).

We therefore infer the following rule. *To form the test functions of Art. 297 we write down the first, viz. p_0; the second may be obtained from the first and the third from the second and so on, by changing each letter as indicated in the schedule* (A) *just above.*

In these changes we always increase the suffix, hence we may write zero for any letter as soon as its suffix becomes greater than the degree of the equation.

We thus form the test functions, each from the preceding, and we stop as soon as we have obtained the proper number, viz. (counting p_0 as one test function) one more than the degree of the equation.

302. Example. *Express the test functions for the quintic*

$$f(z) = p_0 z^5 + p_1 z^4 + p_2 z^3 + p_3 z^2 + p_4 z + p_5 = 0.$$

Here we notice that p_6, p_7, &c. are all zero, so that any term which has the factor p_5 will become zero in the next test function. Following the rule the six test functions are

$$p_0, \qquad p_1, \qquad p_2 - \frac{p_0 p_3}{p_1},$$

$$p_3 - \frac{p_1(p_1 p_4 - p_0 p_5)}{p_1 p_2 - p_0 p_3}, \qquad p_4 - \frac{p_0 p_5}{p_1} - \frac{(p_1 p_2 - p_0 p_3)^2 p_5}{p_1 p_3(p_1 p_2 - p_0 p_3) - p_1{}^2(p_1 p_4 - p_0 p_5)},$$

and lastly, p_5.

If we regard z as of one dimension in space, it is clear that the dimensions of the several coefficients p_0, p_1, &c. are indicated by their suffixes. Hence we may test the correctness of our arithmetical processes by counting the dimensions of the several terms in each of the test functions.

303. When any test function vanishes this process causes an infinite term to appear in the next function. In such a case we may replace the vanishing function by an infinitely small quantity a and then proceed as before. Thus suppose $p_1 = 0$, writing a for p_1 the six functions become p_0, a, $-p_0 p_3/a$, p_3, $p_4 - p_2 p_5/p_3 + p_0 p_5{}^2/p_3{}^2$, p_5. Consider the first four of these functions; the signs of p_0 and p_3 being given, it is easy to see by trial that there will be the same number of variations of sign whether we regard a as positive or negative. Thus, if p_0 and p_3 have the same sign, the middle terms have always opposite signs and there will be just two variations; if p_0 and p_3 have opposite signs, the middle terms are both positive or both negative and there will be just one variation.

304. **Vanishing of a subsidiary function.** In the preceding theory two reservations have been made.

1. In applying Cauchy's theorem it has been assumed that there are no radical points on the axis of y.

2. It has been assumed that P and Q have no common factor. In this case as we continue the process of finding the greatest common measure in order to construct the subsidiary functions $f_3(y)$, &c., we arrive at a function which is this greatest common measure, and the next function is absolutely zero. Thus we are warned of the presence of common factors by the absolute vanishing of one of the subsidiary functions.

It is clear that if $f(z) = 0$ have two roots which are equal and opposite, the even and odd powers of z must separately vanish. It follows from the definition in Art. 292 that $f_1(y)$ and $f_2(y)$ will have these roots common to each. The greatest common measure of $f_1(y)$ and $f_2(y)$ must therefore contain as factors all the roots of $f(z)$ which are equal and opposite. *Conversely*, the greatest common measure of $f_1(y)$ and $f_2(y)$ is necessarily a function of y which contains only even powers of y*, and if it be equated to zero, its roots are necessarily equal and opposite. These roots must obviously satisfy $f(z) = 0$.

Now if any radical point lie on the axis of y, $f(z)$ must have roots of the form $\pm k\sqrt{-1}$ and these are equal and opposite. The two reserved cases therefore are included in the one case in which $f_1(y)$ and $f_2(y)$ have common factors.

305. Let the greatest common measure of $f_1(y)$ and $f_2(y)$ be $\psi(y^2)$. If then we put $f(z) = \psi(-z^2) \phi(z)$, the function $\phi(z)$ is such that no two of its roots are equal and opposite, and to this function we may therefore apply Cauchy's theorem without fear of failure. By Art. 295, the number of roots of $\phi(z)$ which have their real parts positive is equal to the number of variations of sign in the coefficients of the highest powers of the subsidiary functions of $\phi(z)$. But, since $\psi(-z^2)$ is real when we write $z = y\sqrt{-1}$, the subsidiary functions of $\phi(z)$ become, when each is multiplied by $\psi(y^2)$, the subsidiary functions of $f(z)$. The presence of this common factor will not affect the number of variations of signs in the series. Suppose then we agree to omit the consideration of the factors of $\psi(-z^2)$, we may test the positions of the remaining radical points by discussing either of the functions $f(z)$ or $\phi(z)$.

We may therefore make the following addition to the rule given in Art. 297. *If we apply that rule, using only the subsidiary functions which do not wholly vanish, we obtain the number of roots which have their real parts positive, excluding those roots which are in pairs equal and opposite to each other.*

---

* If $p_n = 0$, we have an additional root, viz. $z = 0$, which is not included in this remark. But this root may be either divided out of the equation $f(z) = 0$, or it may be included in the following reasoning as a part of the function $\phi(z)$.

These omitted roots are of course given by equating to zero the last subsidiary function which does not wholly vanish. Putting $y \sqrt{-1} = z$, we may deduce the corresponding roots of the original equation.

It will be seen that for every pair of imaginary roots of y there will be one value of z which has its real part positive, and for every pair of real roots of y there will be two values of z of the form $\pm k \sqrt{-1}$. The former indicate an unstable, the latter a stable motion according to the rule of Art. 283.

306. Usually we may best find the nature of these roots by solving the equation formed by equating to zero the last subsidiary function. But if this be troublesome we may conveniently use Sturm's theorem. Since the powers of y in any subsidiary function decrease two at a time, we may effect Sturm's process of finding the greatest common measure exactly as described in Art. 297. We may also show by the same kind of reasoning as in Art. 295 that, for every variation of sign when $y = +\infty$ in Sturm's functions, there will be a pair of imaginary values of y. We may thus make a second addition to the rule given in Art. 297.

In forming the successive subsidiary functions, as soon as we arrive at one which wholly vanishes, we write instead of it the differential coefficients of the last which does not vanish and proceed to form the succeeding functions by the same rule as before. Every variation of sign in the first column will then indicate one root with its real part positive. The remaining roots will have their real parts negative or zero.

307. **Equal Roots.** We know by Art. 283 that whether a single root of the form $a + b \sqrt{-1}$ indicate stability or instability, several equal roots will indicate the same, except when $a = 0$. In this latter case while solitary roots of the form $\pm b \sqrt{-1}$ imply stability, several equal roots indicate instability. It is therefore generally important to determine if the roots of the latter form are repeated or not.

When the equal roots are of the first form and there happen to be no others equal and opposite to them, their number is fully counted in using Cauchy's theorem. When the equal roots are of the second form, i.e. $\pm b \sqrt{-1}$, they appear in the common factor $\psi(-z^2)$. If we can solve the equation $\psi(-z^2) = 0$, we know at once whether the repeated roots are of the first or second forms. If we analyse the equation by Sturm's theorem (Art. 306) and stop as usual at the first Sturmian function which does not vanish, we must remember that these equal roots will be counted as if they were one root. The last Sturmian function which does not vanish gives by its factors the sets of equal roots with a loss of one root in each set. If we differentiate this function and continue the process described in Art. 297, we are really applying Sturm's theorem anew to this function, and will arrive at another Sturmian function containing the sets of equal roots with a loss of two of each set. Thus by continuing the process the number of repetitions may be counted.

Numerical Examples. Ex. 1. Determine how many roots of the equation
$$z^{10} + z^9 - z^8 - 2z^7 + z^6 + 3z^5 + z^4 - 2z^3 - z^2 + z + 1 = 0$$
have their real parts positive.

Forming the first two rows by the rule of Art. 297 we have

y^{10}	1,	-1,	1,	1,	-1,	1,
y^9	1,	-2,	3,	-2,	1,	

where we have written on the left-hand side the highest power of each subsidiary function, and have omitted the negative signs given in the second, fourth and sixth columns of Art. 292. We may notice that the presence of negative terms shows that the equation indicates an unstable motion (Art. 299). Hence *if we merely wish to determine the question of stability or instability the process terminates at the first negative sign.* To illustrate the other rules we continue as follows.

Operating by the rule of Art. 297 we have

$$y^8 \qquad 1, \quad -2, \quad 3, \quad -2, \quad 1.$$

These are the same as the figures in the last line, hence the next subsidiary function will wholly vanish. Therefore $\psi(-z^2) = z^8 - 2z^6 + 3z^4 - 2z^2 + 1$. By Art. 306 we replace the next function by the differential coefficient

$$y^7 \quad \begin{cases} 8, & -12, & 12, & -4, \text{ divide by 4,} \\ 2, & -3, & 3, & -1, \end{cases}$$

$$y^6 \quad \begin{cases} -\tfrac{1}{2}, & \tfrac{3}{2}, & -\tfrac{3}{2}, & 1, \text{ multiply by 2,} \\ -1, & 3, & -3, & 2, \end{cases}$$

$$y^5 \quad \begin{cases} 3, & -3, & 3, \text{ divide by 3,} \\ 1, & -1, & 1, \end{cases}$$

$$y^4 \quad \begin{cases} 2, & -2, & 2, \text{ divide by 2,} \\ 1, & -1, & 1. \end{cases}$$

Here again the next function vanishes. There are therefore equal roots given by $z^4 - z^2 + 1 = 0$. The nature of these roots may be found by solving this equation. Disregarding this, we may (Art. 307) replace the next function by the differential coefficient

$$y^3 \quad \begin{cases} 4, & -2, \text{ divide by 2,} \\ 2, & -1, \end{cases}$$

$$y^2 \quad -1, \qquad 2, \text{ after multiplication by 2,}$$

$$y \qquad 3,$$

$$y^0 \qquad 2.$$

Looking at the first column, we see that there are four changes of sign. Hence there are four roots whose real parts are positive. We verify this by remarking that the given equation may be written in the form $(z^4 - z^2 + 1)^2 (z^2 + z + 1) = 0$. In this example we have exhibited all the numerical calculations.

Ex. 2. Show that the roots of the equations

$$z^4 + 2z^3 + z^2 + 1 = 0, \qquad z^8 + 2z^7 + 4z^6 + 4z^5 + 6z^4 + 6z^3 + 7z^2 + 4z + 2 = 0,$$

do not satisfy the conditions of stability.

Ex. 3. Show that the roots of the equations

$$z^4 + 3z^3 + 5z^2 + 4z + 2 = 0, \qquad z^6 + z^5 + 6z^4 + 5z^3 + 11z^2 + 6z + 6 = 0,$$

do satisfy the conditions of stability.

The conditions of stability given in this section are taken from the third chapter of the author's essay on *Stability of Motion*. Other methods of testing the roots of the equation $f(z) = 0$ are given in the second chapter of that essay. The conditions for a biquadratic were read before the Mathematical Society in 1874. The theory of linear differential equations with especial reference to the indeterminate case is abridged from a paper by the author in the *Proceedings of the Mathematical Society*, 1883.

Reprinted from *Proceedings of the London Mathematical Society*, **2**
(1868), pp. 60–61

W. K. CLIFFORD

Contribution to stability theory

W. K. Clifford's contribution to stability theory

The following extract is taken from *Proceedings of the London Mathematical Society* volume 2 (1866–1869), pages 60–61. It appears at the end of a paper by J. Clerk Maxwell entitled "On reciprocal diagrams in space and their relation to Airy's function of stress" which was read on 23rd January, 1868.

"Mr. J. J. Walker read a paper 'On the Anharmonic-Ratio Sextic'. The author proposed to himself in this paper the formation of the sextic which gives the six values of the anharmonic ratio of 4 points on a line. The subject has been treated by M. Painvin, 'Equation des rapports anharmoniques', (Nouvelles Annales, t. 19, 1860,)—but Mr. Walker claims to have arrived at his result by a simpler method, and to have put it in a more elegant form. In the course of discussion on this paper, Mr. Maxwell asked if any member present could point out a method of determining in what cases all the possible parts of the impossible roots of an equation are negative. In studying the motion of certain governors for regulating machinery, he had found that the stability of the motion depended on this condition, which is easily obtained for a cubic, but becomes more difficult in the higher degrees.† Mr. W. K. Clifford said that, by forming an equation whose roots are the sums of the roots of the original equation taken in pairs and determining the condition of the real roots of this equation being negative, we should obtain the condition required."

†On Governors. Proceedings of the Royal Society, March 5, 1868.

Journal de Mathématiques Pures et Appliquées, **1** (1836), pp. 290–308.
Translated by A. T. Fuller

C. STURM

**Other demonstrations of the same theorem
(Autres démonstrations du même théorème)**

Other demonstrations of the same theorem*

By C. STURM

J. de Mathématiques pures et appliquées, **1** (1836) 290–308.

Translated by A. T. FULLER

1. *Introduction***

The new demonstrations which I am going to give of the theorem of M. Cauchy derive less than the preceding demonstration* from the method which that illustrious geometer followed in his memoir; they are founded on the decomposition into factors of the function which is set equal to zero. To begin with I am going to demonstrate this theorem for an algebraic equation of arbitrary degree, whilst accepting as already known the principle that every algebraic equation has a root, whether real or complex, of the form† $a+bi$; from which it follows immediately that an equation of mth degree has m roots.

2. *Factorization*

Let the proposed equation be

$$F(z)=0,$$

$F(z)$ being a polynomial†† of degree m, in which the coefficients of the powers of z are real or complex quantities of the form $\alpha+\beta i$. Let the m roots of this equation be

$$a+bi, \ a'+b'i, \ a''+b''i, \ \ldots$$

among which some may be equal. We have immediately

$$F(z)=(z-a-bi) \ (z-a'-b'i) \ (z-a''-b''i) \ \ldots \tag{1}$$

If we replace z by $x+yi$, x and y being real variables, $F(z)$ takes the form $P+Qi$, P and Q being integral and real functions of x and y, and the preceding equation becomes

$$P+Qi=[x-a+(y-b)i][x-a'+(y-b')i] \ \ldots \tag{2}$$

---

*The preceding paper in *J. de Maths. pures et appliquées*, **1**, 278–289, was "Demonstration of a theorem of M. Cauchy, relative to the complex roots of equations", by C. Sturm and J. Liouville. (Translator's remark.)

**The original paper was not divided into sections. The section numbers and headings in the present version have been added by the translator to improve readability.

†The translator has replaced $\sqrt{-1}$ by i throughout the paper.

††Sturm used the term *fonction entière*. Originally this term was used as a synonym for polynomial (e.g. Serret 1866).

3. Complex plane

We may regard the variables x and y as coordinates of a general point M with respect to a system of rectangular axes drawn on a plane, and then the problem of finding the roots of the equation $F(z)=0$, i.e.

$$P+Qi=0,$$

reduces to finding in this plane all the points whose coordinates satisfy simultaneously the two real equations

$$P=0, \qquad Q=0.$$

Let us designate these points by K, K', K", etc. Their coordinates are a and b for point K, a' and b' for point K', etc.

Let us put

$$x-a+(y-b)i=r(\cos t+i \sin t),$$
$$x-a'+(y-b')i=r'(\cos t'+i \sin t'),$$

etc.

The product of all these factors will be, from the known formula,

$$rr'r'' \ldots [\cos(t+t'+t''+ \ldots)+i \sin(t+t'+t''+ \ldots)].$$

By virtue of equation (2), this product must equal $P+Qi$; thus

$$P=rr'r'' \ldots \cos(t+t'+t''+ \ldots),$$
$$Q=rr'r'' \ldots \sin(t+t'+t''+ \ldots),$$

and

$$\frac{P}{Q}=\cot (t+t'+t''+ \ldots).$$

The cotangent signifies here the quotient of cosine divided by sine. Because we have put $x-a+(y-b)i=r(\cos t+i \sin t)$, we have

$$x-a=r \cos t, \qquad y-b=r \sin t.$$

We see that $x-a$ and $y-b$ are the projections on the two rectangular axes of the straight line which joins the fixed point K to the general point M with coordinates x and y. Consequently r represents the length of this line, and t represents the angle between its direction and that of a line KX drawn parallel to the axis $0x$ in the direction of positive x; or rather t represents the circular arc between these lines, this arc being measured on a circle which has for centre the point K. The arc t is zero when the line KM coincides with the line KX parallel to the x-axis, and it can take arbitrary values, whether positive or negative, even greater than a circumference, if this line KM is turned indefinitely round the point K. Similarly t', t'', . . . will be the angles or circular arcs between the lines K′M, K″M, . . . and the parallels to the x-axis drawn through the points K′, K″, . . .

4. *Change of angle when a contour is traced*

We have now to determine how many of these points K, K′ K″, . . . (for which $P=0$, $Q=0$) are to be found in the interior of a closed contour ABC drawn arbitrarily on the plane x0y.

Let us consider the point M as a moving point which traces the contour ABC starting from a point A of this contour, and always going in the same direction (without reversing) until it returns to the departure point A. When point M is at A the angle or the arc t has a definite value which we designate by α; it is the value of the angle AKX. Suppose that the fixed point K is in the interior of contour ABC. When the point

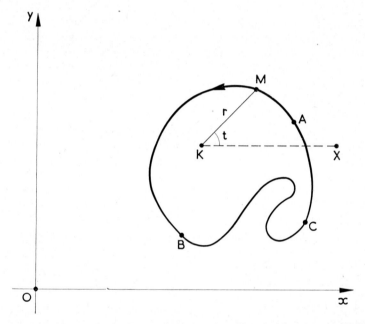

Fig. 1. Showing that t increased by 2π when K is inside contour ABC.

M traces the contour, arc t gradually changes, and can sometimes increase and sometimes decrease, perhaps by more than a circumference, depending on the form of the contour. (See Fig. 1*.) But when point M has returned to A, arc t will be found equal to its original value α augmented by a circumference. Thus we have $t=\alpha$ at the instant when

---

*No figures were used in the original paper; those given here have been added by the translator.

M leaves A, and $t=\alpha+2\pi$ when it returns to A after having traced the complete contour.

But if the point K is outside the contour ABC, the arc t, after having gradually increased and decreased alternately, will finish by taking again its original value α, at the instant when point M returns to A. (See Fig. 2.)

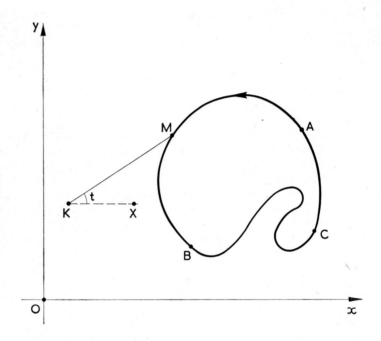

Fig. 2. Showing that the net change in t is zero when K is outside contour ABC.

The same holds for the other arcs t', t'', . . . which have for centres the points K', K'', . . .

Let us suppose that some of the points K, K', K'', . . . are situated outside the contour ABC, and the others are inside. Let μ be the number of the interior points. Let us designate by σ the sum of the values α, α', α'', . . . of the arcs t, t', t'' . . . at the instant when point M leaves point A. While point M traces contour ABC, the sum $t+t'+t''+$ . . . varies gradually, and when point M returns to A, we shall have

$$t+t'+t''+ \ldots = \sigma+2\mu\pi$$

since each of the arcs t, t', t'', . . . which has for centre an interior point must be increased by 2π, when M returns to A; whereas the arcs which have for centres exterior points take their original values.

5. Sign changes of the cotangent

For a general position of the moving point we have

$$\frac{P}{Q} = \cot\,(t+t'+t''+\ldots).$$

We shall see now that $\cot\,(t+t'+t''+\ldots)$ must vanish for different points of the contour ABC in passing from positive to negative, 2μ times more than in passing from negative to positive.

The cotangent of a variable arc vanishes (at the same time as its cosine) when this arc becomes equal to an odd multiple of $\pi/2$. In vanishing, the cotangent passes from positive to negative, or from negative to positive, according as the arc increases or decreases in becoming equal to this multiple. But the cotangent does not change sign if the arc attains this multiple without passing it. The arc $t+t'+t''+\ldots$ changing gradually during the movement of point M, will become equal (once or several times), to each of the 2μ odd multiples of $\frac{\pi}{2}$ lying between σ and $\sigma+2\mu\pi$. If we consider an arbitrary one of these multiples, the arc $t+t'+t''+\ldots$ must become equal to it in increasing once more often than in decreasing; since $t+t'+t''+\ldots$ begins by having (at the point of departure A) a value σ smaller than this multiple, and finishes by having a greater value $\sigma+2\mu\pi$ (when A is returned to). Hence $\cot\,(t+t'+t''+\ldots)$, in vanishing for this particular multiple, passes from positive to negative once more often than from negative to positive. If it happens that the variable sum $t+t'+t''+\ldots$ becomes equal to some odd multiple of $\frac{\pi}{2}$, which does not lie between σ and $\sigma+2\mu\pi$, the sum reaches this multiple in increasing as often as in decreasing; and by consequence $\cot\,(t+t'+t''+\ldots)$, in vanishing for such a multiple passes from positive to negative as often as from negative to positive.

Since the odd multiples of $\frac{\pi}{2}$ comprised between σ and $\sigma+2\mu\pi$ are 2μ in number, since $\cot\,(t+t'+t''+\ldots)$ in vanishing for each of these multiples passes from positive to negative one more time than from negative to positive; and since for an odd multiple of $\frac{\pi}{2}$ not lying between σ and $\sigma+2\mu\pi$, it passes as often from positive to negative as from negative to positive, we can conclude the following.*

cot $(t+t'+t''+\ldots)$, or the quantity P/Q which equals it, in vanishing for different points of the contour ABC, passes from positive to negative 2μ times more often than from negative to positive. This is the theorem of M. Cauchy.

*The italics in the next sentence have been introduced by the translator.

6. Improved demonstration

We can give still another demonstration, analogous to the preceding one, but in which we do not accept as already known the principle of the existence of roots. This principle, on the contrary, will become a consequence of the theorem in question. We shall even see with this new demonstration that it extends to non-algebraic equations. It is based on the propositions which follow.

7. *Change of angle determined by two real functions*

PROPOSITION 1. Let p and q be real functions of two real variables, x and y. Let us consider x and y as coordinates of an arbitrary point M with respect to a system of rectangular axes $0x$, $0y$; and suppose that each of the functions p and q has a finite, unique and definite value for every point on a contour ABC traced on the plane $x0y$ (the functions can become infinite for points situated outside or inside this contour). Let us agree also that p and q are never simultaneously zero for any point on this contour. If we consider the point M, whose coordinates are x, y, as tracing contour ABC (in the direction ABC), the quantity p/q can vanish in changing sign at different points of this contour. Let δ be the excess if the number of times when p/q in vanishing passes from positive to negative, over the number of times when p/q in vanishing passes from negative to positive (this excess δ can be a positive or negative number, or zero). If we write

$$p + qi = r(\cos t + i \sin t)$$

I assert that* *when the point M, having left the point A and traced the entire contour ABC, returns to A, the arc t after having gradually changed will be equal to the original value* α *(which it had at the point of departure A) plus* $\delta\pi$.

Proof. At the instant when the moving point M leaves point A, p and q have determined values, and when M returns to A, p and q take again these same values. Hence $\cos t$ and $\sin t$ also take again their original values. Thus α being the value of the arc t at the moment when point M leaves position A, when it returns t will be equal to this original value α, or possibly to this same value α plus or minus a multiple of the circumference. Thus on returning to point A we shall have

$$t = \alpha \pm 2k\pi$$

k being a positive integer or zero.
If we have

$$t = \alpha \pm 2k\pi,$$

t in changing gradually during the movement of M on contour ABC, will become equal, once or several times, to each of the $2k$ odd multiples

*Translator's italics.

of $\frac{\pi}{2}$ lying between α and $\alpha+2k\pi$. It will reach each of these multiples once more often in increasing than in decreasing, since this arc t to begin with (at the point of departure A) has a value α smaller than the multiple of $\frac{\pi}{2}$ in question, and finishes by having a value greater (when point M returns to A). Thus cot t, in vanishing for this multiple, will pass from positive to negative once more often than from negative to positive. If arc t becomes equal to an odd multiple of $\frac{\pi}{2}$ not contained between α and $\alpha+2k\pi$, it will reach this multiple in increasing as many times as in decreasing. Then cot t, in vanishing for this multiple, will pass from $+$ to $-$ as many times as from $-$ to $+$. We conclude that cot t or p/q, in vanishing for different points of contour ABC, will pass from positive to negative $2k$ times more than from negative to positive. Thus the number we have called δ is equal to $2k$, and we have

$$t=\alpha+\delta\pi$$

when point M returns to A.

If after having traced the entire contour, we have

$$t=\alpha-2k\pi,$$

we may prove in the same manner that cot t or p/q must vanish in passing from positive to negative $2k$ times *less* than from negative to positive. We then have $\delta=-2k$; and on returning to the point A

$$t=\alpha+\delta\pi,$$

(since $t=\alpha-2k\pi$).

If, on the return of point M to A, t takes again its original value α, cot t in vanishing passes from $+$ to $-$ as many times as from $-$ to $+$. Thus we have $\delta=0$, and on returning to point A, the formula

$$t=\alpha+\delta\pi$$

will again be satisfied.

8. Sign changes determined by a product

PROPOSITION 2. Let p, q, p', q', p'', q'' etc. be functions of the two variables x and y, each function having a unique and finite value for every point in the contour ABC. If point M whose coordinates are x and y traces contour ABC (in the direction ABC), let δ, δ', δ'', $\ldots$ respectively be the numbers which express how many times each of the quantities

$$\frac{p}{q}, \frac{p'}{q'}, \frac{p''}{q''}, \ldots,$$

in vanishing for different points of this contour, passes from positive to negative more than from negative to positive. We assume that none of these fractions p/q, p'/q', $\ldots$ becomes $0/0$ on the contour itself. If we put

$$P+Qi=(p+qi)\,(p'+q'i)\,(p''+q''i)\,\ldots$$
and
$$\Delta=\delta+\delta'+\delta''+\ldots$$
the number Δ expresses how many times more the quantity P/Q in vanishing passes from positive to negative than from negative to positive.

(Each of the numbers δ, δ', δ'', ... and Δ can be positive, negative, or zero.)

Proof. Putting
$$p+qi=r(\cos t+i\sin t),$$
$$p'+q'i=r'(\cos t'+i\sin t'),$$
etc.

we have
$$\frac{P}{Q}=\cot\,(t+t'+t''+\ldots).$$

At the instant when point M leaves point A, the arcs t, t', t'', ... have determined values α, α', α'', ... Let us designate by σ the sum $\alpha+\alpha'+\alpha''$... When point M has traced the complete contour ABC and returned to A, we have from Proposition 1:
$$t=\alpha+\delta\pi,\qquad t'=\alpha'+\delta'\pi,\qquad t''=\alpha''+\delta''\pi,\text{ etc.}$$
and consequently
$$t+t'+t''+\ldots=(\alpha+\alpha'+\alpha''+\ldots)+(\delta+\delta'+\delta''+\ldots)\pi$$
$$=\sigma+\Delta\pi.$$

We conclude, by the reasoning used before, that $\cot\,(t+t'+t''+\ldots)$, which is nothing else than P/Q, in vanishing for different points of contour ABC, passes from positive to negative Δ times more often than from negative to positive.

COROLLARY.* *If we put*
$$P+Qi=(p+qi)\,(p'+q'i)$$
and if the excess δ' which corresponds to p'/q' is zero, then
$$\Delta=\delta$$
i.e. the excess of the number of passages through zero from $+$ to $-$ over the number of passages through zero from $-$ to $+$ will be the same for p/q and for P/Q, which is here
$$\frac{pp'-qq'}{pq'+qp'}$$

This case holds in particular, when the quantity p' does not vanish on contour ABC; since then p'/q' or $\cot t'$ does not vanish on this contour, so that we have
$$\delta'=0.$$

*Translator's italics.

196

One will again have $\delta'=0$, if one assumes that p' is identically zero since then p'/q' or cot t', being identically zero, does not change sign on contour ABC. But in making $p'=0$,

$$\frac{P}{Q} \quad \text{or} \quad \frac{pp'-qq'}{pq'+qp'}$$

reduces to $-q/p$. Thus the excess δ is the same for the two quantities

$$\frac{p}{q} \text{ and } -\frac{q}{p}$$

as is easy in any case to recognize *a priori*. (See section 16).

9. Sign changes determined by points inside a contour

PROPOSITION 3.* *Let K, K', K'', . . . be points, μ in number, situated in the interior of contour ABC, and some of which may coincide. Let a and b be the coordinates of point K, a' and b' those of K', a'' and b'' those of K'', etc. If we put*

$$P+Qi=[x-a+(y-b)i]\ [x-a'+(y-b')i] \ . \ . \ .,$$

the quantity P/Q in vanishing for different points of the contour ABC passes from positive to negative 2μ times more than from negative to positive, so that for P/Q we shall have

$$\Delta=2\mu.$$

Proof. If we put

$$x-a+(y-b)i=p+qi=r(\cos t+i \sin t),$$
$$x-a'+(y-b')i=p'+q'i=r'(\cos t'+i \sin t'),$$

etc.,

$t, t', t'', . . .$ will be the angles or arcs of circles between the radius vectors KM, K'M, K''M, . . . and the parallels to the axis of x drawn through the points K, K', K'', . . . When point M has traced the entire contour and returned to A, each of these arcs becomes augmented by a circumference 2π. Therefore, because of Proposition 1, during the motion of point M, each of the quantities cot t or p/q, cot t' or p'/q', . . . passes in vanishing from positive to negative twice more than from negative to positive, so that the numbers δ, δ', δ'', . . . are all equal to $+2$. Hence for P/Q we shall have, in view of Proposition 2,

$$\Delta=\delta+\delta'+\delta''+ \ . \ . \ .=2\mu.$$

10. Functions with no zeros inside a contour

PROPOSITION 4.* *Let P and Q be real functions of the two variables x and y, each function having a finite and unique value for every pair*

*Translator's italics.

of real values of x and y. If the contour ABC does not enclose any point for which P=0 and Q=0 hold simultaneously, I assert that we shall have

$$\Delta=0$$

for P/Q, i.e. if P/Q vanishes for different points of contour ABC, P/Q will pass in vanishing from positive to negative as often as from negative to positive.

This proposition is obvious if, in the interior of contour ABC and on this contour itself, one never has $P=0$.

It is still true when, in the interior of contour ABC and on this contour itself, one never has $Q=0$. For, according to the corollary to Proposition 2, the excess Δ is the same for the two quantities P/Q and $-Q/P$. But Δ is zero for $-Q/P$, since by hypothesis Q vanishes neither on nor inside contour ABC; hence Δ is zero also for P/Q. Moreover, here is another reason. At the instant when point M leaves point A, P/Q has a determined value and sign; and when point M returns to A, P/Q takes again the same value and sign. Hence when point M traces contour ABC, P/Q can change sign only an even number of times, always in vanishing (since only P can become zero), and in passing alternately from positive to negative and from negative to positive. Thus we get

$$\Delta=0.$$

Let us now consider an arbitrary contour ABC which does not enclose any interior point for which

$$P=0, \qquad Q=0$$

hold simultaneously. We can obviously divide the area in this contour into several regions such that, for all the points situated in an arbitrary one of these regions and on the contour which is its boundary, at least one of the functions P, Q always has values different from zero and of the same sign. If the contours which bound two of these regions have a common part, we can assume that in one of these two contiguous regions, it is P which is never zero, and in the other it is Q. For, if it were the same function (P or Q) which was never zero in these two regions, we could re-unite them into a single region in which this same function would never be zero, by suppressing the common part of the two contours enclosing them. After thus suppressing these redundant separation lines, the function P will not be zero for any point common to two contiguous contours, since, as we have said, P can never be zero on one of these two contours, and Q can never be zero on the other.

This agreed, on tracing an arbitrary one of these sub-contours, the quantity P/Q does not vanish, or at least it vanishes in passing from positive to negative as many times as from negative to positive, as we have just seen. Therefore, in tracing the original fixed contour ABC which results from the suppression of all the common parts, it is clear that P/Q will again pass in vanishing from positive to negative as many times as from negative to positive, or that Δ will be zero (since P/Q does not vanish on any common part).

11. *Completion of proof of Cauchy's theorem*

It is now easy to establish the theorem of **M. Cauchy**. Let

$$F(z)=0$$

be the proposed equation, which becomes

$$P+Qi=0$$

when we put

$$z=x+yi.$$

Let μ be the number of its roots

$$a+bi,\ a'+b'i,\ a''+b''i,\ \text{etc.,}$$

corresponding to points **K, K', K''**, . . . situated in the interior of an arbitrary contour **ABC**, such that

$$P=0, \qquad Q=0$$

hold simultaneously for each of these points. Also let Δ be the excess of the number of times P/Q, in vanishing for different points of contour **ABC**, passes from positive to negative, over the number of times when P/Q, in vanishing on the same contour, passes from negative to positive. We have to prove that we always have

$$\Delta=2\mu$$

whatever the value of μ.

This theorem is immediate if μ is zero, i.e. if inside contour **ABC** there is no point for which one has

$$P=0, \qquad Q=0$$

simultaneously; for then one also has

$$\Delta=0$$

from our Proposition 4.

Suppose that the number of roots enclosed in the contour **ABC** is not zero; $F(z)$ is then divisible by the product of the μ factors $z-a-bi$, $z-a'-b'i$, etc., (among which some can be equal). In designating the quotient by $\phi(z)$, one thus has

$$F(z)=(z-a-bi)\ (z-a'-b'i)\ \ldots \times \phi(z).$$

On replacing z by $x+yi$, $F(z)$ becomes $P+Qi$; the product of the μ factors $z-a-bi$, $z-a'-b'i$, etc., becomes a quantity of the form $p+qi$; $\phi(z)$ becomes also $p'+q'i$; and we have

$$P+Qi=(p+qi)\ p'+q'i)$$

Suppose as before that the moving point **M**, of which the coordinates are x, y, traces contour **ABC** (in the direction **ABC**).

The function $\phi(z)$ or $p'+q'i$ is not zero for any point of the interior of contour ABC. Therefore, from our Proposition 4, in tracing contour ABC, we shall have

$$\delta'=0$$

for the quantity p'/q'. From Proposition 3, for p/q we shall have

$$\delta=2\mu.$$

Hence for P/Q, in view of Proposition 2,

$$\Delta=\delta+\delta'=2\mu.$$

Thus the theorem is completely proved.

It is important to note that this proof is applicable not only to a polynomial function of z which one equates to zero, but also to every function* $F(z)$ which, becoming zero for different values of z of the form $a+bi$, always gives, on being divided by $z-a-bi$ or a certain integer power of this factor, a quotient which becomes neither zero nor infinite for this value of z.

We could also modify the form of this last demonstration, by showing with the aid of our lemmas, that the theorem enunciated must be true for an equation which has μ roots enclosed in contour ABC, if it is true for an equation which has $\mu-1$ of them; after having proved (as already done in Proposition 4) that it holds when $\mu=0$.

12. *Proof that an algebraic equation of degree m has m roots*

We may deduce from the above that an algebraic equation of arbitrary degree always has as many roots as there are units in its degree.

Supposing that the equation

$$F(z)=0$$

is algebraic and of degree m, it will have the following form

$$z^m+A_1(\cos\,\alpha_1+i\,\sin\,\alpha_1)z^{m-1}+\ldots$$
$$\ldots+A_m(\cos\,\alpha_m+i\,\sin\,\alpha_m)=0. \qquad (3)$$

I assert that it will have m roots of the form $a+bi$.

Let us put

$$z=x+yi=r(\cos\,(t+i\,\sin\,t).$$

Here r is the distance of the point M (x, y) from the origin 0 and t is the angle which this straight line 0M makes with the axis of x. In designating by $P+Qi$ what $F(z)$ becomes, we find $P+Qi$ equal to

$$\cos\,mt+i\,\sin\,mt \qquad \text{multiplied by}$$
$$r^m+A_1r^{m-1}[\cos\,(\alpha_1-t)+i\,\sin\,(\alpha_1-t)]$$
$$+A_2r^{m-2}[\cos\,(\alpha_2-2t)+i\,\sin\,(\alpha_2-2t)]+\text{ etc.}$$

Let us designate by $p+qi$ the first factor

*$F(z)$ is implicitly assumed to be finite for finite z (see Proposition 4). (Translator's remark.)

200

$$\cos mt + i \sin mt$$

and by $p' + q'i$ the second factor $r^m +$ etc.

We can draw around the origin 0 a contour sufficiently large for the real part p' of this second factor to be constantly positive for all the points situated on this contour or outside. For this real part p' is

$$r^m + A_1 r^{m-1} \cos(\alpha_1 - t) + A_2 r^{m-2} \cos(\alpha_2 - 2t) + \text{etc.}$$

and we see* that it will be positive if the distance r from the origin to an arbitrary point M of contour ABC is equal to or greater than the greatest of the moduli $A_1, A_2, \ldots A_m$ augmented by unity. In assuming that this condition is satisfied, the function p' will be *a fortiori* positive for all points situated outside this contour.

The factor $p' + q'i$ thus cannot be zero for any point on the contour ABC or outside; moreover the first factor $p + qi$ or $\cos mt + i \sin mt$ is not zero for any point of the plane $x0y$. Hence $P + Qi$, which is the product of these two factors, cannot be zero for any point on or outside contour ABC. Thus all the roots of the form $a + bi$ which can belong to the proposed equation

$$F(z) = 0 \text{ or } P + Qi = 0$$

correspond to points situated inside this contour. From the general theorem the total number of these roots is equal to half the number Δ which expresses how many times more often the quantity P/Q in vanishing on this contour ABC passes from positive to negative than from negative to positive.

As we have

$$P + Qi = (p + qi)(p' + q'i)$$

the number Δ is, from our Proposition 2, the sum of the two analogous numbers, δ, δ' relative to the quantities p/q, p'/q'. But for p'/q' we have

$$\delta' = 0$$

since p' is positive for all points of the contour ABC. I assert that for p/q we have

$$\delta = 2m.$$

In fact, p/q is nothing other than $\cot mt$. But the arc t, having a determined value α at the moment when point M (which moves on contour ABC) leaves point A, becomes equal to $\alpha + 2\pi$ when this point returns to A, so that mt becomes $m\alpha + 2m\pi$. From this we conclude that

*If $\max(A_1, A_2, \ldots A_m) = B$, we have

$$\text{Re } p' \geqslant r^m - A_1 r^{m-1} - A_2 r^{m-2} - \ldots \geqslant r^m - B(r^{m-1} + r^{m-2} + \ldots)$$

$$= r^m - B\frac{r^m - 1}{r - 1} = \frac{r^m}{r-1}(r - 1 - B + Br^{-m}).$$

Hence if $r > B + 1$ we get

$$\text{Re } p' > 0.$$

(Translator's footnote.)

cot mt passes in vanishing from positive to negative $2m$ times more than from negative to positive; thus for p/q we have indeed $\delta=2m$.

Since the value of Δ relative to P/Q is equal to $\delta+\delta'$, and since we have found $\delta'=0$ and $\delta=2m$, we conclude that

$$\Delta=2m.$$

Therefore the total number of roots of the algebraic equation $F(z)=0$ is equal to its degree m (since it must equal half Δ).

13. *On a further proof of Cauchy's theorem*

The reasoning I have just used, to deduce from the theorem of M. Cauchy the proposition that every algebraic equation of mth degree has m roots, can again serve to prove (differently from the method in sections 5 and 6 of the preceding paper) that if one draws a sufficiently small contour around a point K corresponding to a single root of an arbitrary equation

$$F(z)=0$$

or a multiple root of order n, one will find on tracing this small contour,

$$\Delta=2 \text{ or } \Delta=2n.$$

In other words the quantity P/Q in vanishing on this contour will pass from positive to negative 2 or $2n$ times more than from negative to positive. Furthermore, it has been proved in our Proposition 4 and also in the preceding paper, that we always have

$$\Delta=0$$

for a contour which does not enclose roots.

This agreed, if we consider an arbitrary contour which encloses a certain number of roots, we can divide it into several contours, of which the very small ones enclose only a single root (simple or multiple) and the others do not contain any root. Then we can show as in the preceding paper, sections 7 and 8, that the theorem of M. Cauchy, holding for each of these sub-contours of the one kind or the other, must hold also for the contour formed by their reunion. I shall not insist on any advantage for this new demonstration of the theorem, which it suffices to have indicated.

14. *Cauchy's theorem for a quotient of two functions*

The following proposition is again worth noting. Let $F(z)=0$ be an equation (algebraic or not) which becomes

$$P+Qi=0$$

when we put

$$z=x+yi,$$

and which has a certain number μ of roots enclosed in the interior of the contour ABC, not having any roots on this contour itself. Let $f(z)=0$

be another equation which becomes

$$p+qi=0$$

on putting

$$z=x+yi$$

and which has v roots inside the same contour. We assume that none of the quantities P, Q, p, q can become infinite for finite values of x and of y. If we divide $P+Qi$ by $p+qi$ we shall have a quotient of the form $p'+q'i$, in which the quantities p' and q' always have finite values for all points of the contour ABC. I say that* *in tracing the contour ABC, the quantity p'/q' will pass in vanishing from positive to negative $2(\mu-v)$ times more than from negative to positive, i.e. we shall have for $p'/q'*

$$\delta'=2(\mu-v).$$

Proof. We have, according to the previous theorem,

$$\Delta=2\mu \quad \text{for} \quad \frac{P}{Q},$$

$$\delta=2v \quad \text{for} \quad \frac{p}{q},$$

and from Proposition 2 we have also

$$\Delta=\delta+\delta'.$$

From this there results

$$\delta'=2(\mu-v).$$

Thus when we know δ' and one of the two numbers of roots μ, v, we know the other. In particular we shall have

$$\delta'=0$$

if the two equations

$$F(z)=0 \text{ and } f(z)=0$$

have the same number of roots in the interior of the contour ABC; and conversely.

15. *Determination of Δ for an algebraic equation*

The problem of finding the number of roots of an equation

$$F(z)=0$$

contained in a given contour being reduced to finding the excess Δ for this contour, we are now going to give the means of determining this number Δ when the equation $F(z)=0$ is algebraic.

Suppose that the contour ABC is composed of several parts of lines AB, BC, etc. We have to determine, in tracing successively each of these parts AB, BC, . . . , the excess (positive, negative or zero) of the number of times when the quantity P/Q in vanishing passes from positive to negative over the number of times when it passes from negative to

*Translator's italics.

positive. The number Δ will be equal to the sum of all these partial excesses relative to the different parts of contour ABC. It suffices, then, to consider one of these parts AB. We can find the excess which corresponds to it, whenever the coordinates x and y of an arbitrary point of this line AB can be expressed by rational functions of a certain variable s. One uses for this purpose a method similar to that which I have given in my theorem for the determination of the number of real roots of an equation lying between two arbitrary limits.

P and Q becoming on the line AB two rational functions of the variable s, their quotient P/Q will take the form of a fraction V/V_1 in which V and V_1 are two polynomial functions of s. One performs on these two polynomials V and V_1 the operation necessary to find their greatest common factor, but taking care to change the signs of all the terms of each remainder before taking it as the divisor of the preceding remainder. Thus, supposing that the degree of V with respect to s is greater than or equal to that of V_1, one divides V by V_1 until one arrives at a remainder with a degree less than that of V_1. One changes the signs of all the terms of this remainder, and on designating it (after the change of signs) by V_2, one divides V_1 by V_2. One arrives at a new remainder $(-V_3)$. One divides in the same way V_2 by V_3, and in continuing thus one arrives finally at a last remainder V_r independent of s, or which contains s and divides exactly the preceding remainder V_{r-1}.

If one traces line AB (in the sense ABC), s will have initially at the point of departure A a certain value α; s will subsequently vary gradually and will finish by having at the point B a value β which may be greater or smaller than α. (s can in its variations sometimes increase, sometimes decrease, and need not even remain between the values α and β corresponding to the two extreme points A and B.)

This agreed,* *the excess ϵ of the number of times when the quantity V/V_1 or P/Q in vanishing for different points of the line AB passes from positive to negative, over the number of times when it passes from negative to positive, will be equal to the excess of the number of variations which are found in the sequence of signs of the functions V, V_1, ... V_r for $s=\beta$, over the number of their variations for $s=\alpha$.*

This proposition results from the following considerations. While s varies from α to β, the sequences of signs of the functions $V, V_1, \ldots V_r$ for each value of s cannot change unless one of these functions changes sign and by consequence becomes zero. When it is one of the functions intermediate between V and V_r which vanishes, one proves easily† (as

*Translator's italics.

†From their definition the V's satisfy
$$V_{i-1}(s)=D_i(s)V_i(s)-V_{i+1}(s) \quad (i=1, 2, \ldots r)$$
(with $V_0 \equiv V$ and $V_{r+1} \equiv 0$). This relation shows that if an intermediate $V_i=0$ then V_{i-1} and V_{i+1} have opposite signs. It follows that the passage of an intermediate V_i (s) through zero does not change the number of variations in sign in the sequence V_{i-1}, V_i, V_{i+1}. (Translator's footnote.)

in the proof of the theorem concerning real roots) that the number of variations in the sequence of signs of all the functions remains the same. Also, when s, in increasing or decreasing, reaches and passes a value which makes V zero, the sequence of signs gains or loses a variation or conserves the same number of variations, according as V/V_1 then passes from positive to negative, or passes from negative to positive, or does not change sign. This is true even if V and V_1 have a greatest common factor V_r which vanishes for the value of s in question; in which case all the functions V, V_1, . . . V_r vanish simultaneously. We conclude from this the validity of the proposition enunciated which holds whether or not V and V_1 have a common factor.*

16. *Remaining cases*

If V and V_1 have a greatest common factor V_r, it can happen that we have simultaneously $P=0$, $Q=0$, for a value of s which makes this greatest common factor equal zero, and which corresponds to a point on the line AB between A and B. In this case, P and Q being simultaneously zero at this point, on substituting its coordinates in the formula $x+yi$, we shall have a simple or multiple root of the equation $F(z)=0$.

If the greatest common factor of V and V_1 does not become zero at any point of the line AB between A and B, or if there is no greatest common factor, we can be certain (provided we have not suppressed in advance any common factor of P and Q) that there exists on line AB no point corresponding to a root of the equation $F(z)=0$. It is in accepting this hypothesis that we have demonstrated the theorem of M. Cauchy. The modifications which we must introduce in the case when there are roots on the contour ABC itself require a long and detailed discussion, which we have sought to avoid by omitting this special case.

We have assumed that the degree of V with respect to s is greater than or equal to that of V_1. If the degree of V is less than that of V_1, one still seeks the greatest common factor of V and V_1, in dividing first V_1 by V, then V by the remainder resulting from the first division (after having changed the signs of all the terms); and in continuing thus one forms this sequence of functions: V_1, V, V_2, V_3, . . . V_r. The difference one obtains, on subtracting the number of variations formed by their signs for $s=\alpha$ from the number of variations for $s=\beta$, expresses the excess E of the number of times when the quantity V_1/V, in vanishing on line AB, passes from positive to negative, over the number of times it passes from negative to positive. This number E being thus deter-

---

*The researches which led me to my theorem on the determination of the real roots of equations also led me to this last proposition among several others. But as I did not then see any utility for it, I did not announce it in the analysis of my memoir inserted in the *Bulletin des Sciences* of June 1829. I have made mention of it since in section 20 of the memoir printed in the *Recueil des Savans étrangers:* it admits moreover the simplification expounded in that memoir.

mined, the required excess ϵ (the number of times when the inverse quantity V/V_1, in vanishing on the same line **AB**, passes from positive to negative, over the number of times it passes from negative to positive) will be equal to

$$-E \text{ or } -E+1 \text{ or } -E-1$$

according as this quantity V/V_1 has values of the same sign for $s=\alpha$ and $s=\beta$, or it is positive for $s=\alpha$ and negative for $s=\beta$, or it is negative for $s=\alpha$ and positive for $s=\beta$.

In fact the quantity V/V_1 can change sign on line **AB** by becoming sometimes zero, sometimes infinite. The excess j of the number of times when in becoming zero or infinite it passes from positive to negative, over the number of times when it passes from negative to positive, is equal to the sum of the two numbers ϵ and E. Moreover this excess j is obviously equal to zero or $+1$ or -1, according as V/V_1 has values of the same sign for $s=\alpha$ and $s=\beta$, or V/V_1 is positive for $s=\alpha$ and negative for $s=\beta$, or it is negative for $s=\alpha$ and positive for $s=\beta$. Therefore ϵ is indeed equal to $-E$ in the first case. $-E+1$ in the second case, and $-E-1$ in the third case. This proposition holds, as one may see, even when V and V_1 are not polynomial functions of s.

17. *Contours composed of straight lines and arcs of circles*

We can always take P and Q as rational functions of one and the same variable s, when the line **AB** is a straight line, or a circle, or a circular arc.

If **AB** is a straight line, it suffices to take for s the distance of a general point of this line from a fixed point in it (or in its extension), or again one can suppose that s is simply x or y. If the straight line **AB** is parallel to the axis of x, y is constant, and one should take $s=x$; if it is parallel to the axis of y, x is constant, and one takes $s=y$.

If line **AB** is a circle or arc of a circle whose radius is R and whose centre has coordinates g and h, we put

$$x=g+R \cos t, \qquad y=h+R \sin t$$

and we take

$$s=\tan \tfrac{1}{2}t.$$

Then we have

$$x=g+R\frac{1-s^2}{1+s^2}, \qquad y=h+R\frac{2s}{1+s^2}$$

and P and Q will be rational functions of this new variable s, such that P/Q will take the form V/V_1, V and V_1 being polynomial functions of s.

In practice, what is most simple is to seek by the preceding method the roots contained in rectangles with sides parallel to the axes. We then vary only one (at a time) of the coordinates x and y appearing in P and Q, which are polynomial functions of x and y. We shorten the calculation by supposing to begin with that the two sides of the rectangle which are parallel to one of the axes are situated at infinite distances from this axis. For then, on tracing these sides, for which we have y (or x) $=-\infty$ and $+\infty$, the quantity P/Q will not vanish or will vanish only once, and we can easily see whether in vanishing it passes from positive to negative or from negative to positive.

We can then determine approximately the real and imaginary parts of roots represented by $x+yi$. We can then obtain more exact values for these roots by the usual methods of approximation.

18. *Number of roots with real (or imaginary) parts greater than a given value**

In practice one can further make use of the following proposition, for which one can give a proof similar to the first proof of the present article. Let

$$F(z)=0$$

be an algebraic equation of form (3), which becomes

$$P+Qi=0$$

on putting

$$z=x+yi.$$

If we give to y in P and Q a fixed positive or negative value h and if we let x increase from $-\infty$ to $+\infty$, *the excess of the number of times when P/Q, in vanishing, passes from positive to negative, over the number of times when P/Q, in vanishing, passes from negative to positive, will be equal to the excess of the number of roots $x+yi$ of the equation $F(z)=0$ for which y is greater than h, over the number of roots for which y is less than h.*

The degree m of the equation $F(z)=0$ being even, if we give to x in P and Q a fixed value g, and if we let y increase from $-\infty$ to $+\infty$, *the excess of the number of times when P/Q, in vanishing, passes from positive to negative, over the number of times when P/Q passes from negative to positive, will be equal to the excess of the number of roots of the equation $F(z)=0$ for which the real part x is less than g, over the number of the roots for which x is greater than g.*

The degree m being odd, if we set $x=g$ in P and Q, and if we let y increase from $-\infty$ to $+\infty$, *the excess of the number of times when the quantity $(-Q/P)$ in vanishing passes from positive to negative, over the number of times when it passes from negative to positive, will again be equal to the excess of the number of roots of $F(z)=0$ for which x is less than g, over the number of roots for which x is greater than g.*

*The italics in this section have been introduced by the translator.

Reprinted from *Bulletin of the American Mathematical Society,* **18** (1911), pp. 1–18

M. BÔCHER

The published and unpublished work of Charles Sturm on algebraic and differential equations

THE PUBLISHED AND UNPUBLISHED WORK OF CHARLES STURM ON ALGEBRAIC AND DIFFERENTIAL EQUATIONS.

PRESIDENTIAL ADDRESS DELIVERED BEFORE THE AMERICAN MATHEMATICAL SOCIETY, APRIL 28, 1911.

BY PRESIDENT MAXIME BÔCHER.

CHARLES Sturm was born in 1803 at Geneva, then a part of France, and went to Paris at about the age of twenty-one. There he spent the rest of his life and died in 1855, having become a member of the French Academy of Sciences in 1836.

It is not necessary for us to go beyond this bare outline of Sturm's life, since it is not with his worldly fortunes that we shall be concerned. Neither do I propose to give an account of his life-work as a whole.* The brief biography and bibliography prefixed to his posthumous Cours d'Analyse fulfills to some extent both of these purposes. We shall confine ourselves to one branch of investigation pursued by Sturm: the study of the real solutions of algebraic equations and of linear differential equations, both ordinary and partial. It was here that Sturm's most important and suggestive work was done, and it is of interest to try to gain some insight into the relations between the various parts of the subject as they appeared to him.

The papers with which we are concerned may be exhibited in the following table:

---

* In brief we may say that, besides the investigations with which we shall be concerned, Sturm published

(a) An experimental memoir in collaboration with Colladon on the compressibility of liquids.

(b) A large number of minor papers, mostly geometrical.

(c) Several papers on geometrical optics including a long memoir.

(d) Some papers, partly in collaboration with Liouville, on the imaginary roots of equations, which are not without connection with Sturm's work on the real roots of algebraic equations.

THE PAPERS OF 1829, presented to the Academy on the dates given and summarised, as indicated, in the *Bulletin de Férussac:*

May 23. "Sur la résolution des équations numériques." Volume 11, pages 419–422, and volume 12, page 318, footnote.

June 1. No title given. Volume 11, pages 422–424, and volume 12, page 318, footnote. The subject of this memoir is the equation $Ax^a + Bx^\beta + \cdots + Mx^\mu = 0$, where $\alpha, \beta, \ldots, \mu$ are real but not necessarily rational.

June 8. Note. Volume 11, page 425. It is merely stated that this note contains (1) two new proofs of the reality of the roots of the transcendental equations to which the solution of various problems in mathematical physics leads; (2) the general determination of the constant coefficients in the series for representing an arbitrary function between given limits.

July 27. "Sur l'intégration d'un système d'équations différentielles linéaires." Volume 12, pages 314–322.

August 3. "Sur la distribution de la chaleur dans un assemblage de vases." Volume 12, page 322. Nothing but the title of this paper is preserved.

October 19. "Nouvelle théorie relative à une classe de fonctions transcendantes que l'on rencontre dans la résolution des problèmes de la physique mathématique." Volume 12, page 322. Nothing but the title of this paper is preserved unless, as is possible, a brief statement in volume 11, pages 424–425, refers to it.

THE THREE GREAT MEMOIRS.

1835. "Mémoire sur la résolution des équations numériques." *Mémoires des savants étrangers,* volume 6, pages 271–318.

1836. "Mémoire sur les équations différentielles linéaires du second ordre." *Liouville's Journal,* volume 1, pages 106–186. This memoir had been presented to the Academy September 30, 1833, and an abstract of it published in *l'Institut* for November 9, 1833, pages 219–223.

1836. "Mémoire sur une classe d'équations à différences partielles." *Liouville's Journal,* volume 1, pages 373–444. Cf. *l'Institut* for November 30, 1833, pages 247–248.

For the sake of completeness we note that there are also three minor papers of later date.*

It is in the three great memoirs of 1835–36 that Sturm gave its final form to so much of his work as he completed; but the above list strongly suggests, what a closer study amply confirms, that it was in the year 1829 that the great creative period of Sturm's life fell, and that the papers presented to the Academy in that year, so far as they are still accessible, must be examined if we would gain an insight into the lines of thought followed by him in making his great discoveries. In doing this we shall find that certain not uninteresting aspects of his early work find little or no mention in the great memoirs. Most of this early work is preserved to us only in the form of brief abstracts, sometimes even only by ts title, so that some reconstruction becomes necessary. This makes it impossible for us to attain certainty at all points, but perhaps the discussion is not less interesting for this reason.

Sturm's personal and scientific relations to Fourier form an indispensable background to a consideration of the papers presented to the Academy in such rapid succession during the summer of that fruitful year. The two main subjects of Fourier's life work had been the theory of heat and the theory of the solutions of numerical equations. Both of these subjects were carried forward by Sturm, the first in the two memoirs of 1836, the second in that of 1835. But if in the memoirs these tendencies appear quite distinct, we find them, when we turn to the papers of 1829, blended in a most curious and interesting manner.

Fourier's treatise on the solution of numerical equations was not published until 1831, after the author's death; but the manuscript of this work had already in 1829 been communicated to several persons among whom was Sturm, who tells us explicitly in the paper of May 23 what a strong influence it had on his own work.

Fourier had established the theorem that a real algebraic equation of the kth degree, $f(x) = 0$, cannot have more roots in an interval ab, neither of whose extremities is a root, than the difference between the number of variations of sign in the

---

* Namely: a brief extract of a memoir written by Sturm and Liouville together: "Sur le développement des fonctions en séries . . . ," published in *Liouville's Journal*, vol. 2 (1837), pp. 220–223, and also in the *C. R.*, vol. 4, p. 675; and two papers concerning the real roots of algebraic equations in *Liouville's Journal*, vol. 7 (1842), pp. 132–133, 356–368.

set of functions

$$(1) \qquad f(x),\ f'(x),\ f''(x),\ \ldots,\ f^{[k]}(x),$$

(accents denoting differentiation) at the points a and b. Sturm's theorem, as it is still called, replaces the sequence (1) by

$$(2) \qquad f_0(x),\ f_1(x),\ f_2(x),\ \ldots,$$

which coincides with (1) in the first two places, while each subsequent f_n is the negative of the remainder obtained by dividing f_{n-2} by f_{n-1},

$$(3) \qquad f_{n-2}(x) = q_{n-1}(x)f_{n-1}(x) - f_n(x) \quad (n = 2, 3, \ldots).$$

The advantage of this set over the set (1) is that the difference in the number of variations in (2) at a and b is *precisely equal* to the number of roots between a and b. Since this theorem is given in the first of the notes of 1829 and is elaborated at length in the first of the great memoirs, one might be tempted to suppose that this formed the starting point in Sturm's researches. Fortunately Sturm himself has preserved us from this mistake, for on the closing page of the first memoir of 1836 he tells us that the above theorem was merely a by-product of his extensive investigations on the subject of linear difference equations of the second order. Curiously enough, however, this subject of difference equations is nowhere else alluded to in Sturm's published writings.

The key to this difficulty lies, I feel sure, in the paper of August 3, 1829, of which as has been said only the title is preserved. This memoir is described as more extensive than the one of July 27, which, as one sees from the summary, was not brief. At Sturm's death there was found among his papers a "very extensive" memoir with almost precisely the same title,* which has also never been published. I shall try to show you how this lost paper forms the starting point in Sturm's investigations, and how all his other work which concerns us here grew directly out of it. For this purpose we must first reconstruct at least the general framework of this paper.

"Sur la communication de la chaleur dans une suite de vases." Cf. Cours d'Analyse, vol. 1, p. xxviii. It is there said: "Ces deux mémoires" (*i. e.*, this one and one on curves of the second order) "sont en état d'être imprimés, et M. Liouville a bien voulu se charger de leur publication." It is to be regretted that this intention was never carried out. Even at this late date the publication would be decidedly interesting if by chance the manuscript could still be found.

Suppose we have a number of vases $P_0, P_1, \ldots, P_n$ placed in any position with reference to one another and filled with various liquids at diverse temperatures. These vases we suppose to be immersed in an atmosphere which circulates freely and thus maintains a constant temperature which we take as the zero of our scale. Each of these vases radiates heat into this atmosphere, and the vases also interchange heat among themselves by radiation. Let us denote the temperature of the vase P_i at the time t by $u(i, t)$. The differential equation for the flow of heat is then, if we assume the Newtonian law of radiation,

$$(4) \qquad c(i) \frac{\partial u(i, t)}{\partial t} = k(i, 0)u(0, t) + \cdots + k(i, n)u(n, t)$$

$$(i = 0, 1, \ldots, n).$$

Here $c(i)$ is a positive constant depending on the specific heat of the vase P_i; when $i \neq j$, $k(i, j) = k(j, i)$ is a positive constant of proportionality which measures the amount of radiation between P_i and P_j; and finally $k(i, i)$ is written merely as an abbreviation for

$$k(i, i) = -h(i) - k(i, 0) - \cdots - k(i, i - 1)$$
$$- k(i, i + 1) - \cdots - k(i, n),$$

where $h(i)$ is a positive constant of proportionality for measuring the radiation of P_i into the atmosphere. It is important for us to understand that the constant $k(i, j)$, when $i \neq j$, depends for its value not merely on the relative positions and the sizes and shapes of the vases P_i and P_j, but that its value is also decreased if one or more of the other vases is so placed as to cut off part of the radiation from P_i to P_j. If these vases are *completely* cut off from each other by intervening vases, the constant $k(i, j)$ has the value zero.

I suspect that it was precisely to the problem just indicated and in particular to the system of equations (4) that Sturm first turned his attention. There is, however, evidence (cf. the paper of July 27) that he had also under consideration problems in small vibrations and in celestial mechanics leading to systems of differential equations analogous to (4) but which may be somewhat more general in form. The paper last cited was devoted to the analytical treatment of such systems of linear homogeneous differential equations with constant coefficients. As the chief result is a method of treating the algebraic *characteristic equation* of the system, we postpone any discussion of this paper until later.

It is not, however, in more general, but rather in more special problems that Sturm found his real inspiration. Consider the case in which the vases $P_0, \ldots, P_n$ are arranged in linear sequence* and in such a way that the radiation between two non-consecutive vases is completely cut off by the intervening ones. This case is characterised analytically by all the constants $k(i, j)$ vanishing except those for which the integers i, j are either equal or differ from one another by unity. We may then write equations (4) as follows:

$$c(0) \frac{\partial u(0, t)}{\partial t} = - [h(0) + k(0, 1)]u(0, t) + k(0, 1)u(1, t),$$

$$c(i) \frac{\partial u(i, t)}{\partial t} = k(i, i - 1)u(i - 1, t) - [h(i) + k(i, i - 1)$$

(5) $$+ k(i, i + 1)]u(i, t) + k(i, i + 1)u(i + 1, t)$$

$$(i = 1, 2, \ldots, n - 1),$$

$$c(n) \frac{\partial u(n, t)}{\partial t} = k(n, n - 1)u(n - 1, t)$$

$$- [h(n) + k(n, n - 1)]u(n, t).$$

By the side of the problem in the theory of heat which we have just formulated we may advantageously consider the problem of the small transverse vibrations of a stretched elastic string whose mass is negligible but which is weighted at a number of points by heavy particles. This problem had first been considered one hundred years earlier by John Bernoulli, and for half a century this and equivalent problems had been, in more or less general forms, subjects of investigation by Daniel Bernoulli, Euler, and Lagrange;† but none of these mathematicians had gone beyond the case where the particles

---

* It is interesting to note that in the title of the manuscript found at the time of Sturm's death, and which may be supposed to be the final form which his memoir took, the phrase "une suite de vases" is used in place of the earlier "un assemblage de vases." This change suggests that as his work developed Sturm desired to give more prominence to this special case; or, indeed, he may have eliminated all consideration of the more general case.

† Cf. Burkhardt's Report in the *Jahresbericht d. deutschen Mathematiker-Vereinigung*, vol. 10 (1901–1908).

are of equal mass and are equally spaced,* and for fifty years the problem had practically remained untouched.

Suppose that the string in its position of equilibrium lies along the axis of x and that particles $P_0, \ldots, P_n$ with masses $c(0), \ldots, c(n)$ lie respectively at the points whose abscissas are $x_0 < x_1 < \cdots < x_n$, and let P_0 and P_n be at the ends of the string. In order to secure the same degree of generality as in the heat problem above mentioned, we assume that during the transverse vibration each particle is drawn back towards its position of equilibrium not merely by the tension of the string but also by an additional force acting towards its position of equilibrium and proportional to the distance from this point. The constant of proportionality here we denote by $h(i)$ in the case of the ith particle, and, calling the tension of the string T, we let

$$k(i, i - 1) = \frac{T}{x_i - x_{i-1}}.$$

The distance of P_i from its position of equilibrium at the time t we denote by $u(i, t)$, and we assume that each particle is free to move only in a direction at right angles to the axis of x, and that the whole motion takes place in one plane. Finally we assume that the string always remains so nearly straight that the squares of the sines or tangents of the angles which its pieces make with the axis of x may be neglected.† Then it is readily seen that the equations of motion of the particles become identical with equations (5) *provided we replace the first derivatives in these equations by second derivatives.* It follows that the mechanical problem last mentioned is mathematically almost equivalent to the problem in the theory of heat considered above. That Sturm chose the latter rather than the former, with which he was surely familiar, is, so far as the greater part of his work goes,‡ a matter of slight importance and is prob-

---

* In all the cases treated during the eighteenth century the particles are either supposed to be acted upon by no external forces, or to be under the influence of gravity acting in the direction of the string. The presence of such an external constant force as this is mathematically equivalent to an unequal spacing of the particles, and will therefore not be explicitly considered by us.

† It should be noticed that we do not assume the ends of the string to be fixed. If we did this, we should have a case strictly analogous to that in which the two extreme vases, P_0 and P_n, in the heat problem are maintained at the temperature zero.

‡ An essential difference occurs only in the work which leads up to the latter part of the second memoir of 1836.

ably to be explained by the fact that the theory of heat was at that moment a more "up to date" subject. The relation between the two problems is however so close that we may be permitted to depart so far from strict historical accuracy as to substitute the vibration problem for the heat problem in our further explanations, since in this way greater concreteness of expression may be gained.

We consider first the simple harmonic vibrations of the string, that is we assume that u has the form

$$(6) \qquad u(i, t) = y(i) \, [A \sin \mu t + B \cos \mu t].$$

By substituting this expression in the equations of motion we find for $y(i)$ the difference equation of the second order

$$(7) \qquad \begin{aligned} k(i, i-1)y(i-1) - [h(i) + k(i, i-1) + k(i, i+1) \\ - \mu^2 c(i)] \, y(i) + k(i, i+1)y(i+1) = 0 \end{aligned}$$

or

$$(7') \qquad \Delta\{k(i, i-1)\Delta y(i-1)\} + [\mu^2 c(i) - h(i)]y(i) = 0$$

together with the terminal conditions

$$(8) \qquad k(1, 0)y(1) + [\mu^2 c(0) - h(0) - k(1, 0)]y(0) = 0,$$

$$(9) \quad [\mu^2 c(n) - h(n) - k(n, n-1)]y(n) + k(n, n-1)y(n-1) = 0.$$

The equation (7) has in general no solution other than zero which satisfies both conditions (8) and (9),—it is only for special values of μ that these conditions can both be fulfilled. Consequently we shall disregard at first condition (9), and consider merely the solution of (7) which satisfies (8). This solution obviously contains an arbitrary constant factor, since (7) and (8) are homogeneous. We therefore replace the condition (8) by the two non-homogeneous conditions

$$(8') \qquad \begin{aligned} y(0) &= k(0, 1), \\ y(1) &= h(0) + k(0, 1) - \mu^2 c(0), \end{aligned}$$

which are precisely equivalent to (8) except that (8') also determines the otherwise arbitrary constant factor, and determines it in such a way that $y(i)$ does not vanish identically.

The solution $y(i)$ determined by (8') does not in general satisfy

(9). It does, however, for a specified value of μ either satisfy the condition $y(n) = 0$, or a condition of precisely the form (9) where either $c(n)$ or $h(n)$ have in general been replaced by another value.* We may therefore say that for every value of μ the function $u(i, t)$ defined by (6) gives a simple harmonic vibration corresponding either to the mechanical problem we wish to consider or to a modification of this problem which consists either in having the particle P_n held fast, or in a change in the mass of this particle, or in a change in the strength of the force which pulls this particle back to its position of equilibrium. This we shall speak of as the modified problem corresponding to a given value of μ, using this term so that, for the special values of μ above referred to, the original problem itself is the modified problem.

In the plane in which the vibration takes place let us now construct an ordinate of length $y(i)$ at each of the points x_i and connect the extremities of each two successive ordinates by a straight line. The broken line thus formed, which we shall call the line $y(i)$, gives essentially the shape of the string in the simple harmonic vibration we are considering; for, if we multiply by $A \sin \mu t + B \cos \mu t$ all the ordinates of this broken line, and this will evidently not essentially affect its shape, we get a broken line which has precisely the shape of the string at the time t. The points where the line $y(i)$ meets the axis of x thus give the *nodes* of the simple harmonic vibration in question. Either from simple mechanical considerations or from the equation (7) we see that at each node the line $y(i)$ crosses the axis. Consequently, since each of the quantities $y(0)$, $y(1)$, $\cdots$, $y(n)$ is obviously a continuous function of μ (in fact a polynomial in μ^2), the nodes also vary continuously with μ, never suddenly appearing or disappearing except at the extremity x_n of the string.

There can be very little doubt that at this point Sturm, by a simple manipulation of equation (7') which we will not stop to give here†, established the important fact, which may easily

---

* This is true even in the case $\mu = 0$ provided we replace $h(n)$ by a negative quantity. In all other cases positive quantities may be used in place of $c(n)$ and $h(n)$.

† Cf. Porter, *Annals of Mathematics*, second series, vol. 3 (1902), p. 55. In the article here cited Professor Porter, at my suggestion, reconstructed a part of Sturm's researches on difference equations without, however, considering either the vibration problem or the heat problem. Cf. also the article by Professor Porter's pupil, Miss Merrill, *Trans. Amer. Math. Soc.*, vol. 4 (1903), p. 423.

have been suggested to him by the mechanical problem itself, that as μ^2 increases the abscissa of each node decreases, new nodes appearing one by one at the point x_n.

It is here that Sturm must have noticed the connection with Fourier's theorem concerning the roots of algebraic equations. To establish this connection we need merely to observe that the number of nodes for a given value of μ^2 (we shall write for convenience $\lambda = -\mu^2$) is simply the number of variations of sign in the set of polynomials in λ

$$(10) \qquad\qquad y(n),\, y(n-1),\, \cdots,\, y(0).$$

Consequently what we have said above is equivalent to saying that the number of roots of the polynomial $y(n)$ between two negative values of λ is precisely equal to the difference between the number of variations in the system (10) for these two values of λ. Sturm found, therefore, that for the particular polynomial $y(n)$ he was in possession of a sequence of polynomials of descending degrees (since $y(i)$ is a polynomial of the ith degree in λ), which served *perfectly* the purpose which the sequence of derivatives serves imperfectly in Fourier's theorem. He must then have asked himself to what properties of the polynomials (10) this fact is due, and have seen that just three properties were used:

(a) The last polynomial, $y(0)$, is a constant not zero.

(b) When one polynomial vanishes the two adjacent ones have opposite signs. This was an immediate consequence of (7), but would follow in the same way if instead of (7) the y's satisfied any difference equation

$$(11) \qquad L(i)y(i+1) + M(i)y(i) + N(i)y(i-1) = 0,$$

where L and N always have the same sign.

(c) The nodes increase with λ. Far less than this, however, would be sufficient for our present purpose, namely that when a node lies at x_n it decrease as λ decreases. This would in particular be the case if $y(n)$ had no multiple root and $y(n-1)$ were simply the derivative of $y(n)$, for this is precisely the property of the derivative on which Fourier's work is based.

We may then suppose that Sturm said to himself: Starting with any polynomial without multiple roots, $f(\lambda)$, in place of $y(n)$, and taking in place of $y(n-1)$ the derivative $f'(\lambda)$, how can I form a sequence of polynomials $f_2(\lambda)$, $f_3(\lambda)$, $\ldots$, to take the place of $y(n-2)$, $y(n-3)$, $\ldots$, which satisfy a relation of the form (11) and of which the last is a constant not zero? This question once formulated, the method of successive divisions and reversal of sign of the remainder, leading to equation (3) which is merely a special case of (11), would readily suggest itself, and Sturm's theorem in its most familiar form was found.

If our surmises so far are correct, it follows that, even at this early date Sturm must have been well aware that any sequence of functions having a small number of easily specified properties would serve the purpose of his theorem just as well as the sequence (2); so that to call such more general sequences Sturmian sequences, as is now done,* is even from a strictly historical point of view entirely suitable. Our belief that Sturm was familiar with this more general point of view need not, however, rest entirely on the line of reasoning so far explained. Not only does he show in his memoir of 1835 how other Sturmian sequences besides (2) may be formed;† but more particularly his paper of July 27, 1829, to which reference has already been made, is mainly devoted to the formation for a special algebraic equation of a Sturmian sequence which is very different from the sequence (2). If we use the notation of determinants, which Sturm does not use, the equation in question is

$$(12) \qquad \begin{vmatrix} g_{11}\lambda + k_{11} & g_{12}\lambda + k_{12} & \cdots & g_{1n}\lambda + k_{1n} \\ g_{21}\lambda + k_{21} & g_{22}\lambda + k_{22} & \cdots & g_{2n}\lambda + k_{2n} \\ \cdots\cdots\cdots\cdots\cdots\cdots\cdots\cdots\cdots\cdots\cdots \\ g_{n1}\lambda + k_{n1} & g_{n2}\lambda + k_{n2} & \cdots & g_{nn}\lambda + k_{nn} \end{vmatrix} = 0,$$

where $g_{ij} = g_{ji}$, $k_{ij} = k_{ji}$, and where the g's and k's are real and the former are the coefficients of a non-singular definite quadratic form. Sturm falls here into the error into which Laplace and Lagrange had fallen before him, and which was first corrected by Weierstrass in 1858, of thinking that this equation can have no multiple roots. He gives, however, the correct theorem that the roots are all real; and, what is important for us here, he states that the determinant in (12) and the polynomials obtained by striking off from it the last 1, 2, 3, $\cdots$ rows and columns form

---

* Cf. Weber's Algebra, 2 ed., vol. 1, p. 303.
† Cf. also the closing lines of his abstract of May 23, 1829.

a Sturmian sequence,* provided each of these polynomials is multiplied by such a power of -1 as to make the coefficient of its leading term positive.†

The paper of May 23, 1829, subsequently published as the memoir of 1835, did more than all of his other papers together to win for its author recognition both in France and throughout Europe. It appears to us here in its true light,‡ as a digression from his investigations in the domain of mechanics and mathematical physics. This digression was indeed carried a little farther, as the paper of June 1 testifies. Here it is shown how Fourier's methods can be applied with very slight change to obtain an upper limit for the number of real roots in a given interval for the type of transcendental equation there considered. It is clear, moreover, from a brief remark near the middle of page 424 that Sturm was here also in possession of a method of forming a Sturmian sequence.

Let us now return to the problem of the vibrating string which we were considering above. We saw that as μ^2 increases the abscissa of each node decreases. Now from (8′) and (7′) it may readily be inferred that when $\mu = 0$,

$$0 < y(1) < y(2) < \cdots < y(n),$$

so that here there is no node. On the other hand from (8′) and (7) we see that $y(i)$ is a polynomial of the ith degree in μ^2 whose leading coefficient has the sign of $(-1)^i$. Consequently, for very large values of μ^2 we have a node in each of the intervals

$$x_i < x < x_{i+1}, \qquad (i = 0, 1, \cdots, n),$$

that is, we have the maximum possible number of nodes, namely n. Accordingly as μ^2, starting with the value zero, increases, we have at first no node, then for a while one node,

---

* This is true only with the qualification that no two of these polynomials have a common root; cf. Weber's Algebra, 2 ed., vol. 1, p. 308. This necessary qualification is not mentioned in Sturm's abstract, though it is by no means impossible that it may have been given in the extended memoir.

† In other words, these factors are all $+1$ or alternately $+1$ and -1 according as the quadratic form of which the g's are the coefficients is positive or negative.

‡ There are further details elaborated in this memoir to which it is not necessary for us to refer.

then for a certain interval two nodes, etc., until finally the nth node appears at x_n and from that point on we constantly have n nodes. We thus see that there are just n positive values of μ^2, for which a node lies at x_n, that is, that the equation in μ^2, $y(n) = 0$, has n distinct positive roots, and consequently, since it is of the nth degree, that it has no imaginary or negative or multiple roots. If we denote the roots arranged in order of increasing magnitude by $\mu'^2, \mu''^2, \cdots, \mu^{[n]2}$ it is clear from what has been said that for positive values of μ^2 $y(i)$ has just k nodes $(k \leqq n)$ in the interval $x_0 < x < x_n$ when and only when $\mu^{[k]2} < \mu^2 < \mu^{[k+1]2}$, where, for convenience, we let $\mu^{[0]} = 0$, $\mu^{[n+1]} = +\infty$.

The next step is to show that in this interval there exists one and only one value of μ^2 for which $y(i)$ satisfies the condition (9), and this follows readily from the fact* that, when $y(n) \neq 0$, $y(n - 1)/y(n)$ increases as μ^2 increases, and hence increases from $-\infty$ to $+\infty$ as μ^2 increases through the interval we are now considering. This establishes the following:

THEOREM OF OSCILLATION.† There exist just $n + 1$ values of μ^2, all real and positive, for which the difference equation (7) has a solution, not identically zero, which satisfies the terminal conditions (8), (9). Denoting these values, arranged in order of increasing magnitude, by $\mu_0^2, \mu_1^2, \cdots, \mu_n^2$, the solution $y_k(i)$ of (7) corresponding to μ_k^2 and satisfying (8), (9) has exactly k nodes.

We obtain in this way $n + 1$ simple harmonic vibrations of the weighted string, which differ from one another in the number of their nodes. The most general motion of the string will be obtained by compounding these simple harmonic vibrations. Here the formulæ, which are readily obtained, for making the vibration correspond to arbitrarily given initial conditions are closely analogous to the well known ones for the representation of periodic functions at n equally spaced points by a finite trigonometric series. These latter formulæ had been obtained by Lagrange in considering a special case of the vibration problem with which we have been concerned.

In precisely the same way, the problem of the distribution of

---

* Cf. Porter, loc. cit. This fact is also necessary in the proof, referred to above, that the nodes decrease as μ^2 increases.

† See the articles by Porter and Miss Merrill above cited. This theorem, never published by Sturm, is the prototype of the important and still increasing class of theorems to which Klein attached this name more than fifty years later.

heat in a row of vases is solved by the formula

$$(13) \qquad A_0 e^{-\lambda_0 t} y_0(i) + A_1 e^{-\lambda_1 t} y_1(i) + \cdots + A_n e^{-\lambda_n t} y_n(i),$$

where $\lambda_k = -\mu_k^2$. Here also the coefficients A_k can be determined so as to correspond with given initial conditions. It was, however, not merely the analytic solution of this problem which interested Sturm, but even more, perhaps, a discussion of the properties of the solution.

If we mark the vases at any moment $+$ or $-$ according as their temperatures are above or below the temperature of the surrounding atmosphere, it is obvious from physical considerations that as time passes the number of variations of sign in the sequence cannot increase. This fact may be established analytically by means of the equations (5) of which the function (13) is a solution, and at the same time we can see precisely how the number of variations decreases. For a fixed value of t we plot the function (13) as a broken line, precisely as above we plotted the line $y(i)$. This line, however, unlike the line $y(i)$, does not necessarily cross the axis of x at every point where it meets it; indeed it may meet the axis of x not merely at isolated points but it may also coincide with it throughout a whole segment extending between two points x_i. Let us call each of the isolated points and segments where the broken line representing (13) meets the axis of x a node of (13). To each node we attribute a multiplicity as follows: If the node lies at, or reaches up to, one of the end-points x_0 or x_n, we take as its multiplicity the number of points x_i contained in it. Otherwise we take either this number or a number one greater, in such a way that the multiplicity shall be odd or even according as in passing through the node the function (13) does or does not change sign. This convention is justified by the fact, readily established by means of equations (5), that such multiple nodes can occur only for isolated values of t; and that for values of t a little smaller than such a value, the function (13) has exactly k simple nodes in the neighborhood of the point or segment where a k-fold node is to appear.* Now the fundamental fact here, which also follows from (5), is that as t increases through a value for which there is a node of multiplicity k, the simple nodes, after coalescing to form the multiple node, all disappear,

---

* We exclude here and in what follows the possibility that the function (13) vanish identically; or, what is the same thing, we assume that not all the A's are zero.

leaving no node at all in the neighborhood of the point or segment in question, except in the one case of a node of odd multiplicity which does not lie at or reach up to one of the endpoints x_0 or x_n; in which case just one simple node remains in the neighborhood in question.

From these considerations it may readily be inferred that the number of nodes of the expression

(14) $$A_p y_p(i) + A_{p+1} y_{p+1}(i) + \cdots + A_q y_q(i),$$

where $A_p \neq 0$, $A_q \neq 0$, $0 \leqq p < q \leqq n$, cannot be less than p or greater than q, a multiple node being counted at pleasure either once or as often as its multiplicity indicates. For if, by introducing exponentials, we modify (14) into an expression of the form (13), the nodes of (14) appear merely as the nodes of (13) when $t = 0$, and the number of such nodes lies, by what was said above, between the number of nodes of the expression (13) in question for a very large negative, and the number for a very large positive value of t. For such extreme values, (13) coincides very nearly with constant multiples of $y_p(i)$ and $y_q(i)$ respectively.

While it does not seem likely from the scanty evidence which Sturm has left us that these latter considerations were all familiar to him in 1829, they can hardly fail to have been in his possession four years later, and it is not unlikely that if the manuscript which was among his papers at the time of his death could be recovered, it would be found to contain a systematic exposition of them along with the other matters we have touched upon.*

Two lines for further investigation now naturally presented themselves. One of these consisted in replacing the difference equation (7) and the boundary conditions (8), (9) by the more general relations of the same form

$$\Delta\{K(i)\Delta y(i)\} - G(i)y(i+1) = 0 \quad (K(i) > 0),$$

(15) $$K(0)\Delta y(0) - hy(0) = 0 \text{ (or } y(0) = 0),$$

$$K(n-1)\Delta y(n-1) + Hy(n-1) = 0 \text{ (or } y(n) = 0).$$

---

* We note in passing that if we equate the expression (13) to zero and assign to i a particular value, the equation thus obtained is precisely of the form considered in the paper of June 1, 1829 concerning which we have already spoken. Cf. the introductory remarks in the summary of that paper.

If here we assume that the quantities $K(i)$, $G(i)$, h, H are continuous increasing functions of λ, the results relating to equation (7) and also their proofs admit of ready extension to the system (15).

On the other hand we may pass over from *difference* to *differential* equations by allowing the integer n to become infinite, the points x_0 and x_n however remaining fixed. In this way the various functions of the integral argument i become functions of a continuous argument x. We thus pass from the massless string weighted by n distinct particles to the string whose mass is continuously but unequally distributed throughout its extent, and from the radiation of heat in a row of vases to the conduction of heat in a heterogeneous bar. It is this latter problem which forms the subject of Sturm's second great memoir of 1836, while the extension of the results concerning the difference equation (15) to the differential equation

$$\frac{d}{dx}\left(K(x)\frac{dy}{dx}\right) - G(x)y = 0$$

is the subject of the first memoir of that year. It is worthy of notice that in both cases Sturm used the method of passing by a limiting process from a difference to a differential equation merely as a heuristic one, making indeed hardly a mention of it in the final memoirs, and treating the differential equations *directly* by methods which are the immediate generalizations of those he had used for the difference equations in his unpublished work.* A careful examination of the abstracts published in 1829 in the *Journal de Férussac* will show that all this, at least so far as it relates to the heat problem, was in his mind even at that early date.† It was probably developed to some extent in the unpublished paper of October 19.

It is not my purpose to discuss here the two great memoirs of 1836, although the richness of their detail tempts one to linger over many points which have, it is to be feared, rather escaped the notice of mathematicians. This richness of detail probably reflects a similar quality in the earlier unpublished

---

* Cf. Fredholm's derivation of the theory of integral equations as a limiting case from the theory of a system of linear algebraic equations. Like Sturm, Fredholm used this limiting process merely as a heuristic one for deriving both the results and the methods for their proofs.

† There is no evidence to show whether the more general difference equation (15) was considered at this time or only at a slightly later date.

researches, and much of the detail there could be readily reproduced.   In these days, when new methods are being suggested
for obtaining a few of the fundamental results of Sturm in their
simplest forms, it is not out of place to remark that if one were
to cut away from Sturm's memoirs everything except what is
necessary to obtain *these* results, the few pages that would be
left would in brevity, rigor, and directness easily stand comparison with anything which has so far been suggested to replace
them.

Coupled with Sturm's name in all of this work on differential
equations one often finds the name of his young friend Liouville.
It is true that Liouville's work on these matters was hardly
inferior in originality and power to that of Sturm himself; but
it must be remembered that Sturm's work was practically complete, even to the writing of the two great memoirs, before Liouville's began, and that, except for alternative proofs which the
latter gave for some of Sturm's results, and for a genial extension
to certain differential equations of higher order, his work dealt
with a single problem, of fundamental importance it is true,
which had not been treated by Sturm,* namely the proof that the
development of an arbitrary function which occurs in Sturm's
papers is valid.   We may therefore fairly speak of the Sturm-
Liouville development according to normal functions, but these
normal functions themselves, and almost everything relating
to their theory,† are due to Sturm alone.

I have tried to show you how all of Sturm's most important
work flowed naturally from his treatment of a single physical
problem, not very important in itself perhaps, certainly of no
great generality or largeness of scope.   Sturm's genius showed
itself first in his method of handling the problem where such
purely formal skill as one associates with the names of Lagrange
or Poisson is less in evidence than a constant intuitional visualization of the problem combined with a sense of accuracy un-
common in his day; secondly in his perception of the relation
of this problem to other questions, and to the way in which he
followed up his work into adjacent fields.   The power of gen-
eralizing is not rare, as the huge bulk of our current mathe-

---

* One paper on this subject written in conjunction with Liouville is
preserved to us in abstract (*Liouville's Journal*, vol. 2, p. 220) but was written
after Liouville's first work on this subject.

† An exception should be made here of the asymptotic expressions for
these functions for large values of the index.   These important expressions
are due to Liouville.

matical literature sadly reminds us; but one who like Sturm can seize on the important and simple modifications of a given problem has certainly one of the most essential elements of mathematical greatness.

HARVARD UNIVERSITY,
CAMBRIDGE, MASS.